T4-AKQ-503

Alvina Bremecke
507 – 3rd St.
Watertown, Wis.

From
Edith Nowacki, 4/85

THE

ENDEAVOR HYMNAL

FOR

YOUNG PEOPLE'S SOCIETIES
SUNDAY SCHOOLS AND
CHURCH PRAYER MEETINGS

UNITED SOCIETY OF CHRISTIAN ENDEAVOR
BOSTON AND CHICAGO

COPYRIGHT 1901
BY THE
UNITED SOCIETY OF CHRISTIAN ENDEAVOR

NOTE: In addition to the many pieces which have been copyrighted separately, this volume contains much original matter which is covered by the general copyright of the book and must not be reprinted without permission.

Stanhope Press
F. H. GILSON COMPANY
BOSTON, U.S.A.

PREFACE

THE ENDEAVOR HYMNAL is the response of the United Society of Christian Endeavor to a widely expressed desire on the part of the young people for a higher and more varied class of hymns for use in the prayer meeting. In the preparation of this book the rich resources of Christian hymnology have been freely drawn upon. While it does not lack in the best class of what are known as gospel hymns, it gives proportionate place to the hymns of praise and devotion which cannot fail to quicken the sense of reverence and worship, and stimulate the spiritual life. Along the lines of Service, Christian Citizenship, Consecration, The Quiet Hour, Missions, and Evangelism, the collection is especially full and comprehensive.

Recognizing the demand for such a work, the Trustees of the United Society in 1899 appointed a Hymnal Committee, consisting of Rev. Charles A. Dickinson, D.D., Rev. Howard B. Grose, and Rev. James L. Hill, D.D. This Committee was subsequently enlarged by the addition of Rev. Maltbie D. Babcock, D.D., Rev. J. Wilbur Chapman, D.D., and Mr. F. H. Jacobs. Constant service has been rendered to the Committee by Mr. George B. Graff, Business Agent of the United Society. Valuable suggestions and lists of hymns have been received from President John Henry Barrows, D.D., Rev. F. B. Meyer, Rev. O. P. Gifford, D.D., Rev. F. E. Clark, D.D., Bishop Samuel Fallows, D.D., Rev. Nehemiah Boynton, D.D., Rev. Floyd W. Tomkins, D.D., Rev. Wilton Merle Smith, D.D., Rev. Wayland Hoyt, D.D., Rev. David James Burrell, D.D., Rev. F. D. Power, D.D., Mr. Robert E. Speer, Rev. W. H. McMillan, D.D., Rev. E. R. Dille, D.D., Mr. John R. Mott, Rev. A. C. Crews, Rev. Ira Landrith, Mr. William R. Moody, Rev. M. Rhodes, D.D., Rev. Clarence E. Eberman, Mr. John Willis Baer, Rev. H. T. McEwen, D.D., Rev. F. M. Lamb, Mr. H. C. Lincoln, Rev. E. F. Hallenbeck, and Mr. Percy S. Foster. Special thanks are due to Rev. R.

DeWitt Mallary and Mrs. James L. Hill, who freely placed their collection of hymns at the disposal of the Committee; to Rev. Joseph Brown Morgan and Rev. Carey Bonner, Editors of the English Christian Endeavor Hymnal, for permission to use pieces written for that excellent book; and to Mr. Frank Leslie Stone and Mr. Charles S. Brown, both for original pieces and correction of the text. To all who have generously assisted in the work, and extended courtesies in the use of original pieces and copyrights, hearty acknowledgments are here made.

The steady aim of the Committee has been to select the best and most singable hymns obtainable, recognizing the variety of tastes and needs, while always keeping in mind the high purpose which the Hymnal is designed to serve. The Committee completes its labors, extending over more than two years, with a greatly deepened appreciation of the ennobling quality of the grand hymns of the Church, and of their inspirational and educational value as a factor in the molding of Christian character. The hope is earnestly cherished that The Endeavor Hymnal may be blessed of God as an efficient aid in the ministry of spiritual song.

THE HYMNAL COMMITTEE.

Boston, *June 1, 1901.*

Inscription of Praise

O come, let us sing unto the Lord: let us make a joyful noise to the Rock of our Salvation.

Serve the Lord with gladness: come before His presence with singing.

It is a good thing to give thanks unto the Lord, and to sing praises unto Thy Name, O Most High.

O sing unto the Lord a new song: sing unto the Lord, bless His name; show forth His salvation from day to day.

I will praise Thee, O Lord, with my whole heart; I will be glad and rejoice in Thee; I will sing praise to Thy name, O Thou Most High.

Order of Arrangement

Index of Subjects

Index of Subjects

GIVING: 159, 234, 272. 279, 312.
God:
Creator. 21, 30, 73, 273.
The Father. 2, 4, 41, 55, 66, 300.
His Love: 2, 5, 48, 86, 106.
King: 3, 29, 79, 209, 210, 211, 218, 231.
Gratitude: 30, 159, 272.
Growth: 116, 121, 134, 147.
Guidance: 36, 58, 59, 67, 84, 102, 106, 114, 227, 277, 291, 297.

HARVEST: 265, 266.
Heaven: 68, 77, 80, 89, 90, 100, 101, 103, 105, 107, 112, 141, 204, 281, 282, 298.
Helpfulness: 124, 136, 152, 159, 161, 166, 171, 190, 246, 313.
Holy Spirit: 38, 39, 54, 58, 114, 199.
Hope: 69, 142, 147, 154, 228, 280, 288.
Humility: 121, 166, 174, 180.

IMMORTALITY: 101, 264, 288.
Invitation: 99, 114, 162, 177, 195, 244, 249, 250, 253.

JESUS: 10, 14, 23, 24, 33, 43, 62, 67, 71, 75, 77, 82, 105, 108, 113, 118, 126, 128, 133, 142, 247, 250, 252, 286.
Joy: 64, 77, 110, 129, 141, 152, 223.

KIND WORDS: 59, 124, 133, 155, 161.
Kindness: 59, 124, 135, 136, 190, 246.

LITTLE THINGS: 59, 87, 120, 124, 128, 136, 155, 161, 190, 272.
Love: 10, 12, 14, 16, 37, 53, 57, 59, 63, 74, 75, 76, 79, 86, 87, 108, 113, 153, 191, 192, 228, 242, 278.

MISSIONS: 131, 145, 150, 230 to 239.

NATIONAL: 187, 209, 210, 211, 213, 214 215, 216, 217, 220 233.
Native Land: 213, 215, 216, 221, 233.
New Year: 267, 268, 269, 270.

OBEDIENCE: 33, 62, 130, 149, 268.

PEACE: 41, 57, 64, 65, 66, 72, 78, 84, 92, 97, 182, 202, 209, 241, 245, 305, 307, 308, 309.
Praise:
General: 1 to 29, 255, 304.
To God: 1 to 5, 17, 19, 21, 25, 26, 27, 29, 30, 129, 259, 264, 267.
To Christ: 6, 8, 10, 11, 13, 14, 15, 16, 22, 23, 24, 26, 28, 37, 121, 141, 271, 307.
To the Trinity: 9, 17, 314.
Prayer: 16, 31 to 56, 62, 67, 70, 73, 84, 111, 160, 163, 175, 188, 199, 210, 240, 290, 291, 292, 293, 296, 298, 303, 306, 313, 314.
Prayer Meeting:
Opening: 290, 291, 292, 293.
General: 294, 295, 296, 297, 298, 299, 300, 301, 302, 303, 304, 305.
Closing: 306, 307, 308, 309, 310, 313, 314.
Processional: 18, 121, 122, 123, 125, 132, 134, 138, 140, 144, 147, 148, 168, 169, 172, 230, 259, 261, 269, 270, 271.
Promises: 20, 269, 270, 294, 299.
Providence: 88, 110, 220.
Purity: 41, 116.

QUIET HOUR: 55, 65, 110, 112, 193 to 208, 241, 298.

RACE, CHRISTIAN: 76, 147.
Redemption: 76, 229, 231, 237, 285.
Refuge: 104, 109, 118, 119, 197, 201.
Repentance: 81, 126, 158.
Rescue: 125, 212, 248.
Responses: 56, 70, 245, 301, 303, 311, 312, 313, 314.

Rest: 12, 57, 64, 66, 71, 72, 89, 98, 195, 197, 207, 289.
Righteousness: 232, 233.
Rock of Ages: 75, 85.

SAILORS. 33, 43, 166, 241, 282, 288, 297.
Salvation: 145, 158, 163, 231, 247, 248, 255, 263, 286.
Saviour: 13, 16, 34, 40, 42, 77, 88, 103, 115, 121, 150, 162, 194, 197, 242, 251, 258, 277, 305, 307.
Seeing Jesus: 77, 83.
Service: 76, 87, 120, 122 to 172, 303.
Shepherd: 65, 79, 91.
Solace: 8, 206.
Soldiers of Christ: 125, 127, 132, 138, 140, 144, 146, 148, 164, 168, 169, 172, 187.
Solos: 88, 243, 254, 263, 306.
Sowing and Reaping: 167, 170, 171, 235, 265.
Submission: 26, 49, 50, 55, 62, 95, 102, 111, 116, 158, 184.
Surrender: 76, 174, 179, 180, 193.

TEMPERANCE: 20, 54, 122, 125, 212, 219, 243, 248, 274.
Temptation: 135, 137, 243.
Testimony: 133, 155, 161.
Thankfulness: 2, 21, 30, 265.
Thanksgiving: 265, 266, 267.
Today: 162, 275.
Tongue: 59, 124, 135.
Trust: 20, 51, 62, 65, 71, 86, 94, 95, 97, 102, 104, 105, 106, 110, 111, 117, 130, 173, 193, 204, 205, 219, 287.
Truth: 220, 228.

VICTORY: 132, 138, 140, 148, 153, 169, 192, 218, 232, 264, 269.

WATCHFULNESS: 43, 153, 160, 281, 312.
Welcome: 276.
Work: 128, 131, 135, 143, 149, 153, 156, 167, 171.
Worship: 3, 4, 13, 21, 257, 264, 300.

ZEAL: 16, 135, 175.

A Scriptural Opening

Leader: O come, let us worship and bow down: let us kneel before the Lord our Maker.

Response: For He is our God; we are His people, and the sheep of His pasture.

Leader: The Lord is nigh unto all that call upon Him;

Response: To all that call upon Him in truth.

Leader: Who shall ascend into the hill of the Lord, and who shall stand in His holy place?

Unison: He that hath clean hands, and a pure heart; he that walketh uprightly, and worketh righteousness, and speaketh the truth in his heart. He that slandereth not with his tongue, nor doeth evil to his friend, nor taketh up a reproach against his neighbor. He shall receive a blessing from the Lord, and righteousness from the God of his salvation.

Leader: If we confess our sins, He is faithful and just to forgive us our sins, and to cleanse us from all unrighteousness.

Unison: O God, I acknowledge my transgressions. Wash me thoroughly from mine iniquity, and cleanse me from my sin. Create in me a clean heart, O God, and renew a right spirit within me.

Leader: He is faithful that hath promised. Let us therefore come boldly unto the throne of grace, that we may obtain mercy, and find grace to help in time of need.

Unison: Our Father who art in heaven,
Hallowed be Thy name.
Thy kingdom come.
Thy will be done in earth as it is in heaven.
Give us this day our daily bread.
And forgive us our debts as we forgive our debtors.
And lead us not into temptation,
But deliver us from evil:
For Thine is the kingdom and the power and the glory, forever.
Amen. (Matt. 6 : 9-13.)

The Endeavor Hymnal

I Angel Voices, Ever Singing

Rev. Francis Pott, 1861 (8. 5. 8. 5. 8. 4. 3) Sir Arthur Sullivan, 1872

1. An - gel voi - ces, ev - er sing - ing Round Thy throne of light,
2. Thou who art be - yond the far - thest Mor - tal eye can scan,
3. Yea, we know Thy love re - joi - ces O'er each work of Thine;
4. Here, great God, to - day we of - fer Of Thine own to Thee;
An - gel harps, for - ev - er ring - ing, Rest not day nor night;
Can it be that Thou re - gard - est Songs of sin - ful man?
Thou didst ears and hands and voi - ces For Thy praise com - bine;
And for Thine ac - cept - ance prof - fer, All un - wor - thi - ly,
Thou-sands on - ly live to bless Thee, And con - fess Thee Lord of might.
Can we feel that Thou art near us, And wilt hear us? Yea, we can.
Crafts-man's art and mu - sic's meas - ure For Thy pleas - ure Didst de - sign.
Hearts and minds, and hands and voi - ces, In our choic - est Mel - o - dy.
A-MEN.

2 A Gladsome Hymn

A. N. Blatchford *(8. 7. 8. 7. and Refrain)* Nora C. Byrne

1. A glad-some hymn of praise we sing, And thank-ful-ly we gath-er
2. From shades of night He calls the light, And from the sod the flow-er;
3. Full in His sight His chil-dren stand, By His strong arm de-fend-ed;
To bless the love of God a-bove, Our ev-er-last-ing Fa-ther.
From ev-'ry cloud His bless-ings break, In sun-shine or in show-er.
And He, whose wis-dom guides the world, Our foot-steps hath at-tend-ed.
Refrain
f
In Him re-joice with heart and voice, Whose glo-ry fad-eth nev-er;
cres.
Whose prov-i-dence is our de-fence, Who lives and loves for-ev-er!

Used by per.

God Eternal, Mighty King

3

Anon. (7s. D.) R. De W. Mallary, 1901

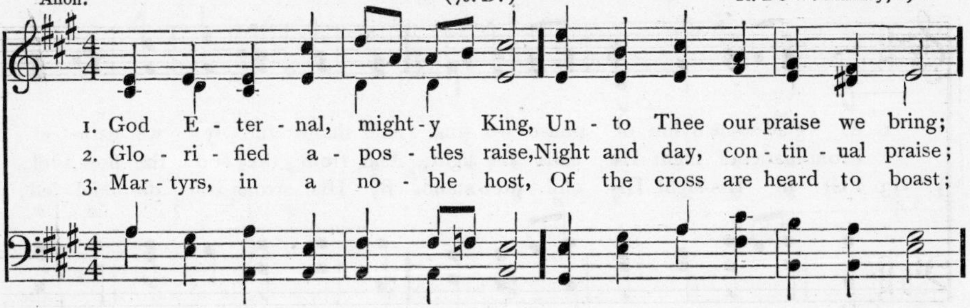
1. God E - ter - nal, might - y King, Un - to Thee our praise we bring;
2. Glo - ri - fied a - pos - tles raise, Night and day, con - tin - ual praise;
3. Mar - tyrs, in a no - ble host, Of the cross are heard to boast;

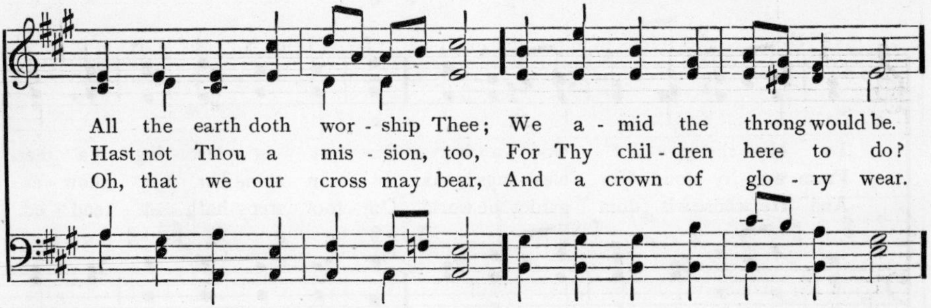
All the earth doth wor - ship Thee; We a - mid the throng would be.
Hast not Thou a mis - sion, too, For Thy chil - dren here to do?
Oh, that we our cross may bear, And a crown of glo - ry wear.

Ho - ly, ho - ly, ho - ly! cry An - gels, round Thy throne on high;
With the proph - ets' good - ly line We in mys - tic bond com - bine;
God E - ter - nal, might - y King, Un - to Thee our praise we bring;

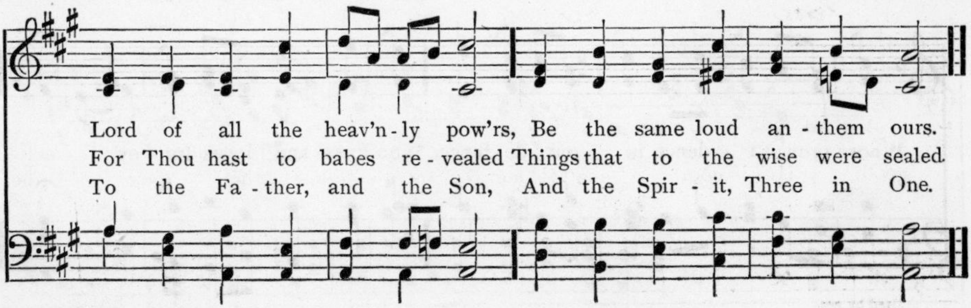
Lord of all the heav'n - ly pow'rs, Be the same loud an - them ours.
For Thou hast to babes re - vealed Things that to the wise were sealed.
To the Fa - ther, and the Son, And the Spir - it, Three in One.

Copyright, 1901, by U. S. C. E.

4 Glory and Honor

Flora Kirkland

Chas. Gounod

Glo - ry and hon - or to God our heav'nly Fa - ther, Praise and a -
dore Him who reigns in might and maj - es - ty. Tell of His good - ness, pro -
claim His name to ev - 'ry land 'Till all the na - tions shall own Him King for
ev - er-more. Sing and give praise to the Lord the King of kings, For He is
O sing, give praise,
good, He is good, and His mer - cy ev - er - last - ing. Sing to the
is good, is good, O sing,

Glory and Honor

Lord, tho' a host en-camp a - gainst thee, For His pow'r and His love o'er -
O sing,
shad-ow thee. Sing praise to the God of bat - tles. Glo - ry and hon - or to the
ff
ff
God of our sal- va - tion! Glo - ry and hon- or un - to God our Sun and Shield!
O lift joy-ous songs of praise, Praise for all His lov- ing kind-ness-es. Give to God the
wor- ship due His ho- ly name, give glo - ry and praise; praise for ev - er-more.
1
2

* Use small notes if desirable

5 Lord, with Glowing Heart

Francis S. Key, 1823 (*Sanctuary* 8. 7. 8. 7. D.) J. B. Dykes, 1871

1. Lord,with glow - ing heart I'd praise Thee For the bliss Thy love be-stows,
2. Praise,my soul, the God that sought thee, Wretched wan-derer, far a - stray;
3. Lord, this bos - om's ar - dent feel - ing Vain-ly would my lips ex - press;
For the par-d'ning grace that saves me, And the peace that from it flows;
Found thee lost, and kind - ly brought thee From the paths of death a - way;
Low be - fore Thy foot - stool kneel - ing, Deign Thy sup-pliant's pray'r to bless;
Help, O God, my weak en - deav - or; This dull soul to rap - ture raise;
Praise, with love's de - vout - est feel - ing, Him who saw thy guilt - born fear;
Let Thy grace, my soul's chief treas - ure, Love's pure flame with - in me raise;
Thou must light the flame, or nev - er Can my love be warmed to praise.
And, the light of hope re - veal-ing, Bade the blood-stained cross appear.
And, since words can nev - er meas-ure, Let my life show forth Thy praise. A - MEN.

Crown Him with Many Crowns

6

Mathew Bridges, 1848 (*Diademata* S. M. D.) George J. Elvey, 1868

1. Crown Him with ma - ny crowns, The Lamb up - on His throne;
2. Crown Him, the Lord of love! Be - hold His hands and side,—
3. Crown Him, the Lord of life! Who tri - umphed o'er the grave;
4. Crown Him, the Lord of heav'n, One with the Fa - ther known,
Hark! how the heav'n - ly an - them drowns All mu - sic but its own!
Rich wounds, yet vis - i - ble a - bove In beau - ty glo - ri - fied;
Who rose vic - to - rious to the strife For those He came to save;
One with the Spir - it through Him giv'n From yon - der glo - rious throne!
A - wake, my soul, and sing Of Him who died for thee;
No an - gel in the sky Can ful - ly bear that sight,
His glo - ries now we sing, Who died and rose on high,
To Thee be end - less praise, For Thou for us hast died;
And hail Him as thy match-less King Thro' all e - ter - ni - ty.
But downward bends his won - d'ring eye At mys - ter - ies so bright.
Who died e - ter - nal life to bring, And lives that death may die.
Be Thou, O Lord, thro' end - less days A - dored and mag - ni - fied.

7 City of God

Samuel Johnson (8. 6. 8. 6) R. De W. Mallary, 1901

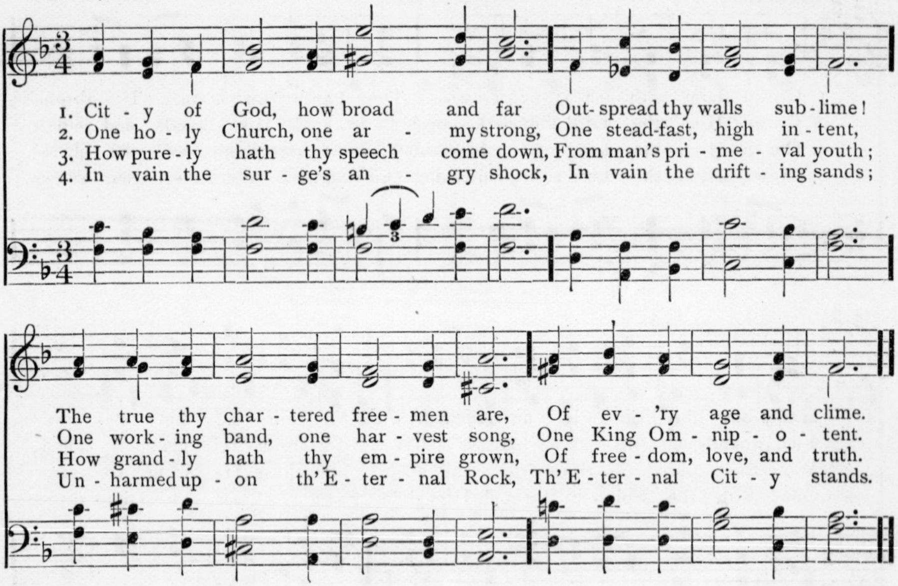
1. Cit - y of God, how broad and far Out-spread thy walls sub - lime!
2. One ho - ly Church, one ar - my strong, One stead-fast, high in - tent,
3. How pure - ly hath thy speech come down, From man's pri - me - val youth;
4. In vain the sur - ge's an - gry shock, In vain the drift - ing sands;
The true thy char - tered free - men are, Of ev - 'ry age and clime.
One work - ing band, one har - vest song, One King Om - nip - o - tent.
How grand - ly hath thy em - pire grown, Of free - dom, love, and truth.
Un - harmed up - on th' E - ter - nal Rock, Th' E - ter - nal Cit - y stands.

Copyright, 1901, by U. S. C. E.

8 When Morning Gilds the Skies

German, 1828. Tr. E. Caswell, 1854 (*Laudes Domini* 6s. 6l.) J. Barnby, 1868

1. When morning gilds the skies, My heart a - wak-ing cries May Je - sus Christ be praised!
2. In heav'n's e-ter - nal bliss, The loveliest strain is this, May Je - sus Christ be praised!
3. Be this, while life is mine, My can - ti - cle di - vine, May Je - sus Christ be praised!
A - like at work and pray'r, To Je-sus I re - pair; May Je - sus Christ be praised!
Let earth, and sea, and sky From depth to height reply, May Je - sus Christ be praised!
Be this th' e-ter-nal song Through a-ges all a - long, May Je - sus Christ be praised!

O Day of Rest and Gladness

9

C. Wordsworth (*Mendebras* 7s. 6s. D.) Arr. by L. Mason

1. O day of rest and glad - ness, O day of joy and light,
2. To - day on wea - ry na - tions The heav'n-ly man - na falls;
3. New gra - ces ev - er gain - ing From this our day of rest,
O balm of care and sad - ness, Most beau - ti - ful, most bright;
To ho - ly con - vo - ca - tions The sil - ver trum - pet calls,
We reach the rest re - main - ing To spir - its of the blest.
On thee, the high and low - ly, Bend - ing be - fore the throne,
Where gos - pel light is glow - ing With pure and ra - diant beams,
To Ho - ly Ghost be prais - es, To Fa - ther and to Son;
Sing, Ho - ly, Ho - ly, Ho - ly, To the great Three in One.
And liv - ing wa - ter flow - ing With soul - re - fresh - ing streams.
The Church her voice up - rais - es To Thee, blest Three in One.

10 Jesus, These Eyes Have Never Seen

R. Palmer, 1858 (*Lambeth C. M.*) S. Webbe, 1740–1816

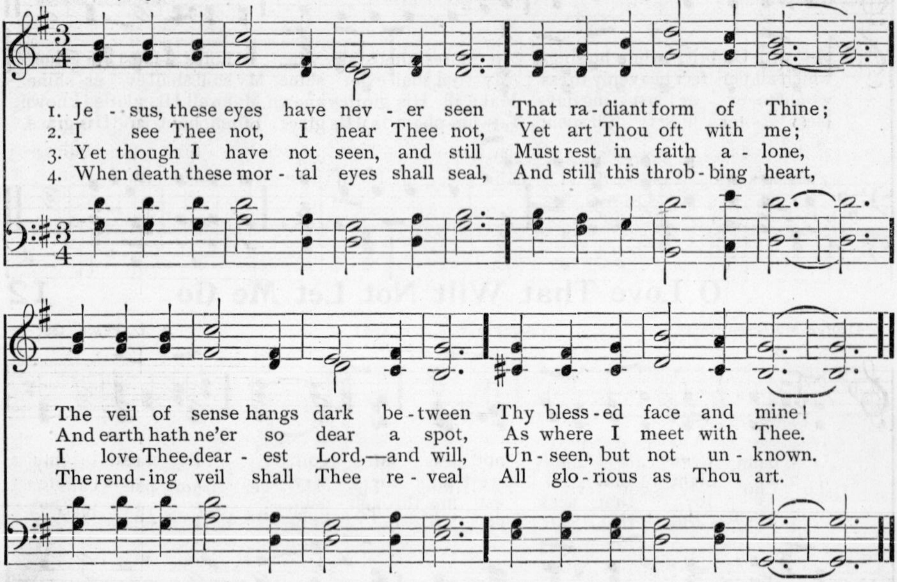
1. Je - sus, these eyes have nev - er seen That ra - diant form of Thine;
2. I see Thee not, I hear Thee not, Yet art Thou oft with me;
3. Yet though I have not seen, and still Must rest in faith a - lone,
4. When death these mor - tal eyes shall seal, And still this throb - bing heart,
The veil of sense hangs dark be - tween Thy bless - ed face and mine!
And earth hath ne'er so dear a spot, As where I meet with Thee.
I love Thee, dear - est Lord,—and will, Un - seen, but not un - known.
The rend - ing veil shall Thee re - veal All glo - rious as Thou art.

11 Oh, Could I Speak the Matchless Worth

Samuel Medley (*Ariel C. P. M.*) Lowell Mason

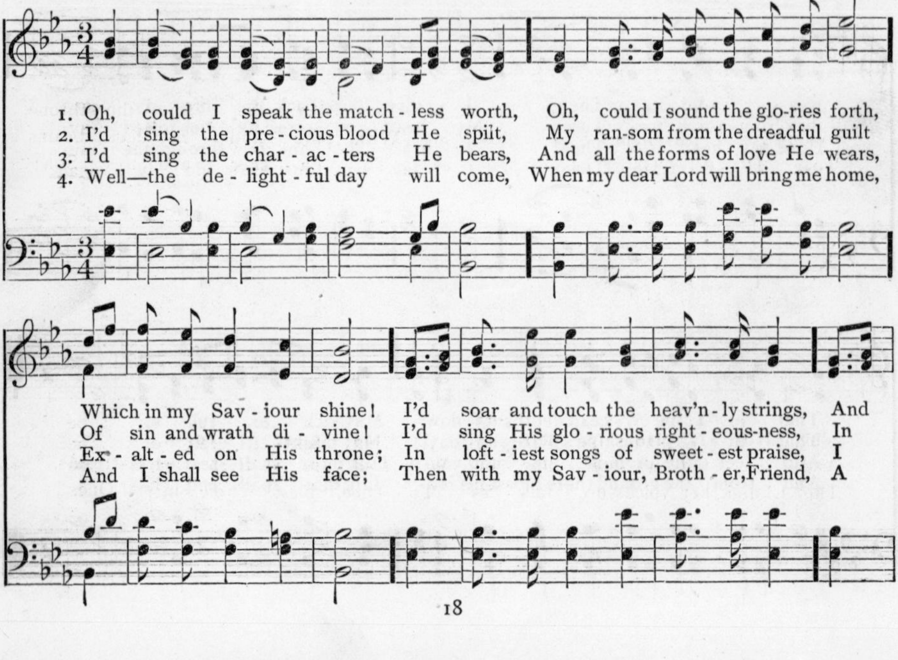
1. Oh, could I speak the match - less worth, Oh, could I sound the glo - ries forth,
2. I'd sing the pre - cious blood He spilt, My ran - som from the dreadful guilt
3. I'd sing the char - ac - ters He bears, And all the forms of love He wears,
4. Well—the de - light - ful day will come, When my dear Lord will bring me home,
Which in my Sav - iour shine! I'd soar and touch the heav'n - ly strings, And
Of sin and wrath di - vine! I'd sing His glo - rious right - eous - ness, In
Ex - alt - ed on His throne; In loft - iest songs of sweet - est praise, I
And I shall see His face; Then with my Sav - iour, Broth - er, Friend, A

Oh, Could I Speak the Matchless Worth

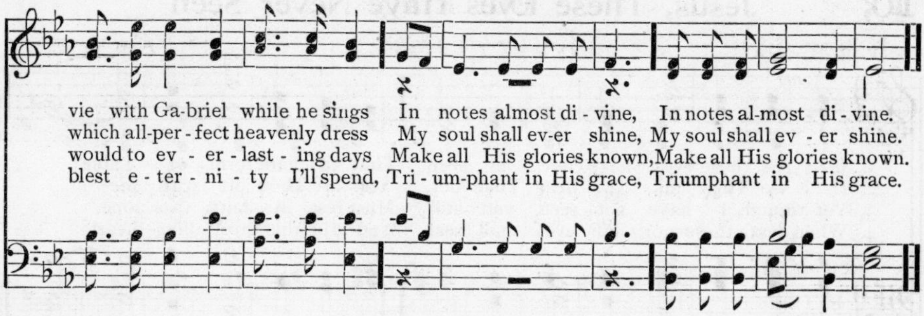
vie with Ga-briel while he sings In notes almost di - vine, In notes al-most di - vine.
which all-per - fect heavenly dress My soul shall ev-er shine, My soul shall ev - er shine.
would to ev - er - last - ing days Make all His glories known, Make all His glories known.
blest e - ter - ni - ty I'll spend, Tri - um-phant in His grace, Triumphant in His grace.

O Love That Wilt Not Let Me Go 12

George Matheson, 1882 (*Margaret* 8. 8. 8. 8. 6) A. L. Peace, 1885

1. O Love that wilt not let me go, I rest my wea - ry soul in Thee; I give Thee back the life I owe, That in Thine o - cean depths its flow May rich - er, full - er be.
2. O Light that fol - lowest all my way, I yield my flick-'ring torch to Thee; My heart re - stores its bor-rowed ray, That in Thy sunshine's blaze its day May bright - er, fair - er be.
3. O Joy that seek - est me through pain, I can - not close my heart to Thee; I trace the rain - bow through the rain, And feel the prom-ise is not vain That morn shall tear - less be.
4. O Cross that lift - est up my head, I dare not ask to fly from Thee; I lay in dust life's glo - ry dead, And from the ground there blossoms red Life that shall end - less be.

13 Our King

F. R. Havergal (7. 6. 7. 6. D. *With Refrain*) G. F. Le Jeune

mf
1. O Sav - iour, pre - cious Sav - iour, Whom yet un - seen we love;
2. O bring - er of sal - va - tion, Who won - drous - ly hast wrought,
mf
p
O Name of might and fa - vor, All oth - er names a - bove:
Thy - self the rev - e - la - tion Of love be - yond our thought:
p
cres.
We wor - ship Thee, we bless Thee, To Thee a - lone we sing;
In Thee all ful - ness dwell - eth, All grace and pow'r di - vine;
cres.
f
We praise Thee, and con - fess Thee Our ho - ly Lord and King!
The glo - ry that ex - cel - leth, O Son of God, is Thine.
f

Our King

We wor - - - - - - - - - ship Thee, we bless Thee,
We wor - ship Thee, we bless Thee, To Thee a - lone we sing;
We praise
We praise Thee, and con - fess Thee Our ho - ly Lord and King!

O Jesus, King 14

Bernard of Clairvaux, 1153
Tr. by E. Caswall, 1849

(*Holy Cross C. M.*)

Felix Mendelssohn

1. O Je - sus, King most won - der - ful, Thou Con - quer - or re - nowned,
2. When once Thou vis - it - est the heart, Then truth be - gins to shine,
3. O Je - sus, Light of all be - low, Thou Fount of liv - ing fire,
4. Thee, Je - sus, may our voi - ces bless; Thee may we love a - lone;
Thou sweet - ness most in - ef - fa - ble, In whom all joys are found!
Then earth - ly van - i - ties de - part, Then kin - dles love di - vine.
Sur - pass - ing all the joys we know, And all we can de - sire.
And ev - er in our lives ex - press The im - age of Thine own.

15 Majestic Sweetness Sits Enthroned

Samuel Stennett (*Ortonville C. M.*) Thomas Hastings

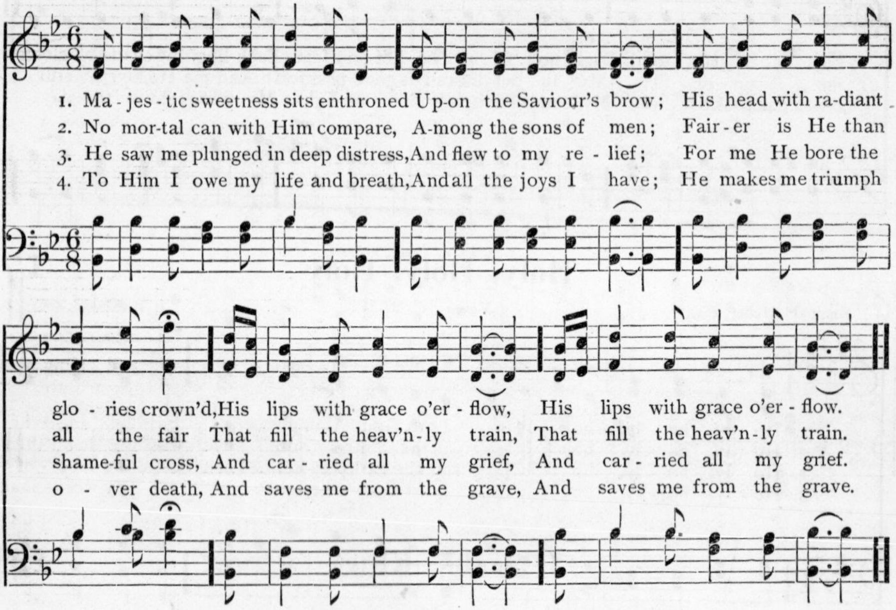
1. Ma - jes - tic sweetness sits enthroned Up-on the Saviour's brow; His head with ra-diant
2. No mor-tal can with Him compare, A-mong the sons of men; Fair - er is He than
3. He saw me plunged in deep distress, And flew to my re - lief; For me He bore the
4. To Him I owe my life and breath, And all the joys I have; He makes me triumph
glo - ries crown'd, His lips with grace o'er - flow, His lips with grace o'er - flow.
all the fair That fill the heav'n-ly train, That fill the heav'n-ly train.
shame-ful cross, And car - ried all my grief, And car - ried all my grief.
o - ver death, And saves me from the grave, And saves me from the grave.

16 I Bless the Christ of God

Horatius Bonar (*Praise Song S. M. D.*) Felix Mendelssohn

1. I bless the Christ of God, I rest on love di - vine, And with un - fal-t'ring
2. I praise the God of peace; I trust His truth and might; He calls me His, I
3. 'Tis He who sav - eth me, And free - ly par-don gives; I love be-cause He
lip and heart, I call the Sav-iour mine. His cross dis-pels each doubt; I
call Him mine, My God, my joy, my light. In Him is on - ly good, In
lov - eth me; I live be-cause He lives. My life with Him is hid, My

I Bless the Christ of God

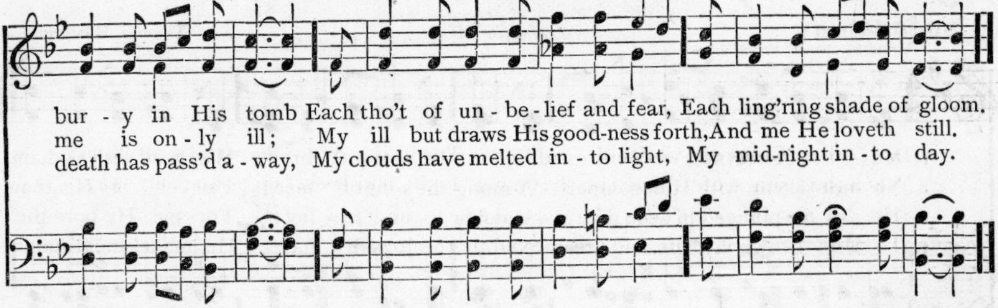

bur - y in His tomb Each tho't of un - be - lief and fear, Each ling'ring shade of gloom.
me is on - ly ill; My ill but draws His good-ness forth, And me He loveth still.
death has pass'd a - way, My clouds have melted in - to light, My mid-night in - to day.

Holy, Holy, Holy 17

Reginald Heber, 1827 (*Nicæa P. M.*) J. B. Dykes, 1861

1. Ho - ly, ho - ly, ho - ly! Lord God Al-might - y! Ear - ly in the
2. Ho - ly, ho - ly, ho - ly! all the saints a - dore Thee, Cast-ing down their
3. Ho - ly, ho - ly, ho - ly! tho' the darkness hide Thee, Tho' the eye of
4. Ho - ly, ho - ly, ho - ly! Lord God Al-might - y! All Thy works shall

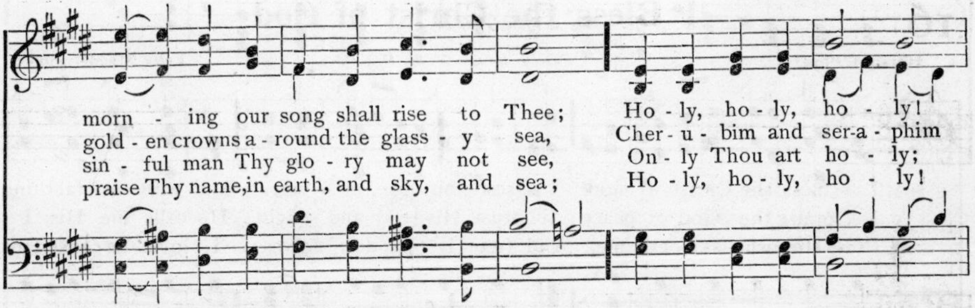

morn - ing our song shall rise to Thee; Ho - ly, ho - ly, ho - ly!
gold - en crowns a - round the glass - y sea, Cher - u - bim and ser - a - phim
sin - ful man Thy glo - ry may not see, On - ly Thou art ho - ly;
praise Thy name, in earth, and sky, and sea; Ho - ly, ho - ly, ho - ly!

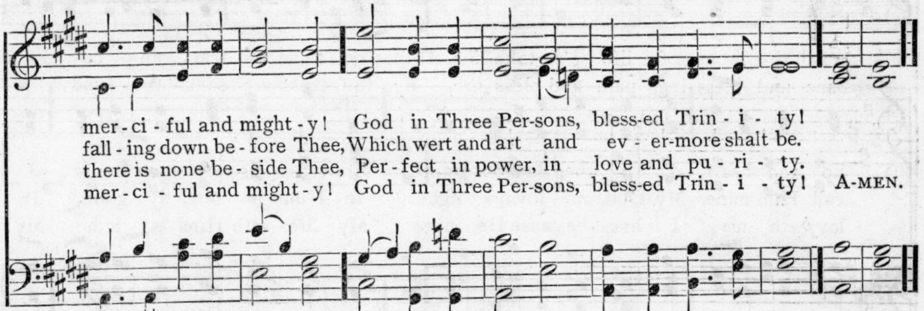

mer - ci - ful and might - y! God in Three Per-sons, bless-ed Trin - i - ty!
fall - ing down be - fore Thee, Which wert and art and ev - er-more shalt be.
there is none be - side Thee, Per - fect in power, in love and pu - ri - ty.
mer - ci - ful and might - y! God in Three Per-sons, bless-ed Trin - i - ty! A-MEN.

18 In the Cross of Christ I Glory

John Bowring, 1825

(*8s. 7s. D.*)

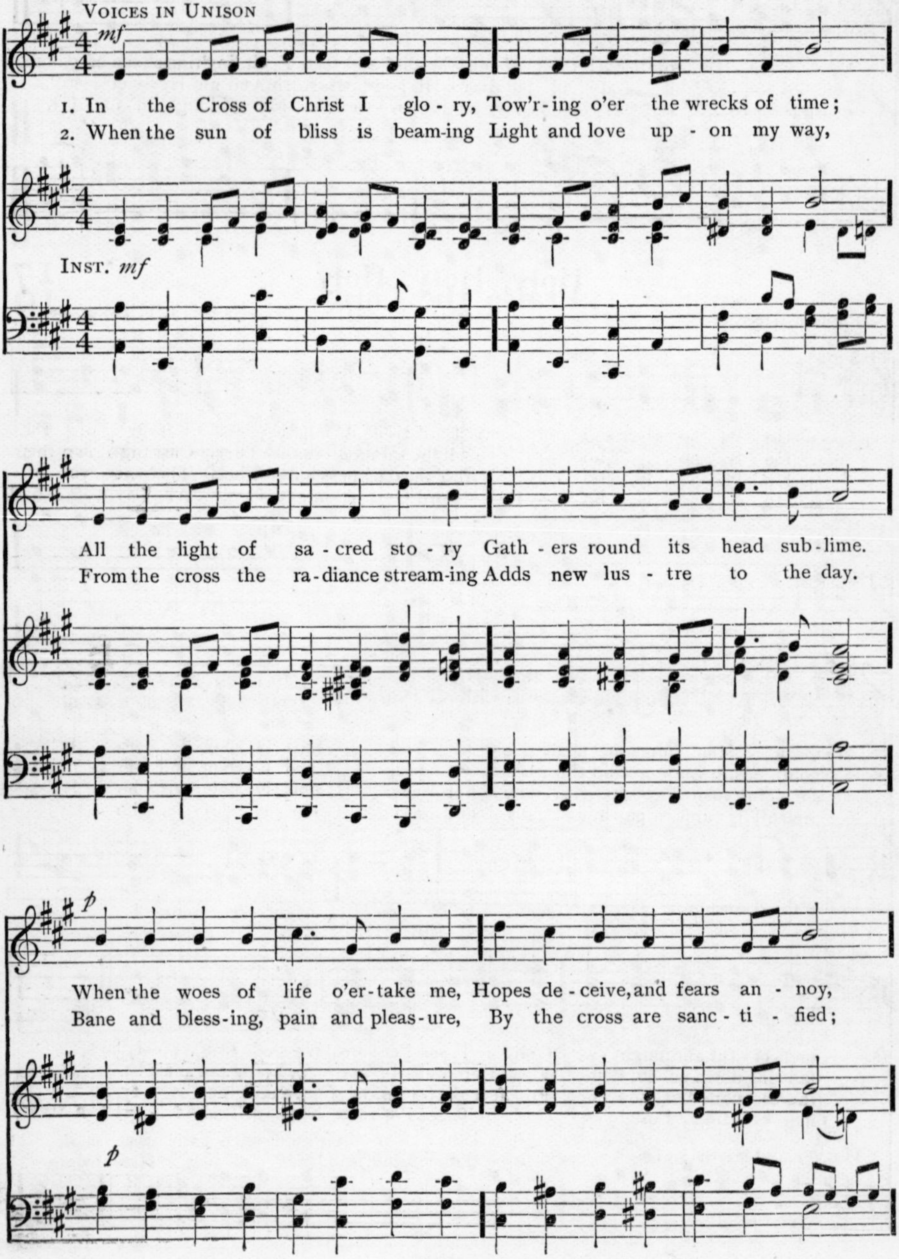
VOICES IN UNISON
mf
1. In the Cross of Christ I glo - ry, Tow'r-ing o'er the wrecks of time;
2. When the sun of bliss is beam-ing Light and love up - on my way,
INST. mf
All the light of sa - cred sto - ry Gath - ers round its head sub - lime.
From the cross the ra - diance stream-ing Adds new lus - tre to the day.
p
When the woes of life o'er-take me, Hopes de - ceive, and fears an - noy,
Bane and bless-ing, pain and pleas - ure, By the cross are sanc - ti - fied;
p

In the Cross of Christ I Glory

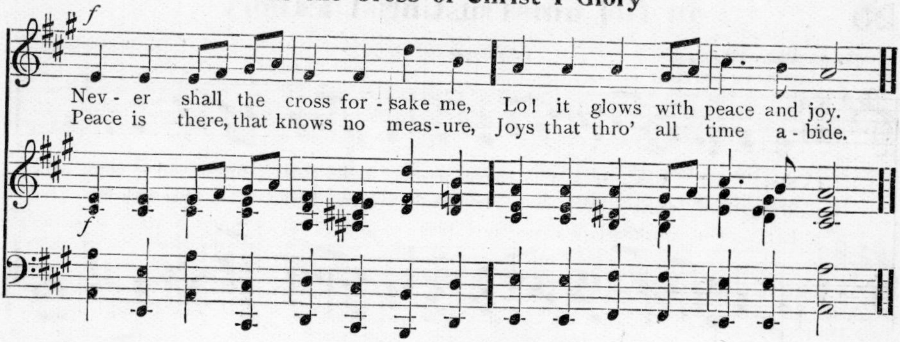
f
Nev - er shall the cross for - sake me, Lo! it glows with peace and joy.
Peace is there, that knows no meas - ure, Joys that thro' all time a - bide.
f

Praise the Lord

19

Anon.

(*Faben* 8. 7. 8. 7. D.)

John H. Willcox, 1849

1. Praise the Lord: ye heav'ns a - dore Him; Praise Him, an - gels, in the height;
2. Praise the Lord, for He is glo - rious; Nev - er shall His prom - ise fail:
Sun and moon, re - joice be - fore Him; Praise Him, all ye stars and light.
God hath made His saints vic - to - rious; Sin and death shall not pre - vail.
Praise the Lord, for He hath spo - ken; Worlds His might - y voice o - beyed:
Praise the God of our sal - va - tion; Hosts on high, His power pro - claim;
Laws which nev - er shall be bro - ken For their guid - ance hath He made.
Heaven and earth and all cre - a - tion, Laud and mag - ni - fy His Name.

20 I am Trusting Thee

Charles Albert Dickinson | (*Bullinger P. M.*) | E. W. Bullinger

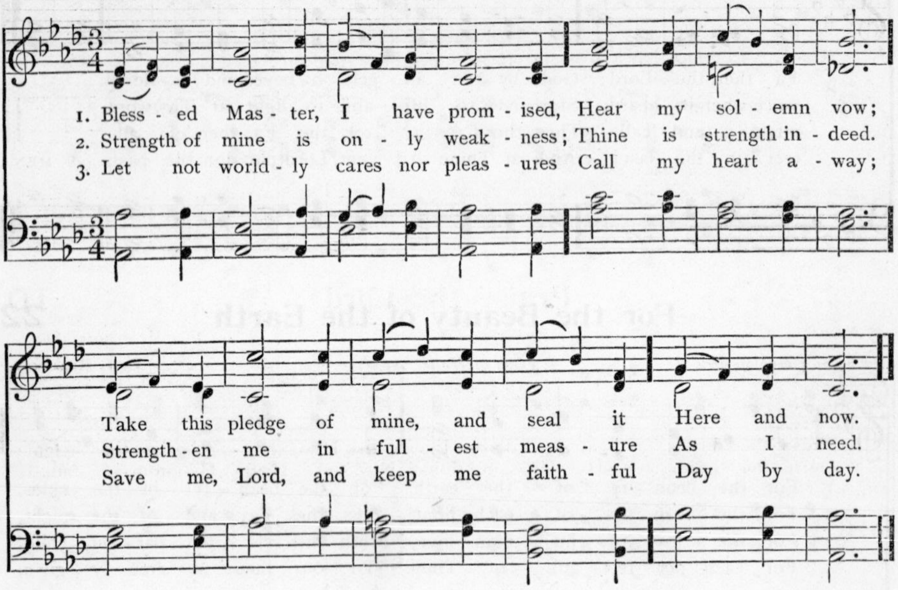
1. Bless - ed Mas - ter, I have prom - ised, Hear my sol - emn vow;
2. Strength of mine is on - ly weak - ness; Thine is strength in - deed.
3. Let not world - ly cares nor pleas - ures Call my heart a - way;
Take this pledge of mine, and seal it Here and now.
Strength - en me in full - est meas - ure As I need.
Save me, Lord, and keep me faith - ful Day by day.

21 Honor and Glory

E. A. Dayman | (*Naaman 10s*) | M. Costa. Arr. W. H. Callcott

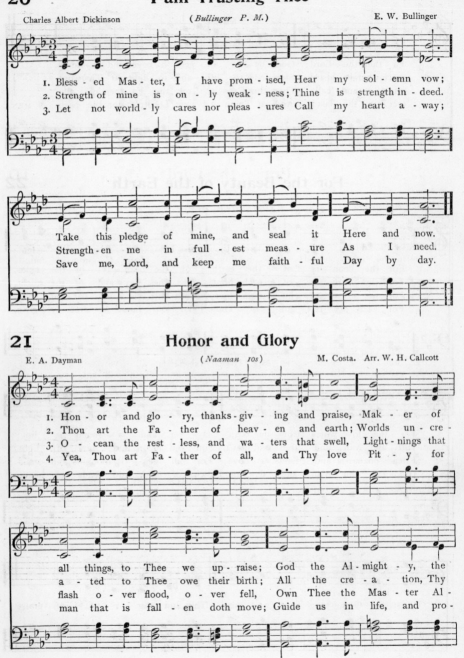

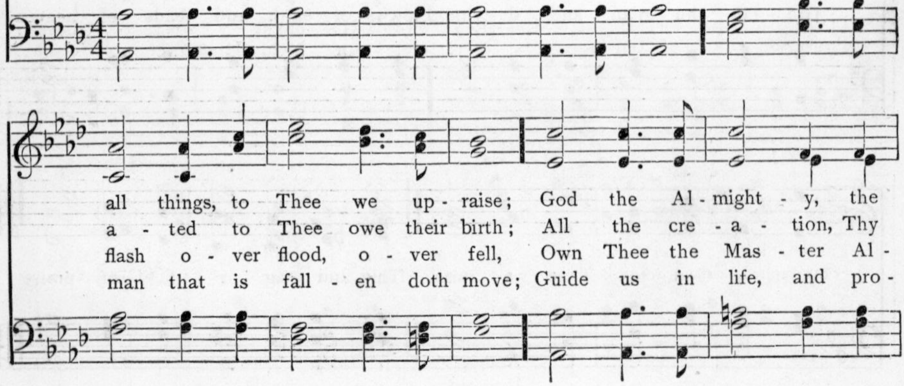
1. Hon - or and glo - ry, thanks - giv - ing and praise, Mak - er of
2. Thou art the Fa - ther of heav - en and earth; Worlds un - cre -
3. O - cean the rest - less, and wa - ters that swell, Light - nings that
4. Yea, Thou art Fa - ther of all, and Thy love Pit - y for
all things, to Thee we up - raise; God the Al - might - y, the
a - ted to Thee owe their birth; All the cre - a - tion, Thy
flash o - ver flood, o - ver fell, Own Thee the Mas - ter Al -
man that is fall - en doth move; Guide us in life, and pro -

Honor and Glory

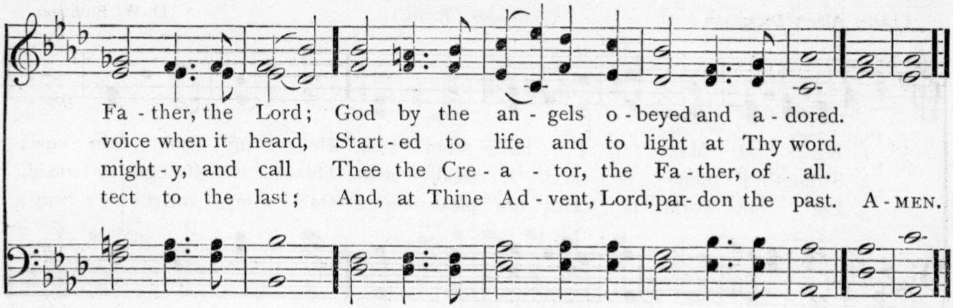

For the Beauty of the Earth 22

F. S. Pierpoint, 1864 (*God of Hosts 7s, 6l.*) E. J. Hopkins

23 Fairest Lord Jesus

Crusaders' Hymn. Tr. R. S. W. *(P. M.)* Arr. by R. S. Willis

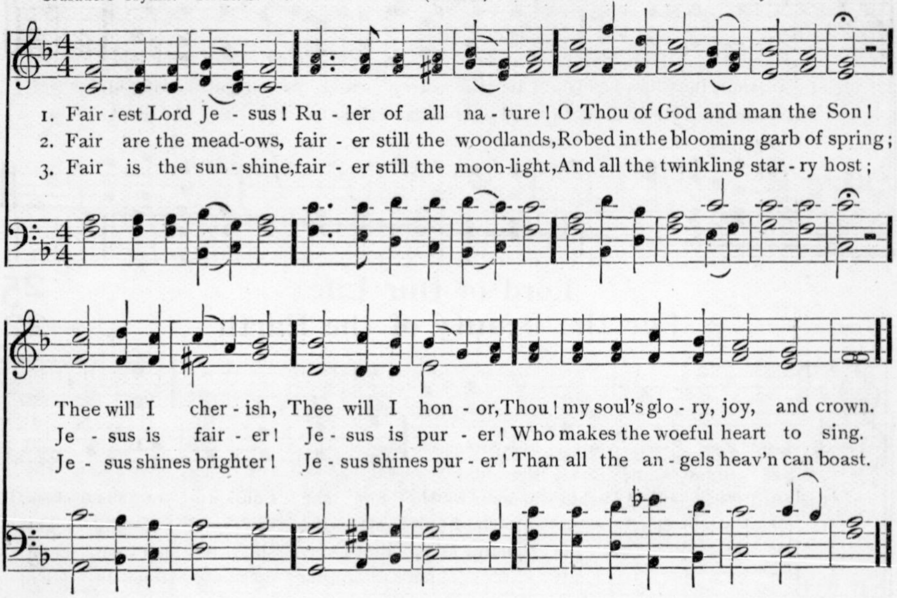
1. Fair - est Lord Je - sus ! Ru - ler of all na - ture ! O Thou of God and man the Son !
2. Fair are the mead-ows, fair - er still the woodlands, Robed in the blooming garb of spring ;
3. Fair is the sun - shine, fair - er still the moon-light, And all the twinkling star - ry host ;
Thee will I cher - ish, Thee will I hon - or, Thou ! my soul's glo - ry, joy, and crown.
Je - sus is fair - er ! Je - sus is pur - er ! Who makes the woeful heart to sing.
Je - sus shines brighter ! Je - sus shines pur - er ! Than all the an - gels heav'n can boast.

24 At the Name of Jesus

C. M. Noel *(6. 5. 6. 5. D.)* W. H. Monk

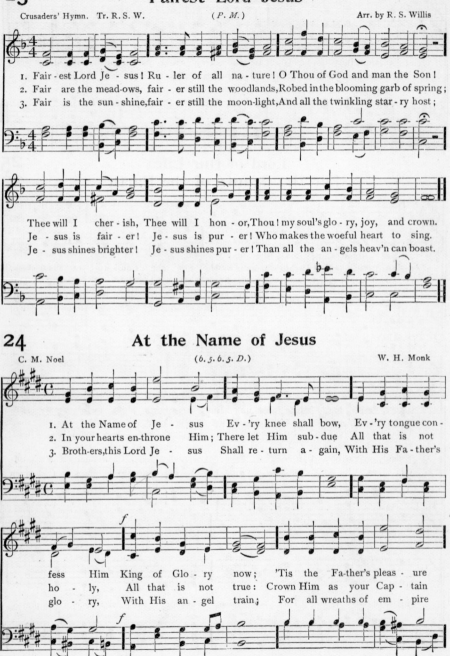

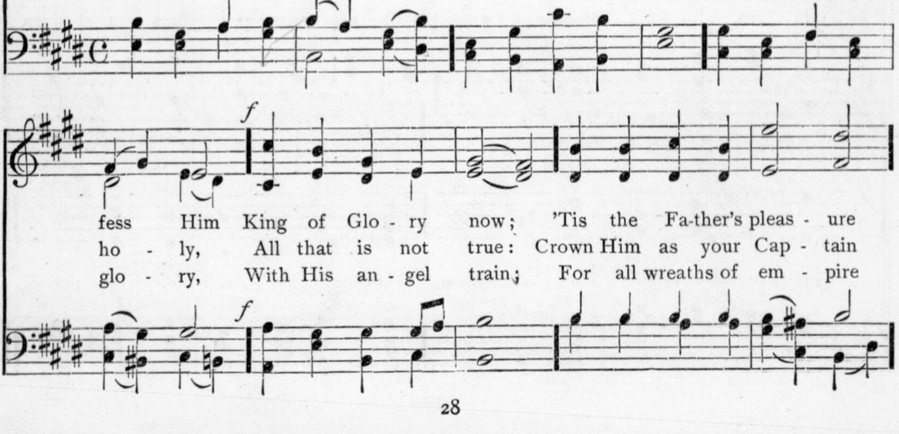
1. At the Name of Je - sus Ev - 'ry knee shall bow, Ev - 'ry tongue con -
2. In your hearts en-throne Him ; There let Him sub - due All that is not
3. Broth-ers, this Lord Je - sus Shall re - turn a - gain, With His Fa - ther's
f
fess Him King of Glo - ry now ; 'Tis the Fa-ther's pleas - ure
ho - ly, All that is not true : Crown Him as your Cap - tain
glo - ry, With His an - gel train ; For all wreaths of em - pire
f

At the Name of Jesus

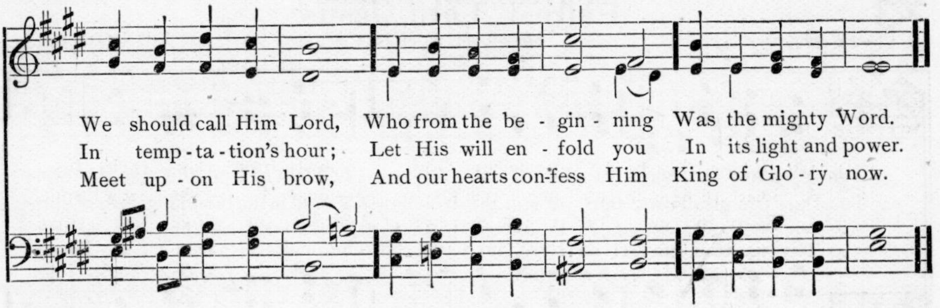
We should call Him Lord, Who from the be - gin - ning Was the mighty Word.
In temp - ta - tion's hour; Let His will en - fold you In its light and power.
Meet up - on His brow, And our hearts con-fess Him King of Glo - ry now.

Lord of Our Life 25

M. A. von Löwenstern, 1644
Tr. by P. Pusey

(*Cloisters* 11s. 5)

J. Barnby

1. Lord of our life, and God of our sal - va - tion, Star of our night, and hope of ev - 'ry na - tion, Hear and re - ceive Thy Church's sup - pli - ca - tion, Lord God al - might - y.
2. See round Thine ark the hun - gry bil - lows curl - ing; See how Thy foes their ban - ners are un - furl - ing, Lord, while their darts en - ven - omed they are hurl - ing, Thou canst pre - serve . . us.
3. Lord, Thou canst help when earth - ly ar - mor fail - eth, Lord, Thou canst save when dead - ly sin as - sail - eth, Lord, o'er Thy Church nor death nor hell pre - vail - eth; Grant us Thy peace, . . Lord.
4. Grant us Thy help till foes are back - ward driv - en, Grant them Thy truth, that they may be for - giv - en, Grant peace on earth, and, aft - er we have striv - en, Peace in Thy heav - en.

26 A Heart of Praise

Chas. Wesley, 1742 (*Beatitude C. M.*) J. B. Dykes, 1875

1. Oh, for a heart to praise my God, A heart from sin set free,
2. A heart re-signed, sub - mis - sive, meek, My dear Re - deem - er's throne,
3. A heart in ev - 'ry thought re - newed, And full of love di - vine,
4. Thy na- ture, gra - cious Lord, im - part; Come quick- ly from a - bove:

A heart that al - ways feels Thy blood, So free - ly shed for me.
Where on - ly Christ is heard to speak, Where Je - sus reigns a - lone.
Per - fect, and right, and pure, and good, A cop - y, Lord, of Thine.
Write Thy new name up - on my heart, Thy new, best name of Love.

27 Above the Clear Blue Sky

John Chandler, 1841 (*Chandler P. M.*) W. H. Harper

1. A-bove the clear blue sky, In heav-en's bright a- bode, The an - gel host on high
2. O bless -ed Lord, Thy truth To all Thy flock im - part, And teach us in our youth
3. O, may Thy ho - ly word Spread all the world a - round! And all with one ac - cord

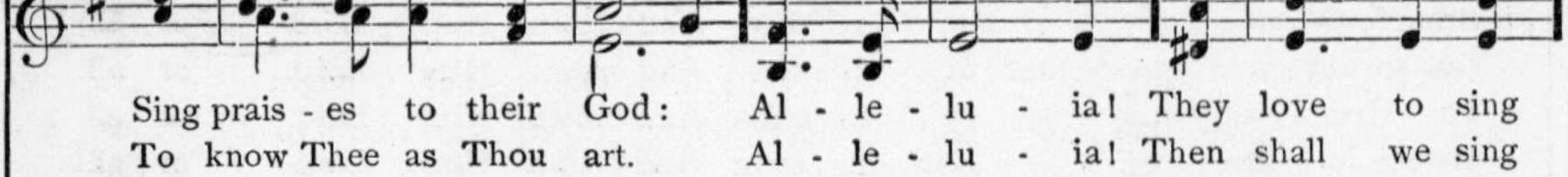

Sing prais - es to their God: Al - le - lu - ia! They love to sing
To know Thee as Thou art. Al - le - lu - ia! Then shall we sing
Up - lift the joy - ful sound: Al - le - lu - ia! All then shall sing

Above the Clear Blue Sky

Al - le - lu - ia! They love to sing To God their King Al - le - lu - ia!
Al - le - lu - ia! Then shall we sing To God our King Al - le - lu - ia!
Al - le - lu - ia! All then shall sing To God their King Al - le - lu - ia!

Lord of All

28

Edward Perronet

(*Coronation* C. M.)

O. Holden

1. All hail the pow'r of Je - sus' name! Let an - gels pros - trate fall;
2. Sin - ners, whose love can ne'er for - get The worm - wood and the gall;
3. Let ev - 'ry kin - dred, ev - 'ry tribe, On this ter - res - trial ball,
4. Oh, that with yon - der sa - cred throng, We at His feet may fall;
Bring forth the roy - al di - a - dem, And crown Him Lord of all;
Go, spread your tro - phies at His feet, And crown Him Lord of all;
To Him all maj - es - ty as - cribe, And crown Him Lord of all;
We'll join the ev - er - last - ing song And crown Him Lord of all;
Bring forth the roy - al - di a - dem, And crown Him Lord of all.
Go, spread your tro - phies at His feet, And crown Him Lord of all.
To Him all maj - es - ty as - cribe, And crown Him Lord of all.
We'll join the ev - er - last - ing song And crown Him Lord of all.

29 God, My King

Bishop Richard Mant, 1824 (*Stuttgart* 8. 7. 8. 7) Gotha Cantional, 1715

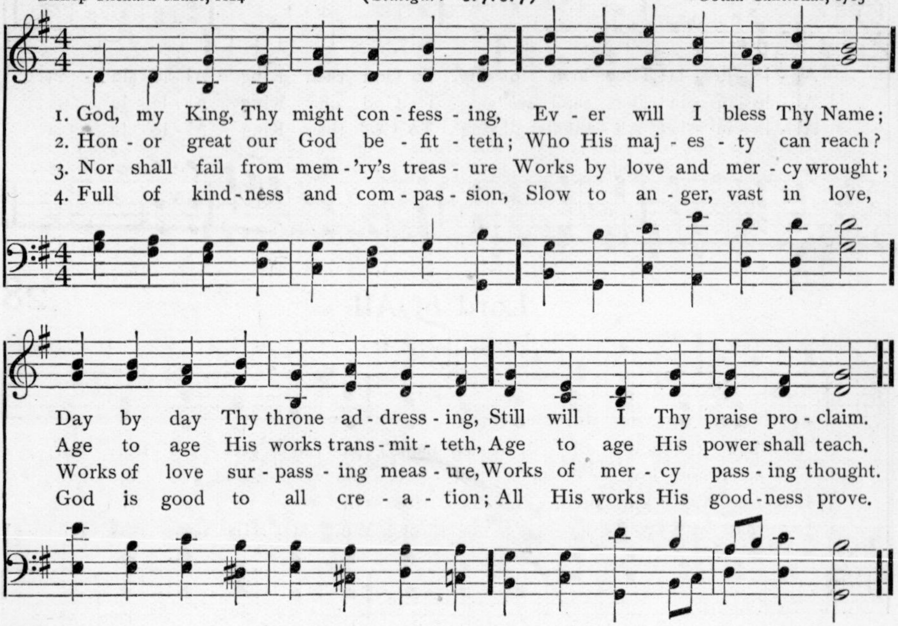
1. God, my King, Thy might con - fess - ing, Ev - er will I bless Thy Name;
2. Hon - or great our God be - fit - teth; Who His maj - es - ty can reach?
3. Nor shall fail from mem - 'ry's treas - ure Works by love and mer - cy wrought;
4. Full of kind - ness and com - pas - sion, Slow to an - ger, vast in love,
Day by day Thy throne ad - dress - ing, Still will I Thy praise pro - claim.
Age to age His works trans - mit - teth, Age to age His power shall teach.
Works of love sur - pass - ing meas - ure, Works of mer - cy pass - ing thought.
God is good to all cre - a - tion; All His works His good - ness prove.

30 My God, I Thank Thee

Adelaide A. Procter, 1864 (*Wentworth* 8. 4. 8. 4. 8. 4) F. C. Maker

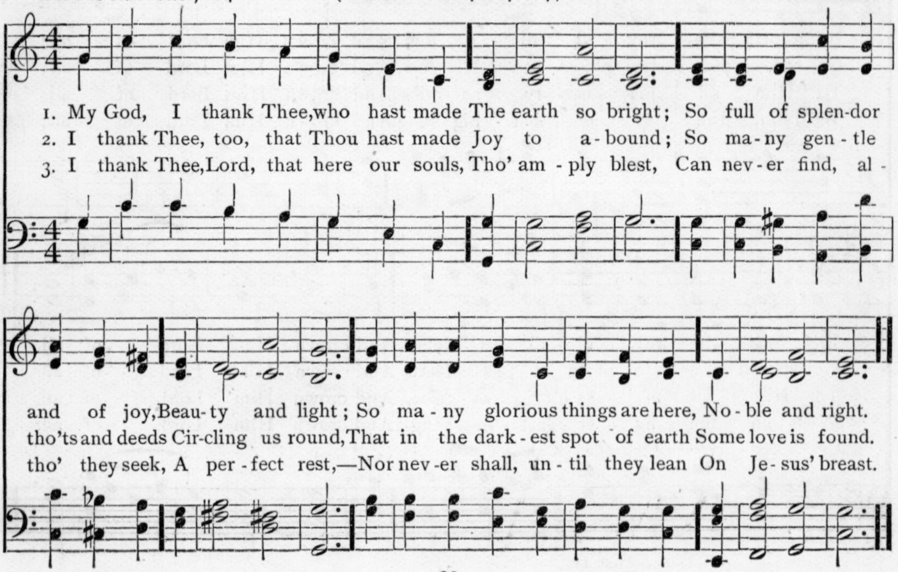
1. My God, I thank Thee, who hast made The earth so bright; So full of splen - dor
2. I thank Thee, too, that Thou hast made Joy to a - bound; So ma - ny gen - tle
3. I thank Thee, Lord, that here our souls, Tho' am - ply blest, Can nev - er find, al -
and of joy, Beau - ty and light; So ma - ny glorious things are here, No - ble and right.
tho'ts and deeds Cir - cling us round, That in the dark - est spot of earth Some love is found.
tho' they seek, A per - fect rest, — Nor nev - er shall, un - til they lean On Je - sus' breast.

Hear Our Prayer 31

Anon. (6s. 5s) John Adcock

1. Hear us, Heav'nly Fa - ther, Thou whose gen - tle care Tends the young and
2. Par - don our of - fen - ces; Guard us from all ill; Make us, like true
3. Let not sin be - guile us From Thy paths to stray; But with Thy great
fee - ble,— Hear our sim - ple pray'r! Hear our pray'r! Fa - ther, hear!
chil - dren, Love Thy ho - ly will. Hear our pray'r! Fa - ther, hear!
mer - cy Keep us night and day. Hear our pray'r! Fa - ther, hear!

Teach Us to Pray 32

(4. 8. 8. 4. 4) J. H. Tenney

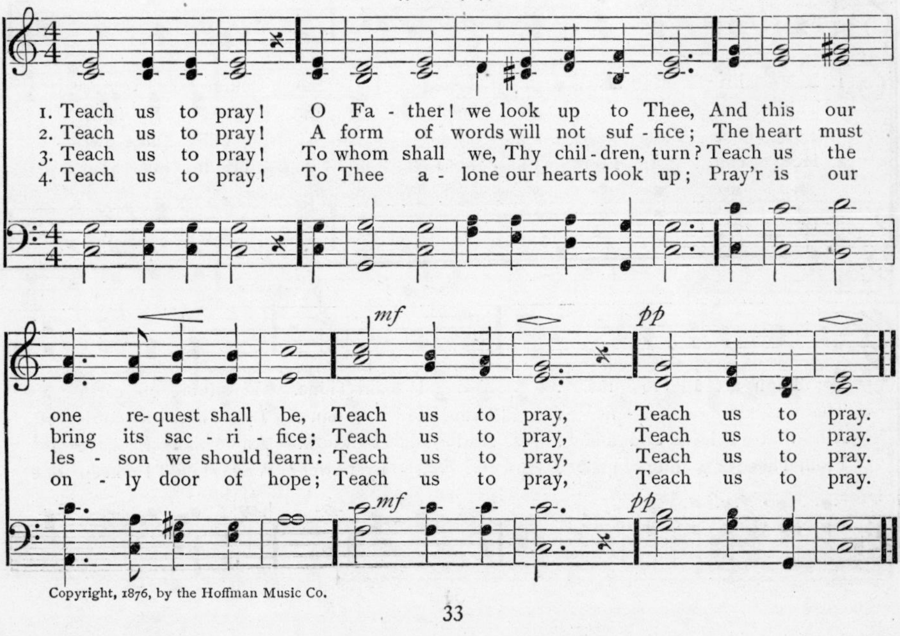
1. Teach us to pray! O Fa - ther! we look up to Thee, And this our
2. Teach us to pray! A form of words will not suf - fice; The heart must
3. Teach us to pray! To whom shall we, Thy chil - dren, turn? Teach us the
4. Teach us to pray! To Thee a - lone our hearts look up; Pray'r is our
one re - quest shall be, Teach us to pray, Teach us to pray.
bring its sac - ri - fice; Teach us to pray, Teach us to pray.
les - son we should learn: Teach us to pray, Teach us to pray.
on - ly door of hope; Teach us to pray, Teach us to pray.

Copyright, 1876, by the Hoffman Music Co.

33 Jesus Calls Us

Cecil F. Alexander (*Talmar* 8s. 7s) Isaac B. Woodbury

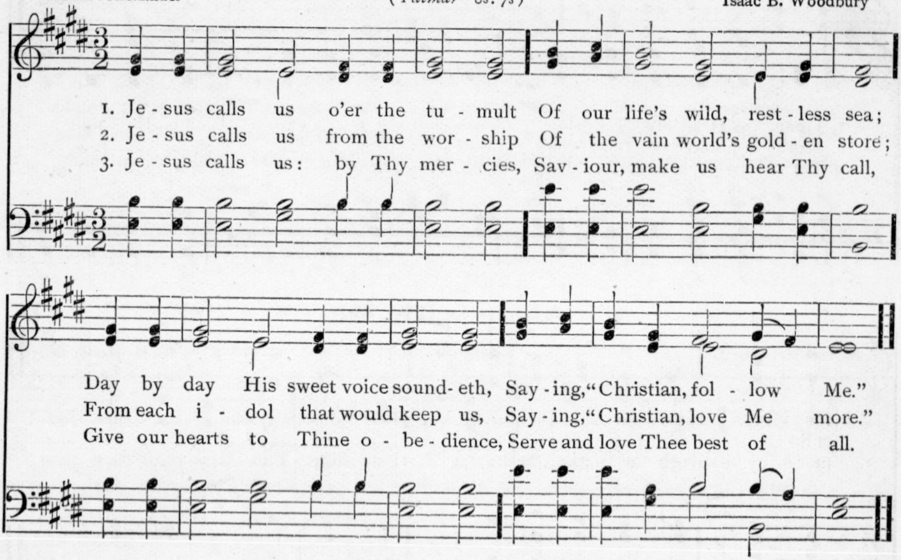
1. Je - sus calls us o'er the tu - mult Of our life's wild, rest - less sea;
2. Je - sus calls us from the wor - ship Of the vain world's gold - en store;
3. Je - sus calls us: by Thy mer - cies, Sav - iour, make us hear Thy call,
Day by day His sweet voice sound- eth, Say - ing, "Christian, fol - low Me."
From each i - dol that would keep us, Say - ing, "Christian, love Me more."
Give our hearts to Thine o - be - dience, Serve and love Thee best of all.

34 I Lift My Heart to Thee

Charles Edward Mudie (*Budleigh* 6. 4. 6. 4. 10. 10) Thomas Molleson Mudie

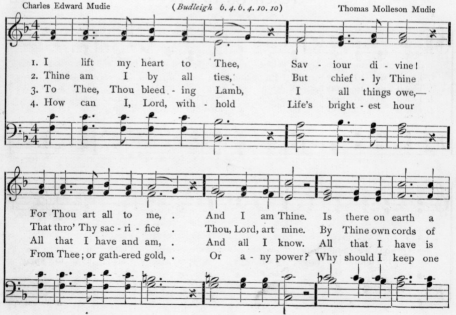

1. I lift my heart to Thee, Sav - iour di - vine!
2. Thine am I by all ties, But chief - ly Thine
3. To Thee, Thou bleed - ing Lamb, I all things owe,—
4. How can I, Lord, with - hold Life's bright - est hour
For Thou art all to me, . And I am Thine. Is there on earth a
That thro' Thy sac - ri - fice . Thou, Lord, art mine. By Thine own cords of
All that I have and am, . And all I know. All that I have is
From Thee; or gath-ered gold, . Or a - ny power? Why should I keep one

PRAYER

I Lift My Heart to Thee

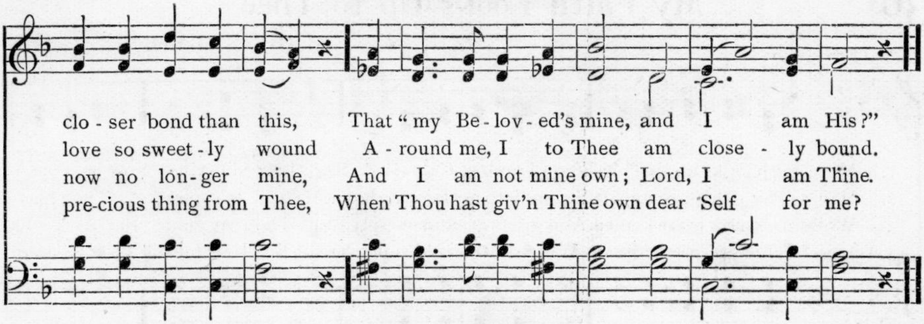
clo - ser bond than this, That "my Be - lov - ed's mine, and I am His?"
love so sweet - ly wound A - round me, I to Thee am close - ly bound.
now no lon - ger mine, And I am not mine own; Lord, I am Thine.
pre - cious thing from Thee, When Thou hast giv'n Thine own dear Self for me?

Abide with Me

35

H. F. Lyte, 1847 (*Eventide 10s*) W. H. Monk, 1861

1. A - bide with me: fast falls the e - ven - tide; The dark - ness deep - ens;
2. Swift to its close ebbs out life's lit - tle day; Earth's joys grow dim, its
3. I need Thy pres - ence ev - 'ry pass - ing hour: What but Thy grace can
4. Hold Thou Thy cross be - fore my clos - ing eyes; Shine thro' the gloom, and
Lord, with me a - bide: When oth - er help - ers fail, and com - forts flee,
glo - ries pass a - way; Change and de - cay in all a - round I see:
foil the tempt - er's power? Who like Thy - self my guide and stay can be?
point me to the skies. Heav'n's morn - ing breaks, and earth's vain shad - ows flee—
Help of the help - less, oh, a - bide with me!
O Thou who chan - gest not, a - bide with me!
Thro' cloud and sun - shine, oh, a - bide with me!
In life, in death, O Lord, a - bide with me! A - MEN.

36 My Faith Looks Up to Thee

R. Palmer, 1830 (*Olivet* 6s. 4s) Lowell Mason

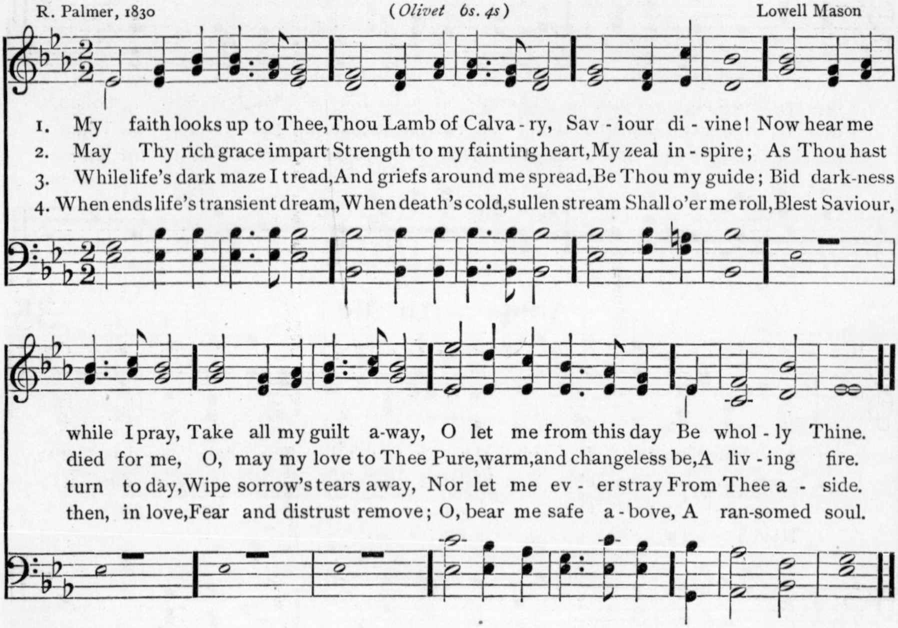
1. My faith looks up to Thee, Thou Lamb of Calva - ry, Sav - iour di - vine! Now hear me
2. May Thy rich grace impart Strength to my fainting heart, My zeal in - spire; As Thou hast
3. While life's dark maze I tread, And griefs around me spread, Be Thou my guide; Bid dark-ness
4. When ends life's transient dream, When death's cold, sullen stream Shall o'er me roll, Blest Saviour,
while I pray, Take all my guilt a-way, O let me from this day Be whol - ly Thine.
died for me, O, may my love to Thee Pure, warm, and changeless be, A liv - ing fire.
turn to day, Wipe sorrow's tears away, Nor let me ev - er stray From Thee a - side.
then, in love, Fear and distrust remove; O, bear me safe a - bove, A ran-somed soul.

37 To Thee, O Saviour Friend

Charles A. Dickinson Howard B. Grose, 1901

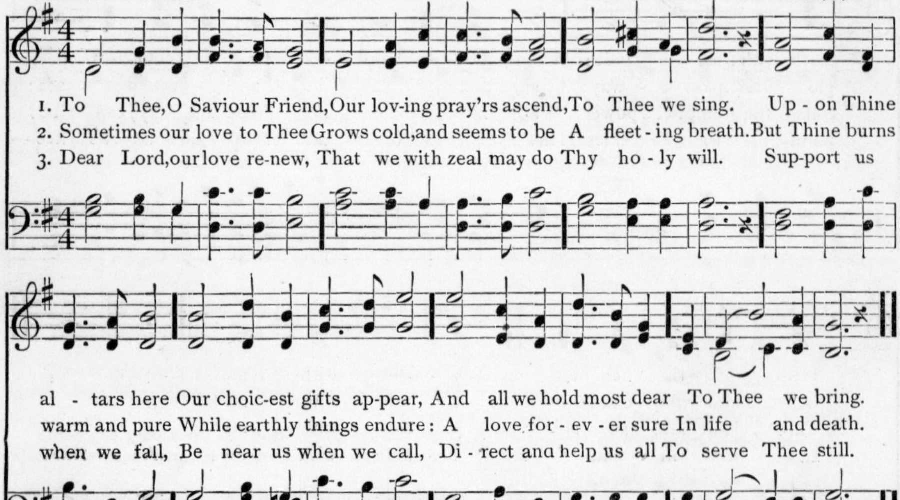
1. To Thee, O Saviour Friend, Our lov-ing pray'rs ascend, To Thee we sing. Up - on Thine
2. Sometimes our love to Thee Grows cold, and seems to be A fleet - ing breath. But Thine burns
3. Dear Lord, our love re-new, That we with zeal may do Thy ho - ly will. Sup-port us
al - tars here Our choic-est gifts ap-pear, And all we hold most dear To Thee we bring.
warm and pure While earthly things endure: A love for - ev - er sure In life and death.
when we fall, Be near us when we call, Di - rect and help us all To serve Thee still.

Copyright, 1901, by U. S. C. E.

Holy Ghost, with Light Divine

38

A. Reed — (*Mercy* 7s) — E. P. Parker. Arr. from Gottschalk

1. Ho - ly Ghost! with light di - vine, Shine up - on this heart of mine;
2. Ho - ly Ghost! with pow'r di - vine, Cleanse this guilt - y heart of mine;
3. Ho - ly Ghost! with joy di - vine, Cheer this saddened heart of mine;
4. Ho - ly Spir - it! all - di - vine, Dwell with - in this heart of mine;
Chase the shades of night a - way, Turn my dark - ness in - to day.
Long hath sin, with - out con - trol, Held do - min - ion o'er my soul.
Bid my ma - ny woes de - part, Heal my wound-ed, bleed - ing heart.
Cast down ev - 'ry i - dol - throne, Reign su - preme—and reign a - lone.

Pray, Always Pray

39

E. H. Bickersteth — (*Müller* 10. 10) — Hermann von Müller

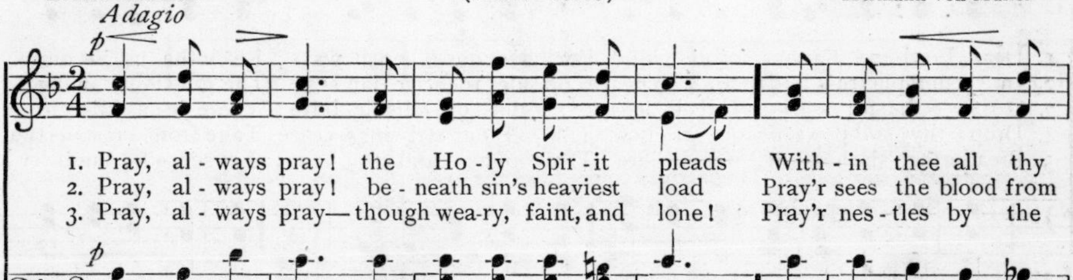
Adagio
p
1. Pray, al - ways pray! the Ho - ly Spir - it pleads With - in thee all thy
2. Pray, al - ways pray! be - neath sin's heaviest load Pray'r sees the blood from
3. Pray, al - ways pray— though wea - ry, faint, and lone! Pray'r nes - tles by the
p

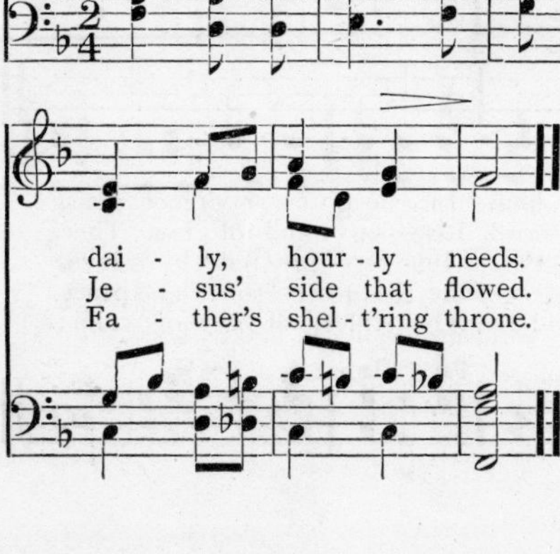
dai - ly, hour - ly needs.
Je - sus' side that flowed.
Fa - ther's shel - t'ring throne.

4 Pray, always pray! amid the world's turmoil
Prayer keeps the heart at rest, and nerves for toil.

5 Pray, always pray! if joys thy pathway throng,
Prayer strikes the harp, and sings the angels' song.

6 Pray, always pray! if loved ones pass the veil,
Prayer drinks with them of springs that cannot fail.

7 All earthly things with earth shall fade away;
Prayer grasps eternity: pray, always pray!

40 Saviour, Listen

Frances R. Havergal (7s) German Evening Hymn

Quietly

1. Now the light has gone a - way, Sav - iour, lis - ten while I pray.
2. Now my even - ing praise I give; Thou didst die that I might live,
3. Thou my best and kind- est Friend, Thou wilt love me to the end!

Help me ev - 'ry day to be Good and gen -tle, more like Thee.
All my bless-ings come from Thee, O how good Thou art to me!
Let me love Thee more and more, Al - ways bet -ter than be - fore.
A - MEN.

41 Forgive Us, Lord

J. G. Whittier, 1872 (*Elton* 8.6.8.8.6) F. C. Maker (1844–)

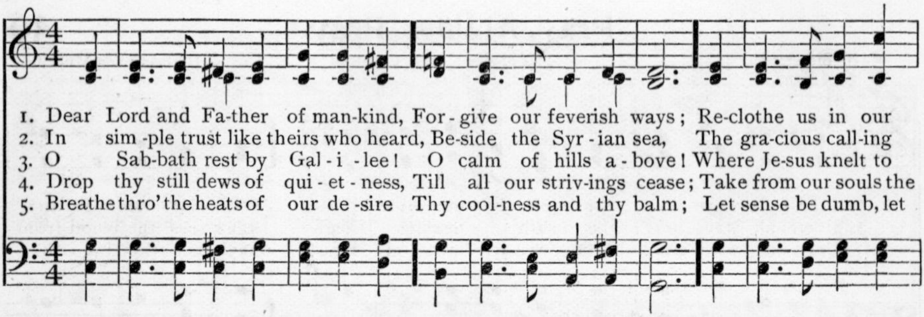
1. Dear Lord and Fa-ther of man-kind, For-give our feverish ways; Re-clothe us in our
2. In sim -ple trust like theirs who heard, Be-side the Syr - ian sea, The gra-cious call-ing
3. O Sab-bath rest by Gal - i - lee! O calm of hills a - bove! Where Je-sus knelt to
4. Drop thy still dews of qui - et - ness, Till all our striv-ings cease; Take from our souls the
5. Breathe thro' the heats of our de-sire Thy cool-ness and thy balm; Let sense be dumb, let

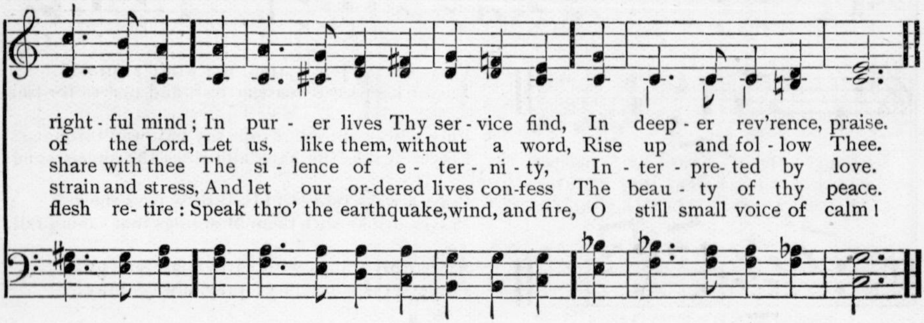
right - ful mind; In pur - er lives Thy ser - vice find, In deep - er rev'rence, praise.
of the Lord, Let us, like them, without a word, Rise up and fol - low Thee.
share with thee The si - lence of e - ter - ni - ty, In - ter - pre- ted by love.
strain and stress, And let our or-dered lives con-fess The beau - ty of thy peace.
flesh re- tire: Speak thro' the earthquake, wind, and fire, O still small voice of calm!

PRAYER

O Holy Saviour, Friend Unseen

42

Charlotte Elliott, 1834 (*Flemming* 8. 8. 8. 6) Arr. from Friedrich F. Flemming, 1810

1. O Ho-ly Sav-iour, Friend un - seen, Since on Thine arm Thou bidd'st me lean,
2. Blest with this fel - low - ship Di - vine, Take what Thou wilt, I'll ne'er re - pine;
3. What though the world de-ceit - ful prove, And earthly friends and joys re - move,
4. Though faith and hope are of - ten tried, I ask not, need not, aught be - side;
5. Blest is my lot, what - e'er be - fall; What can dis - turb me, who ap - pall,

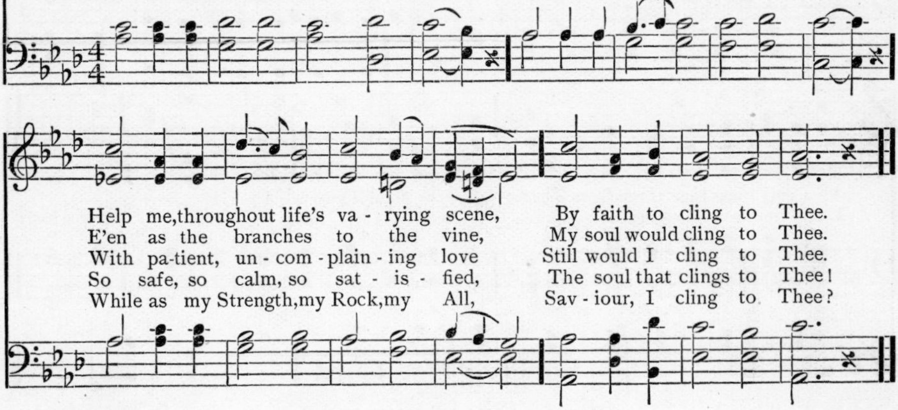

Help me, throughout life's va - rying scene, By faith to cling to Thee.
E'en as the branches to the vine, My soul would cling to Thee.
With pa-tient, un - com - plain - ing love Still would I cling to Thee.
So safe, so calm, so sat - is - fied, The soul that clings to Thee!
While as my Strength, my Rock, my All, Sav - iour, I cling to Thee?

Now the Day is Over

43

S. Baring-Gould, 1865 (*Emmelar* 6s. 5s) Joseph Barnby

1. Now the day is o - ver, Night is draw - ing nigh, Shad - ows of the
2. Je - sus, give the wea - ry Calm and sweet re - pose; With Thy tend'rest
3. Grant to lit - tle chil - dren Vis-ions bright of Thee; Guard the sai - lors

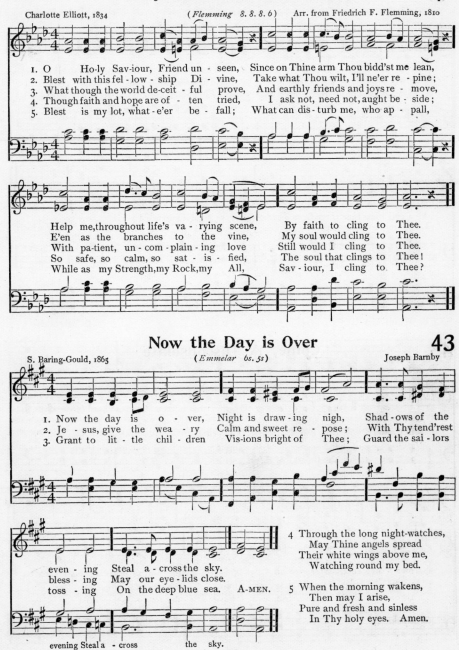

even - ing Steal a - cross the sky.
bless - ing May our eye - lids close.
toss - ing On the deep blue sea. A-MEN.

evening Steal a - cross the sky.

4 Through the long night-watches,
May Thine angels spread
Their white wings above me,
Watching round my bed.

5 When the morning wakens,
Then may I arise,
Pure and fresh and sinless
In Thy holy eyes. Amen.

44 No Time to Pray

Anon. (8. 8. 8. 4) Sir Arthur Sullivan

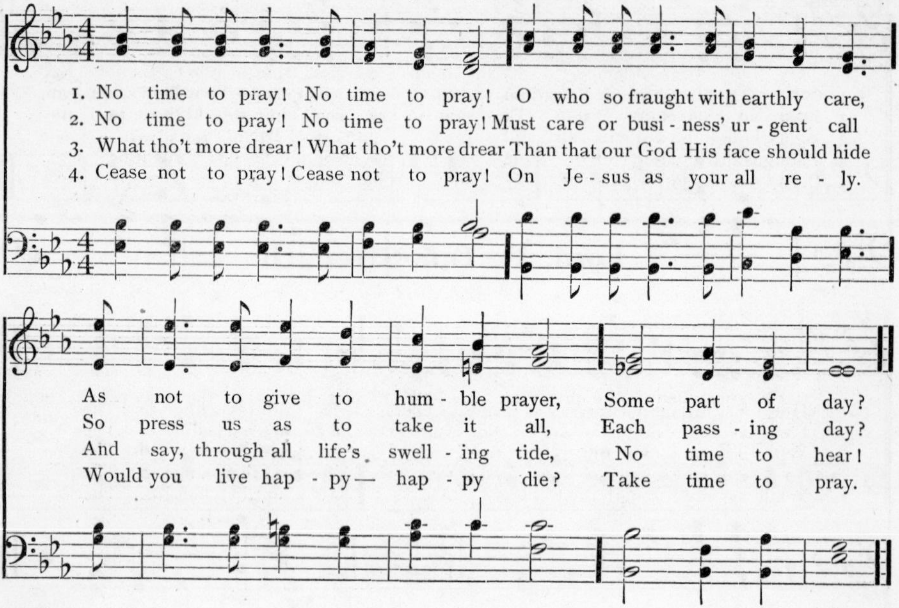
1. No time to pray! No time to pray! O who so fraught with earthly care,
2. No time to pray! No time to pray! Must care or busi - ness' ur - gent call
3. What tho't more drear! What tho't more drear Than that our God His face should hide
4. Cease not to pray! Cease not to pray! On Je - sus as your all re - ly.
As not to give to hum - ble prayer, Some part of day?
So press us as to take it all, Each pass - ing day?
And say, through all life's swell - ing tide, No time to hear!
Would you live hap - py— hap - py die? Take time to pray.

45 Come, Ye Disconsolate

Thos. Moore (11. 10. 11. 10) S. Webbe

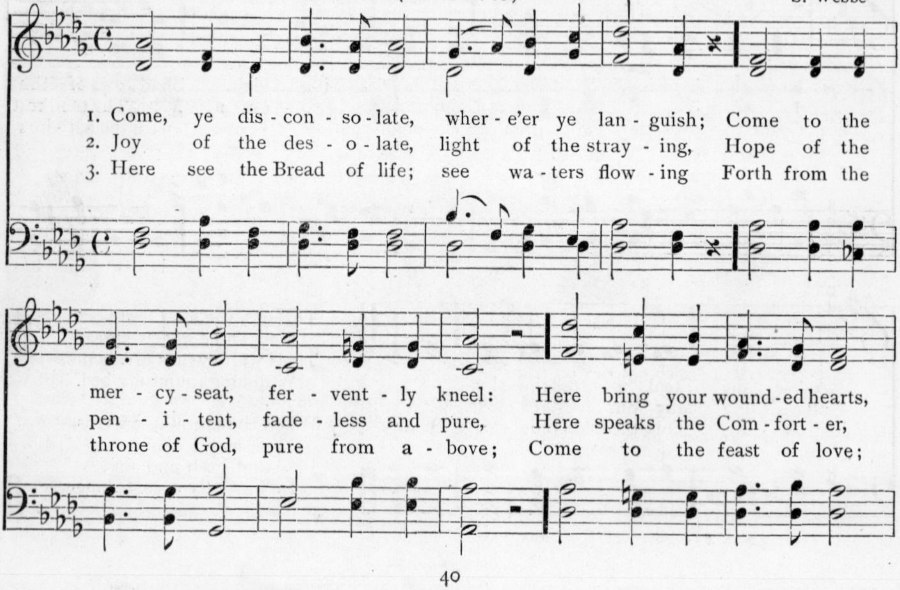
1. Come, ye dis - con - so - late, wher - e'er ye lan - guish; Come to the
2. Joy of the des - o - late, light of the stray - ing, Hope of the
3. Here see the Bread of life; see wa - ters flow - ing Forth from the
mer - cy - seat, fer - vent - ly kneel: Here bring your wound - ed hearts,
pen - i - tent, fade - less and pure, Here speaks the Com - fort - er,
throne of God, pure from a - bove; Come to the feast of love;

Come, Ye Disconsolate

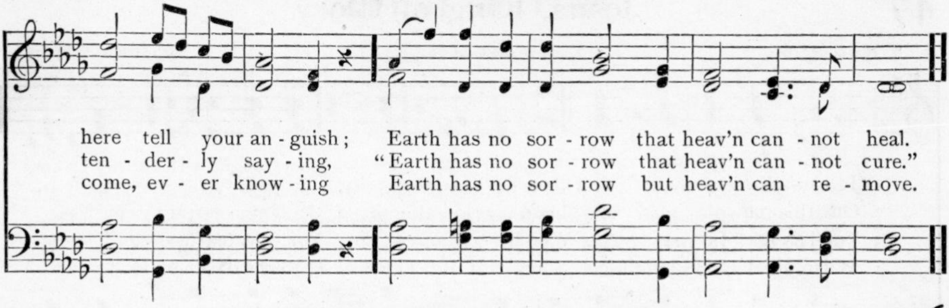
here tell your an - guish; Earth has no sor - row that heav'n can - not heal.
ten - der - ly say - ing, "Earth has no sor - row that heav'n can - not cure."
come, ev - er know - ing Earth has no sor - row but heav'n can re - move.

Lord, Be Our Strength 46

Anon. (*Althorp* 8s. 7s. D.) G. Lomas

1. Fa - ther, hear the pray'r we of - fer! Not for ease that pray'r shall be,
2. Be our strength in hours of weak - ness, In our wan-d'rings, be our guide;
But for strength that we may ev - er Live our lives cour - age - ous - ly.
Thro' en - deav - or, hard - ship, dan - ger, Fa - ther, be Thou at our side!
Not for - ev - er by still wa - ters Would we i - dly, qui - et stay,
Ours to sow the seed in sor - row, Thine to bid it spring and grow;
But would smite the liv - ing foun - tains From the rocks a - long our way.
And the gold - en days of au - tumn Will a pre - cious har - vest show.

47 Jesus, King of Glory

E. Harland, 1863 (*Wakefield* 6s, 5s)

1. Je - sus, King of glo - ry Throned a-bove the sky, Je - sus, ten - der Sav - iour,
2. On this day of glad - ness, Bend-ing low the knee In Thine earthly tem - ple,
3. For Thy faith-ful ser - vants Who have en-tered in; For Thy fear-less sol - diers
4. When the shadows length-en, Show us, Lord, Thy way; Thro' the darkness lead us
Hear Thy chil-dren cry. Par - don our trans - gres - sions, Cleanse us from our sin;
Lord, we wor - ship Thee; Cel - e - brate Thy good - ness, Mer - cy, grace, and truth,
Who have conquered sin; For the countless le - gions Who have followed Thee,
To the heav'n-ly day. When our course is fin - ished, End - ed all the strife,
REFRAIN
By Thy Spir - it help us Heav'n-ly life to win. Je - sus, King of glo - ry,
All Thy lov-ing guid - ance Of our heedless youth.
Heed-less of the dan - ger, On to vic - to - ry.
Grant us with the faith - ful Palms and crowns of life.
Throned a - bove the sky, Je - sus, ten - der Sav - iour, Hear Thy chil-dren cry.

Love Divine, All Loves Excelling

Chas. Wesley, 1747 (*Beecher* 8s. 7s. D.) John Zundel, 1870

1. Love Di - vine, all loves ex - cel - ling, Joy of heav'n to earth come down;
2. Breathe, O breathe, Thy lov - ing Spir - it In - to ev - 'ry trou - bled breast;
3. Come, Al - might - y to de - liv - er, Let us all Thy life re - ceive;
4. Fin - ish then Thy new cre - a - tion, Pure and spot - less let us be;
Fix in us Thy hum - ble dwell - ing, All Thy faith - ful mer - cies crown;
Let us all in Thee in - her - it, Let us find Thy prom - ised rest;
Speed - i - ly re - turn, and nev - er, Nev - er more Thy tem - ples leave.
Let us see Thy great sal va - tion Per - fect - ly re - stored in Thee:
Je - sus, Thou art all com - pas - sion, Pure un - bound - ed love Thou art;
Take a - way our love of sin - ning, Al - pha and O - me - ga be,
Thee we would be al - ways bless - ing, Serve Thee as Thy hosts a - bove,
Chang'd from glo - ry un - to glo - ry, Till in heav'n we take our place
Vis - it us with Thy sal - va - tion, En - ter ev - 'ry trem - bling heart.
End of faith, as its be - gin - ning, Set our hearts at lib - er - ty.
Pray, and praise Thee with - out ceas - ing, Glo - ry in Thy per - fect love.
Till we cast our crowns be - fore Thee, Lost in won - der, love, and praise.

49 Lord, as to Thy Dear Cross We Flee

J. H. Gurney, 1838 (*St. Agnes C. M.*) Rev. John B. Dykes, 1866

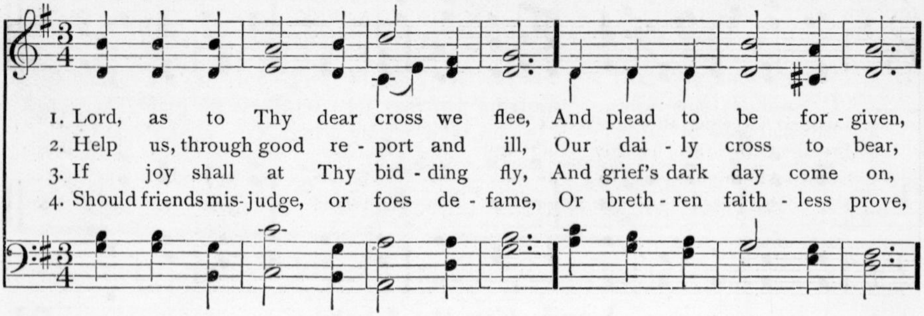
1. Lord, as to Thy dear cross we flee, And plead to be for - given,
2. Help us, through good re - port and ill, Our dai - ly cross to bear,
3. If joy shall at Thy bid - ding fly, And grief's dark day come on,
4. Should friends mis - judge, or foes de - fame, Or breth - ren faith - less prove,

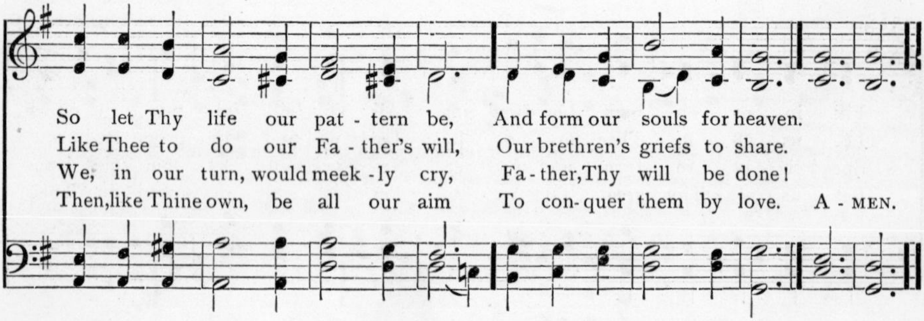
So let Thy life our pat - tern be, And form our souls for heaven.
Like Thee to do our Fa - ther's will, Our brethren's griefs to share.
We, in our turn, would meek - ly cry, Fa - ther, Thy will be done!
Then, like Thine own, be all our aim To con - quer them by love. A - MEN.

50 In the Hour of Trial

James Montgomery, 1834 (*Parole 6s. 5s. D.*) S. Lane

1. In the hour of tri - al, Je - sus, pray for me; Lest, by base de -
2. If, with sore af - flic - tion, Thou in love chas - tise, Pour Thy ben - e -
3. When my lamp low burn - ing, Sinks in mor - tal pain; Earth to earth re -

ni - al, I de - part from Thee. When Thou seest me wa - ver,
dic - tion On the sac - ri - fice. Free - ly on Thine al - tar
turn - ing, Dust to dust a - gain; On Thy truth re - ly - ing,

In the Hour of Trial

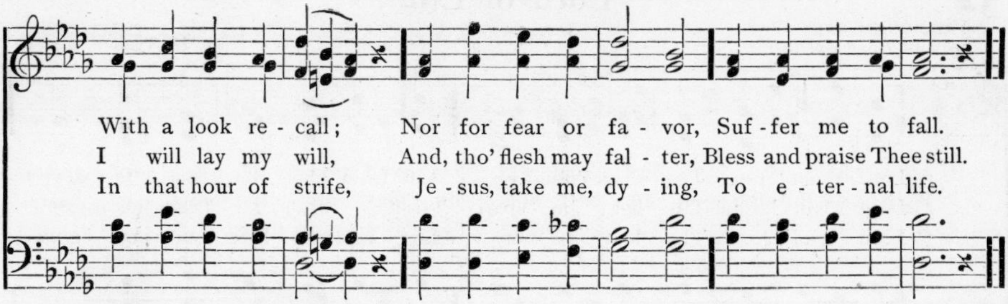
With a look re - call; Nor for fear or fa - vor, Suf - fer me to fall.
I will lay my will, And, tho' flesh may fal - ter, Bless and praise Thee still.
In that hour of strife, Je - sus, take me, dy - ing, To e - ter - nal life.

Lead, Kindly Light 51

J. H. Newman (*Lux Benigna* 10s. 4s) J. B. Dykes

1. Lead, kind - ly Light! a - mid th'en - cir - cling gloom, Lead Thou me on; The night is
2. I was not ev - er thus, nor prayed that Thou Shouldst lead me on; I loved to
3. So long Thy pow'r has bless'd me, sure it still Will lead me on O'er moor and
dark, and I am far from home, Lead Thou me on; Keep Thou my feet; I
choose and see my path; but now Lead Thou me on; I loved the gar - ish
fen, o'er crag and tor - rent, till The night is gone; And with the morn those
do not ask to see The dis - tant scene; one step e - nough for me.
day, and spite of fears, Pride ruled my will. Re - mem - ber not past years.
an - gel fa - ces smile Which I have loved long since, and lost a - while!

52 Lord of Life

Howard B. Grose, 1901 (7. 7. 7. 6.) J. H. Tenney, 1901

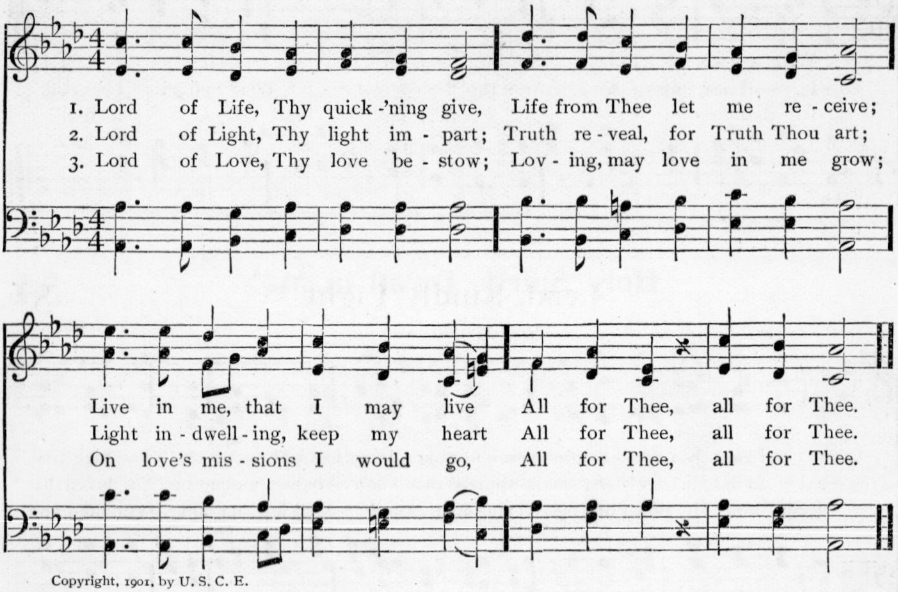
1. Lord of Life, Thy quick-'ning give, Life from Thee let me re-ceive;
2. Lord of Light, Thy light im-part; Truth re-veal, for Truth Thou art;
3. Lord of Love, Thy love be-stow; Lov-ing, may love in me grow;
Live in me, that I may live All for Thee, all for Thee.
Light in-dwell-ing, keep my heart All for Thee, all for Thee.
On love's mis-sions I would go, All for Thee, all for Thee.

Copyright, 1901, by U. S. C. E.

53 More Love to Thee

Elizabeth Payson Prentiss (*Proprior Deo* 6. 4. 6. 4. 6. 6. 4) Sir Arthur Sullivan

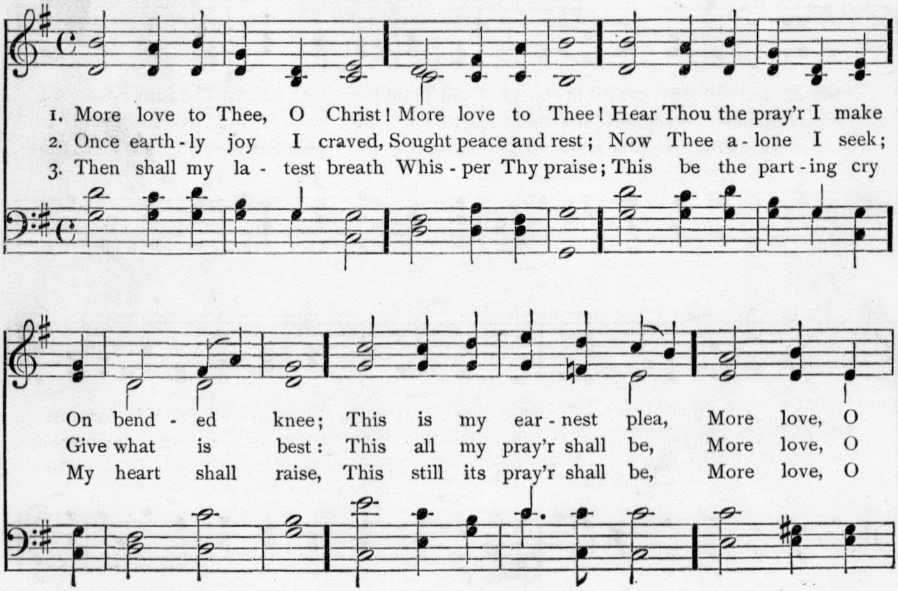
1. More love to Thee, O Christ! More love to Thee! Hear Thou the pray'r I make
2. Once earth-ly joy I craved, Sought peace and rest; Now Thee a-lone I seek;
3. Then shall my la-test breath Whis-per Thy praise; This be the part-ing cry
On bend-ed knee; This is my ear-nest plea, More love, O
Give what is best: This all my pray'r shall be, More love, O
My heart shall raise, This still its pray'r shall be, More love, O

More Love to Thee

Christ, to Thee, More love to Thee, More love to Thee! A - MEN.

Holy Spirit, Dwell in Me 54

E. S. B. (7s. 5s) E. S. Black

1. Ho - ly Spir - it, dwell in me, Teach mine er - ring feet the way; As I jour - ney
2. Ho - ly Spir - it, dwell in me, Fill my soul with Thy rich grace; Let me all the
3. Ho - ly Spir - it, dwell in me, Till life's night has passed a - way; When with rap - ture
here be - low, Guide me ev - 'ry day. Show me what I ought to do,
beau - ty see, In my Sav - iour's face. Till at last His life shall be
I shall wake In e - ter - nal day. I shall dwell with Christ my Lord
Help me shun the wrong, In this va - ried chain of life Make the weak link strong.
Mir - rored in mine own, And the like - ness God can see, To His own dear Son.
In our heav'n - ly home, And He will pre - sent me then, Fault - less at the throne.

Copyright, 1899, by J. Wilbur Chapman. Used by per.

55 Father, Whate'er of Earthly Bliss

A. Steele — L. Mason

1. Fa - ther, what - e'er of earth - ly bliss Thy sov - 'reign will de - nies,
2. Give me a calm and thank - ful heart, From ev - 'ry mur - mur free;
3. Let the sweet hope that Thou art mine My path of life at - tend:
Ac - cept - ed at Thy throne of grace Let this pe - ti - tion rise.
The blessings of Thy grace im - part, And make me live to Thee.
Thy presence thro' my jour - ney shine, And crown my jour - ney's end. AMEN.

56 Heavenly Father

Response — Beethoven

p Andante
Heav'n - ly Fa - ther, gra - cious - ly hear us; Hear the pe - ti - tions we
p
of - fer be - fore Thee, Let Thy mer - cy rest up - on us,
pp
Heav'n - ly Fa - ther, gra - cious - ly hear us, Hear our pray'r, Hear our pray'r. A - MEN.

I am His, and He is Mine

Rev. Wade Robinson *(7s. D.)* J. Mountain

Smoothly
1. Loved with ev - er - last - ing love, Led by grace that love to know;
2. Heaven a - bove is soft - er blue, Earth a - round is sweet-er green!
3. Things that once were wild a - larms Can - not now dis - turb my rest;
4. His for - ev - er, on - ly His; Who the Lord and me shall part?
Spir - it, breath - ing from a - bove, Thou hast taught me it is so!
Some-thing lives in ev - 'ry hue Christ - less eyes have nev - er seen:
Closed in ev - er - last - ing arms, Pil - lowed on the lov - ing breast.
Ah, with what a rest of bliss, Christ can fill the lov - ing heart!
Oh, this full and per - fect peace! Oh, this trans - port all di - vine!
Birds with glad - der songs o'er - flow, Flowers with deep - er beau - ties shine,
Oh, to lie for - ev - er here, Doubt and care and self re - sign,
Heaven and earth may fade and flee, First - born light in gloom de - cline;
Repeat last two lines of each verse as CHORUS p
In a love, which can - not cease, I am His, and He is mine.
Since I know, as now I know, I am His, and He is mine.
While He whis - pers in my ear— I am His, and He is mine.
But, while God and I shall be, I am His, and He is mine.

58 Our Blest Redeemer

H. Auber, 1829 — (*St. Cuthbert* 8. 6. 8. 4) — J. B. Dykes, 1861

1. Our blest Re-deem - er, ere He breathed His ten - der, last fare-well,
2. He came sweet in - fluence to im - part, A gra - cious, will - ing guest,
3. And His that gen - tle voice we hear, Soft as the breath of ev'n,
4. And ev - 'ry vir - tue we pos - sess, And ev - 'ry vic - t'ry won,
5. Spir - it of pu - ri - ty and grace, Our weak - ness, pity - ing, see;

A Guide, a Com - fort - er, bequeathed With us to dwell.
While He can find one hum - ble heart Where-in to rest.
That checks each tho't, that calms each fear, And speaks of heav'n.
And ev - 'ry tho't of ho - li - ness Are His a - lone.
O make our hearts Thy dwelling - place, And wor - thier Thee. A - MEN.

59 Guard Thy Lips

S. G. Fleet, 1818 — (*Leslie* 7s. 6l.) — H. D. Leslie, 1872

1. Words are things of lit - tle cost, Quick - ly spo - ken, quick - ly lost;
2. Oh, how oft - en ours have been I - dle words, and words of sin!
3. Grant us, Lord, from day to day, Strength to watch and grace to pray;

We for-get them, but they stand Wit - ness-es at God's right hand, And their tes - ti -
Words of an - ger, scorn and pride, Or de-sire our faults to hide, Envious tales, or
May our lips, from sin set free, Love to speak and sing of Thee, Till in heav'n we

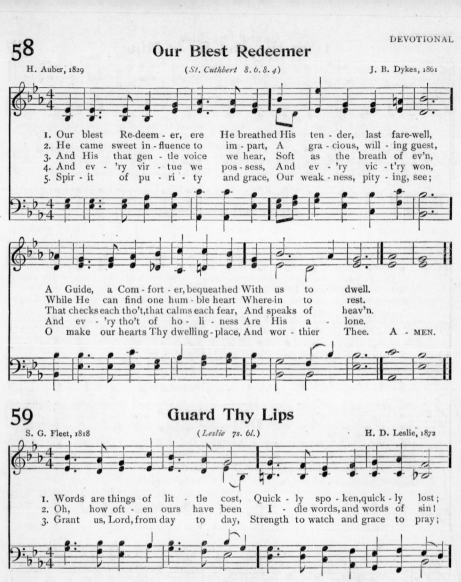

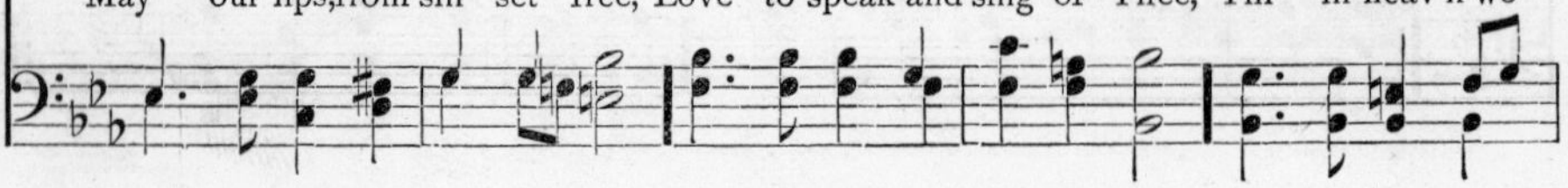

Guard Thy Lips

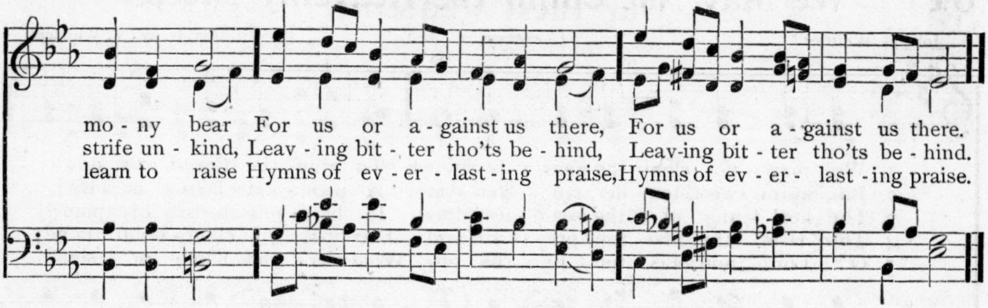
mo - ny bear For us or a - gainst us there, For us or a - gainst us there.
strife un - kind, Leav - ing bit - ter tho'ts be - hind, Leav-ing bit - ter tho'ts be - hind.
learn to raise Hymns of ev - er - last - ing praise, Hymns of ev - er - last - ing praise.

Jesus All the Way

60

Flora Kirkland (*Isaiah 41: 10*) W. S. Weeden

1. I am walk - ing thro' this earth - life, Oft - en wea - ry, oft - en sad;
2. I am trav - 'ling to a cit - y Where the light is nev - er dim,
3. I am look - ing for re - demp - tion Thro' the mer - its of my King;
But my Sav - iour walk - eth with me, And His pres - ence makes me glad.
And my Sav - iour leads so gen - tly, It is sweet to walk with Him.
Bless-ed beams of free sal - va - tion Shine a - bout me as I sing.
CHORUS
Je - sus know - eth ev - 'ry sor - row, Je - sus know - eth ev - 'ry fear;
And He whis - pers thro' life's shad - ows, "Do not trem - ble, I am near!"

Copyright, 1899, by W. S. Weeden. From Christian Hymns. Used by per.

61 We May Not Climb the Heavenly Steeps

John G. Whittier (*Serenity C. M.*) Arr. fr. W. V. Wallace

1. We may not climb the heav'n-ly steeps To bring the Lord Christ down;
2. But warm, sweet, ten-der, e-ven yet A pres-ent help is He;
3. The heal-ing of the seam-less dress Is by our beds of pain;
4. Thro' Him the first fond pray'rs are said Our lips of child-hood frame;
5. O Lord and Mas-ter of us all, What-e'er our name or sign,

In vain we search the low-est deeps, For Him no depths can drown.
And faith has yet its Ol-i-vet, And love its Gal-i-lee.
We touch Him in life's throng and press, And we are whole a-gain.
The last low whis-pers of our dead Are bur-dened with His name.
We own Thy sway, we hear Thy call, We test our lives by Thine!

Used by per. of Oliver Ditson Co., owner of copyright

62 My Jesus, as Thou Wilt

Benjamin Schmolk, 1672–1737 (*6s Iambic*) Carl M. von Weber
Jane Borthwick, tr.

1. My Je-sus, as Thou wilt! Oh, may Thy will be mine; In-to Thy
2. My Je-sus, as Thou wilt! Tho' seen thro' ma-ny a tear, Let not my
3. My Je-sus, as Thou wilt! All shall be well for me; Each chan-ging

hand of love I would my all re-sign; Thro' sor-row, or thro' joy,
star of hope Grow dim or dis-ap-pear; Since Thou on earth hast wept,
fu-ture scene I glad-ly trust with Thee; Straight to my home a-bove

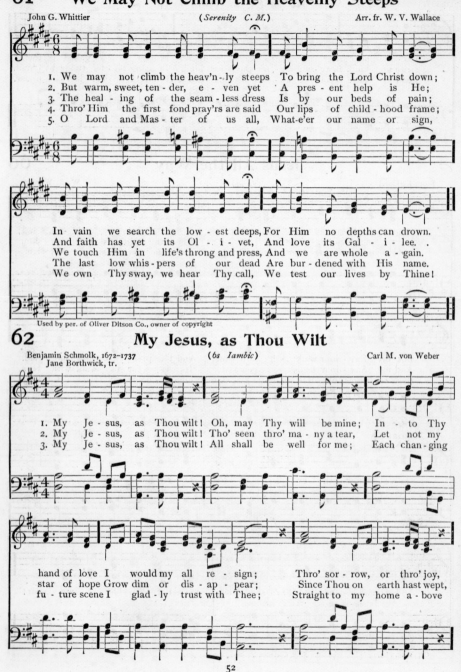

My Jesus, as Thou Wilt

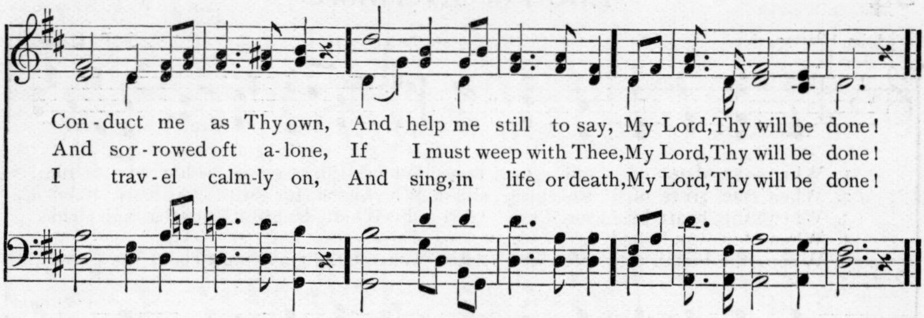
Con - duct me as Thy own, And help me still to say, My Lord, Thy will be done!
And sor - rowed oft a - lone, If I must weep with Thee, My Lord, Thy will be done!
I trav - el calm - ly on, And sing, in life or death, My Lord, Thy will be done!

O Sacred Head, Now Wounded 63

Tr. James W. Alexander (*Aurelia* 7s. 6s. D.) Samuel S. Wesley

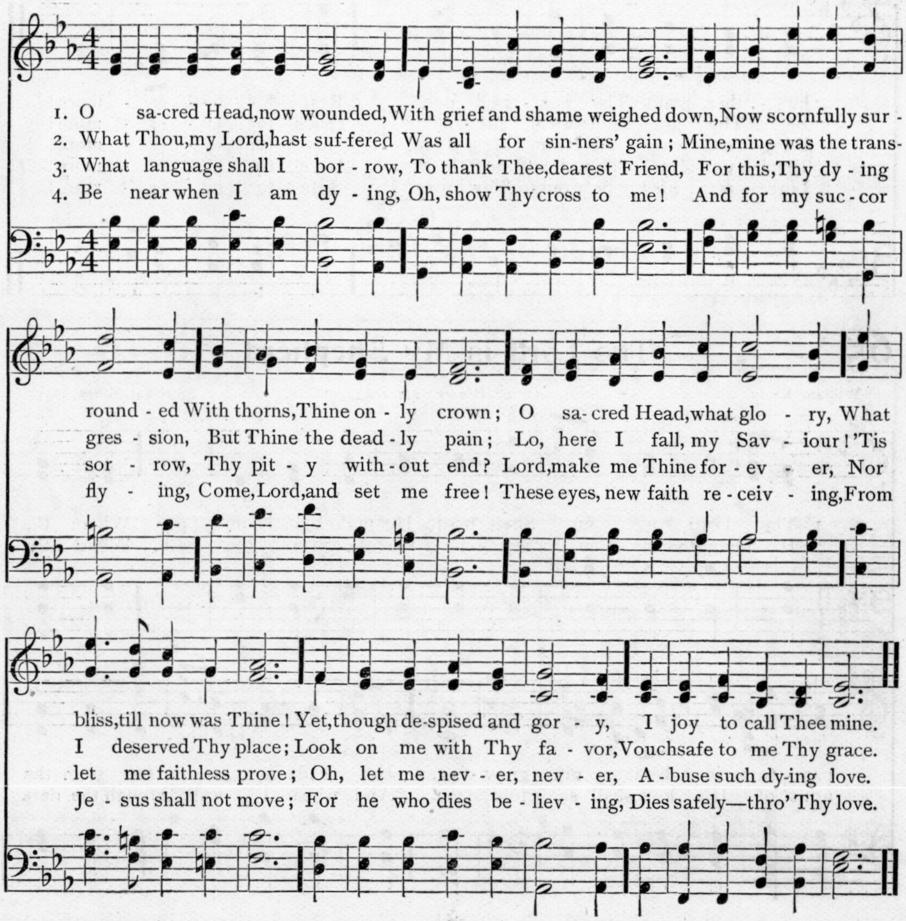
1. O sa - cred Head, now wounded, With grief and shame weighed down, Now scornfully sur - round - ed With thorns, Thine on - ly crown; O sa - cred Head, what glo - ry, What bliss, till now was Thine! Yet, though de - spised and gor - y, I joy to call Thee mine.
2. What Thou, my Lord, hast suf - fered Was all for sin - ners' gain; Mine, mine was the trans - gres - sion, But Thine the dead - ly pain; Lo, here I fall, my Sav - iour! 'Tis I deserved Thy place; Look on me with Thy fa - vor, Vouchsafe to me Thy grace.
3. What language shall I bor - row, To thank Thee, dearest Friend, For this, Thy dy - ing sor - row, Thy pit - y with - out end? Lord, make me Thine for - ev - er, Nor let me faithless prove; Oh, let me nev - er, nev - er, A - buse such dy - ing love.
4. Be near when I am dy - ing, Oh, show Thy cross to me! And for my suc - cor fly - ing, Come, Lord, and set me free! These eyes, new faith re - ceiv - ing, From Je - sus shall not move; For he who dies be - liev - ing, Dies safely—thro' Thy love.

64 Life For Evermore

John Ellerton, 1871 — (*Vesperi Lux* 7s. 5) — J. B. Dykes

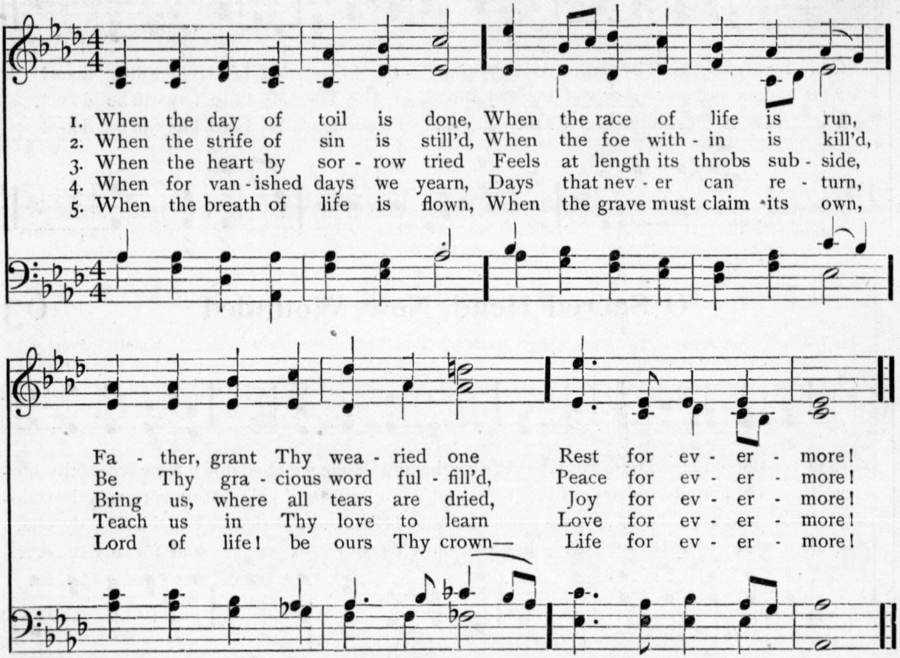
1. When the day of toil is done, When the race of life is run,
2. When the strife of sin is still'd, When the foe with - in is kill'd,
3. When the heart by sor - row tried Feels at length its throbs sub - side,
4. When for van - ished days we yearn, Days that nev - er can re - turn,
5. When the breath of life is flown, When the grave must claim its own,
Fa - ther, grant Thy wea - ried one Rest for ev - er - more!
Be Thy gra - cious word ful - fill'd, Peace for ev - er - more!
Bring us, where all tears are dried, Joy for ev - er - more!
Teach us in Thy love to learn Love for ev - er - more!
Lord of life! be ours Thy crown— Life for ev - er - more!

65 The Lord is My Shepherd

William Knox — (*Still Water* 11s. 10s) — Spiritual Songs, 1833

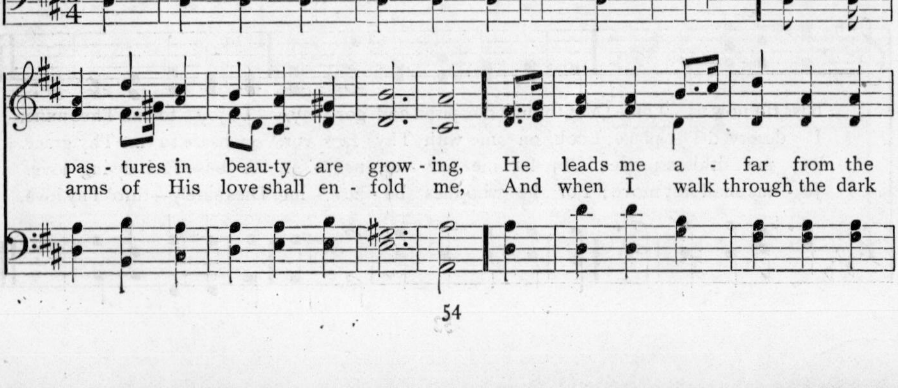
1. The Lord is my Shep - herd, He makes me re - pose Where the
2. He strength - ens my spir - it, He shows me the path, Where the
pas - tures in beau - ty are grow - ing, He leads me a - far from the
arms of His love shall en - fold me, And when I walk through the dark

DEVOTIONAL

The Lord is My Shepherd

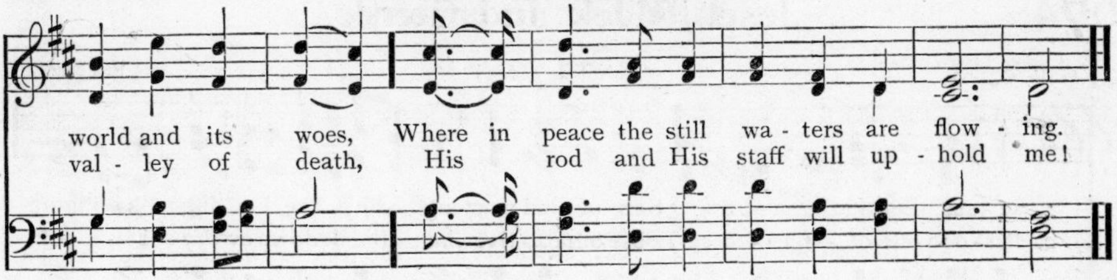
world and its woes, Where in peace the still wa - ters are flow - ing.
val - ley of death, His rod and His staff will up - hold me!

66

Bow Down Thine Ear

Horatius Bonar

R. De Witt Mallary

1. When the wea - ry, seek - ing rest, To Thy good - ness flee; When the heav - y - la - den cast All their load on Thee; When the trou - bled, seek - ing peace, On Thy name shall call; When the sin - ner, seek - ing life, At Thy feet shall fall:
2. When the world-ling, sick at heart, Lifts his soul a - bove; When the prod - i - gal looks back To his Fa - ther's love; When the proud man, from his pride, Stoops to seek Thy face; When the bur-den'd brings his guilt To Thy throne of grace:
3. When the stran - ger asks a home, All his toils to end; When the hun - gry crav - eth food, And the poor a friend; When the sai - lor on the wave Bows the fer - vent knee; When the sol - dier on the field Lifts his heart to Thee:
Hear then in love, O Lord, the cry In heav'n, Thy dwell - ing - place on high.

Copyright, 1901, by U. S. C. E.

67 Jesus, Meek and Gentle

G. R. Prynne (*Derby* 6. 5. 6. 5) F. Filitz

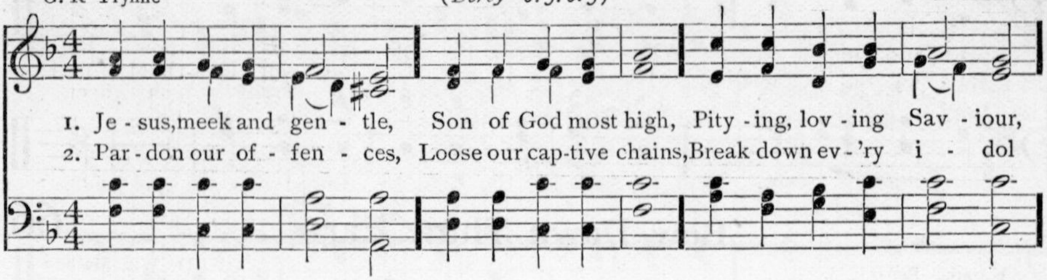
1. Je - sus, meek and gen - tle, Son of God most high, Pity - ing, lov - ing Sav - iour,
2. Par - don our of - fen - ces, Loose our cap - tive chains, Break down ev - 'ry i - dol

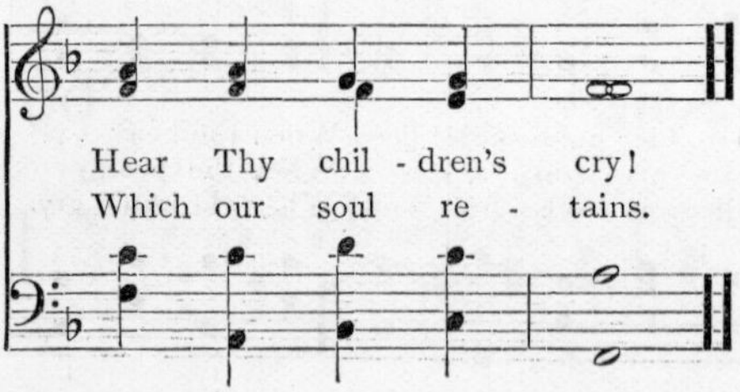
Hear Thy chil - dren's cry!
Which our soul re - tains.

3 Give us holy freedom,
Fill our hearts with love,
Draw us, Holy Jesus,
To the realms above.

4 Lead us on our journey,
Be Thyself the Way
Through terrestrial darkness,
To celestial day.

68 I Would Not Live Alway

William Augustus Muhlenberg, 1826 (*Frederick* 11s) G. Kingsley

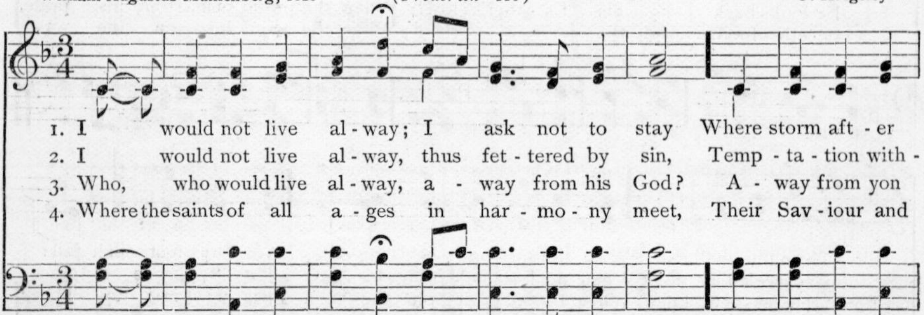
1. I would not live al - way; I ask not to stay Where storm aft - er
2. I would not live al - way, thus fet - tered by sin, Temp - ta - tion with -
3. Who, who would live al - way, a - way from his God? A - way from yon
4. Where the saints of all a - ges in har - mo - ny meet, Their Sav - iour and

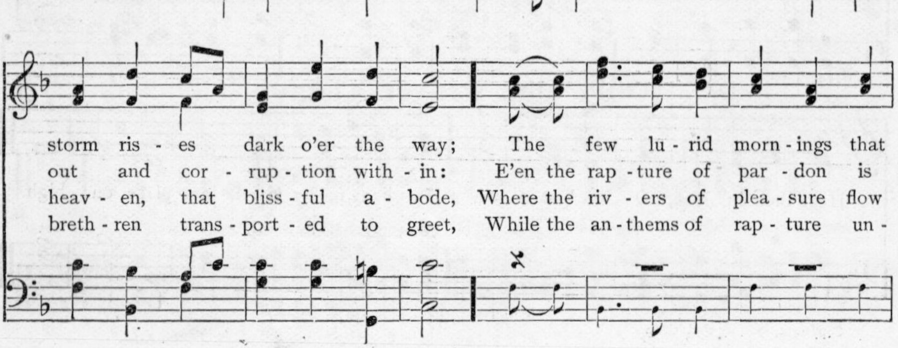
storm ris - es dark o'er the way; The few lu - rid morn - ings that
out and cor - rup - tion with - in: E'en the rap - ture of par - don is
heav - en, that bliss - ful a - bode, Where the riv - ers of plea - sure flow
breth - ren trans - port - ed to greet, While the an - thems of rap - ture un -

I Would Not Live Alway

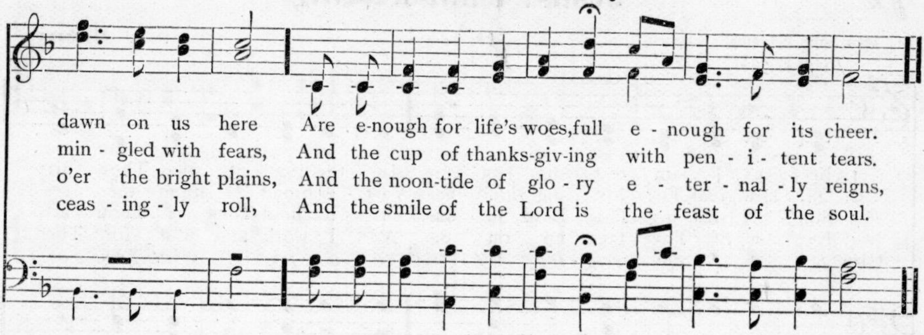
dawn on us here Are e-nough for life's woes,full e - nough for its cheer.
min - gled with fears, And the cup of thanks-giv-ing with pen - i - tent tears.
o'er the bright plains, And the noon-tide of glo - ry e - ter - nal - ly reigns,
ceas - ing - ly roll, And the smile of the Lord is the feast of the soul.

Hope's Song

69

Anon. Mrs. F. H. Jacobs

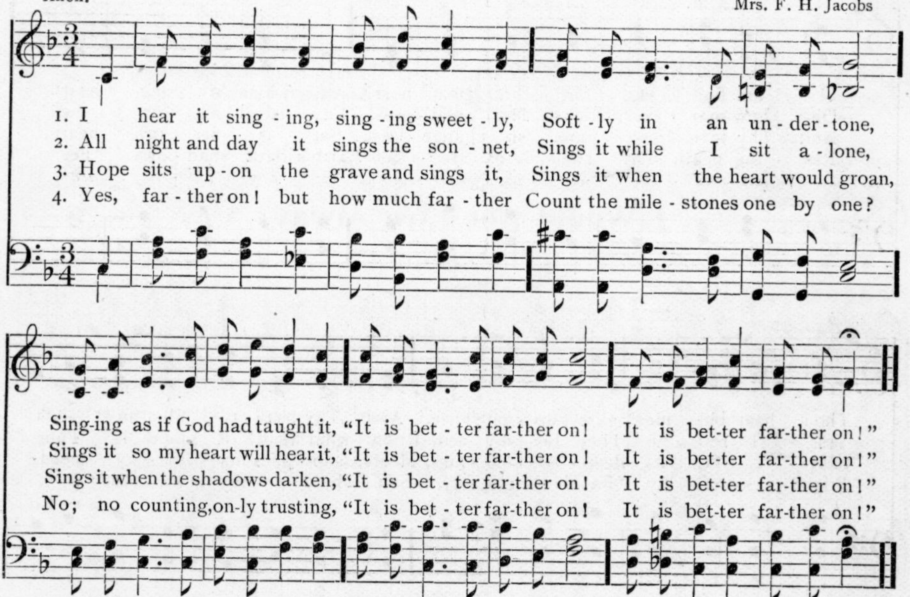
1. I hear it sing - ing, sing - ing sweet - ly, Soft - ly in an un - der - tone,
2. All night and day it sings the son - net, Sings it while I sit a - lone,
3. Hope sits up - on the grave and sings it, Sings it when the heart would groan,
4. Yes, far - ther on! but how much far - ther Count the mile - stones one by one?
Sing-ing as if God had taught it, "It is bet - ter far-ther on! It is bet-ter far-ther on!"
Sings it so my heart will hear it, "It is bet - ter far-ther on! It is bet-ter far-ther on!"
Sings it when the shadows darken, "It is bet - ter far-ther on! It is bet-ter far-ther on!"
No; no counting, on-ly trusting, "It is bet - ter far-ther on! It is bet-ter far-ther on!"

Copyright, 1901, by F. H. Jacobs

Only One Prayer Today

70

J. Barnby

Only one pray'r today, One earnest, tearful plea; O Thou who knowest all my heart, Have mercy, Lord, on me. AMEN.

71 Jesus! I am Resting

Jean Sophia Pigott (8s. 7s. 5s) J. Mountain

Joyfully
1. Je - sus! I am rest - ing, rest - ing In the joy of what Thou art;
2. Oh, how great Thy lov - ing kind - ness, Vast - er, broad - er than the sea!
3. Sim - ply trust - ing Thee, Lord Je - sus, I be - hold Thee as Thou art,
4. Ev - er lift Thy face up - on me, As I work and wait for Thee;
CHO. Je - sus, I am rest - ing, rest - ing In the joy of what Thou art;
FINE
I am find - ing out the great - ness Of Thy lov - ing heart.
Oh, how mar - vel - lous Thy good - ness, Lav - ished all on me!
And Thy love so pure, so change - less, Sat - is - fies my heart;
Rest - ing 'neath Thy smile, Lord Je - sus, Earth's dark shad - ows flee.
I am find - ing out the great - ness Of Thy lov - ing heart.
p
Thou hast bid me gaze up - on Thee, And Thy beau - ty fills my soul,
Yes, I rest in Thee, Be - lov - ed, Know what wealth of grace is Thine,
Sat - is - fies its deep - est long - ings, Meets, sup - plies its ev - 'ry need,
Bright - ness of my Fa - ther's glo - ry, Sun - shine of my Fa - ther's face,
p
cres.
p
D.C. CHORUS
For, by Thy trans - form - ing pow - er, Thou hast made me whole.
Know Thy cer - tain - ty of prom - ise, And have made it mine.
Com - pass - eth me round with bless - ings: Thine is love in - deed!
Keep me ev - er trust - ing, rest - ing, Fill me with Thy grace.
cres.
p

Wonderful Peace

Rev. W. D. Cornell

Rev. W. G. Cooper

1. Far a-way in the depths of my spir-it to-night, Rolls a
2. What a treas-ure I have in this won-der-ful peace, Bur-ied
3. I am rest-ing to-night in this won-der-ful peace, Rest-ing
4. And me-thinks when I rise to that cit-y of peace, Where the
mel-o-dy sweet-er than psalm; In ce-les-tial-like strains it un-
deep in the heart of my soul; So se-cure that no pow-er can
sweet-ly in Je-sus' con-trol; For I'm kept from all dan-ger by
Au-thor of peace I shall see, That one strain of the song which the
ceas-ing-ly falls O'er my soul like an in-fi-nite calm.
mine it a-way, While the years of e-ter-ni-ty roll.
night and by day, And His glo-ry is flood-ing my soul.
ran-som'd will sing In that heav-en-ly cit-y will be:
CHORUS
Peace! peace! Won-der-ful peace, Coming down from the Fa-ther a-bove; Sweep
o-ver my spir-it for-ev-er I pray, In fath-om-less bil-lows of love.

Used by permission of D. B. Towner, owner.

73 The Throne of Grace

Oliver Holden, 1800 (*St. Bees 7s*) J. B. Dykes

1. They who seek the throne of grace, Find that throne in ev - 'ry place;
2. In our sick - ness or our health, In our want or in our wealth,
3. When our earth - ly com - forts fail, When the foes of life pre - vail,
4. Then, my soul, in ev - 'ry strait To thy Fa - ther come and wait;

If we live a life of pray'r, God is pres - ent ev - 'ry-where.
If we look to God in pray'r, God is pres - ent ev - 'ry-where.
'T is the time for ear - nest pray'r; God is pres - ent ev - 'ry-where.
He will an - swer ev - 'ry pray'r; God is pres - ent ev - 'ry-where.

74 I've Found a Friend

J. G. Small, 1866 (*Constance 8s. 7s. D.*) Sir Arthur Sullivan

1. I've found a Friend; Oh, such a Friend! He lov'd me ere I knew Him;
2. I've found a Friend; Oh, such a Friend! He bled, He died to save me;
3. I've found a Friend; Oh, such a Friend! All pow'r to Him is giv - en,

He drew me with the cords of love, And thus He bound me to Him.
And not a - lone the gift of life, But His own self He gave me.
To guard me on my on - ward course, And bring me safe to heav - en:

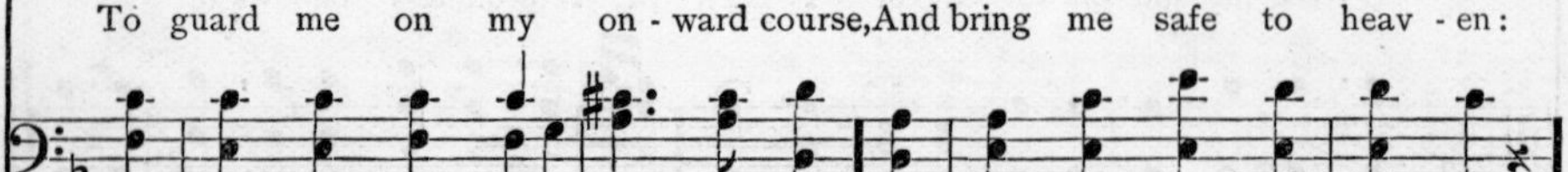

I've Found a Friend

And round my heart still close - ly twine Those ties which naught can sev - er;
Naught that I have my own I call, I hold it for the Giv - er;
E - ter - nal glo - ry gleams a - far, To nerve my faint en - deav - or;
For I am His and He is mine, For - ev - er and for - ev - er.
My heart, my strength, my life, my all, Are His, and His for - ev - er.
So now to watch, to work, to war; And then to rest for - ev - er.

Jesus, My Chief Pleasure 75

Ad. from Johann Franck, 1618 (*6s. 5s. D.*) R. De W. Mallary, 1901

1. Je - sus, my chief pleas - ure, Match-less pearl of grace! Ea - ger oft my
2. Je - sus is the treas - ure To my heart most dear. Hence, de - lud - ing
long - ing To be - hold Thy face. When the tem - pest ra - ges I will
pleas - ure! Hence, dis - turb - ing fear! Flee! ye shades of sad - ness, Joy shall
safe - ly hide In the Rock of A - ges, Where Thy saints a - bide.
be my cup; Christ, the Prince of glad - ness, Comes with me to sup.

Copyright, 1901, by U. S. C. E.

76 I Am Thine

Charles M. Sheldon — Charles S. Brown

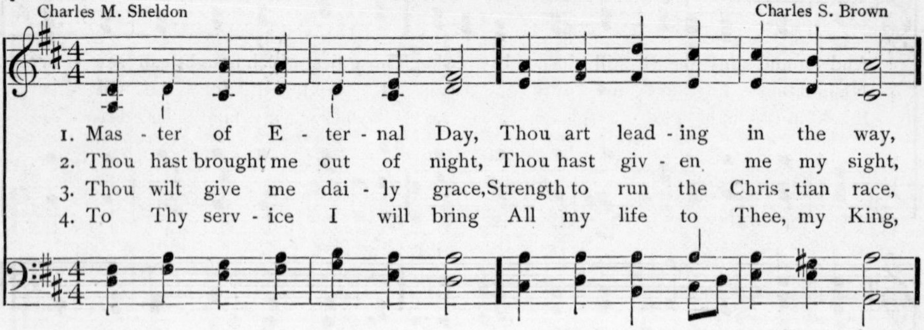
1. Mas - ter of E - ter - nal Day, Thou art lead - ing in the way,
2. Thou hast brought me out of night, Thou hast giv - en me my sight,
3. Thou wilt give me dai - ly grace, Strength to run the Chris - tian race,
4. To Thy serv - ice I will bring All my life to Thee, my King,

Thou wilt nev - er let me stray,— I am Thine, I am Thine.
Hast re-deemed me by Thy might,— I am Thine, I am Thine.
Till at last I see Thy face,— I am Thine, I am Thine.
And for - ev - er I will sing,— I am Thine, I am Thine.

Copyright, 1901, by U. S. C. E.

77 Face to Face

Mrs. Frank A. Breck — Grant Colfax Tullar

Moderato

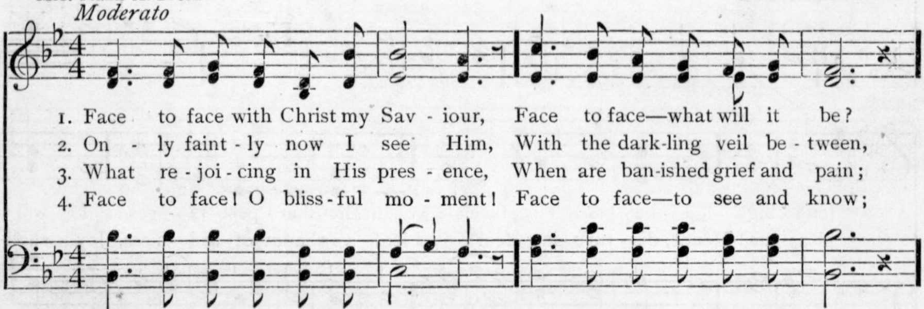
1. Face to face with Christ my Sav - iour, Face to face—what will it be?
2. On - ly faint - ly now I see Him, With the dark-ling veil be - tween,
3. What re - joi - cing in His pres - ence, When are ban-ished grief and pain;
4. Face to face! O bliss - ful mo - ment! Face to face—to see and know;

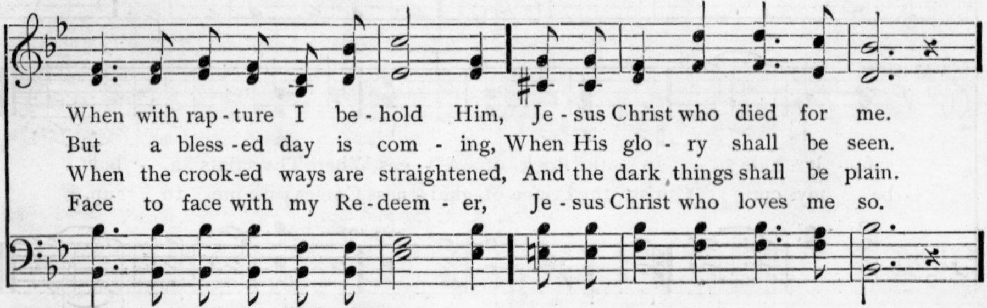
When with rap - ture I be - hold Him, Je - sus Christ who died for me.
But a bless - ed day is com - ing, When His glo - ry shall be seen.
When the crook-ed ways are straightened, And the dark things shall be plain.
Face to face with my Re - deem - er, Je - sus Christ who loves me so.

Copyright, 1899, by Tullar-Meredith Co. By per.

Face to Face

CHORUS
Face to face shall I be-hold Him, Far be-yond the star-ry sky;
Face to face in all His glo-ry, I shall see Him by and by!

A Little While

78

Mrs. Jane Crewdson (*Emilia* 11s. 10s) F. L. Benjamin

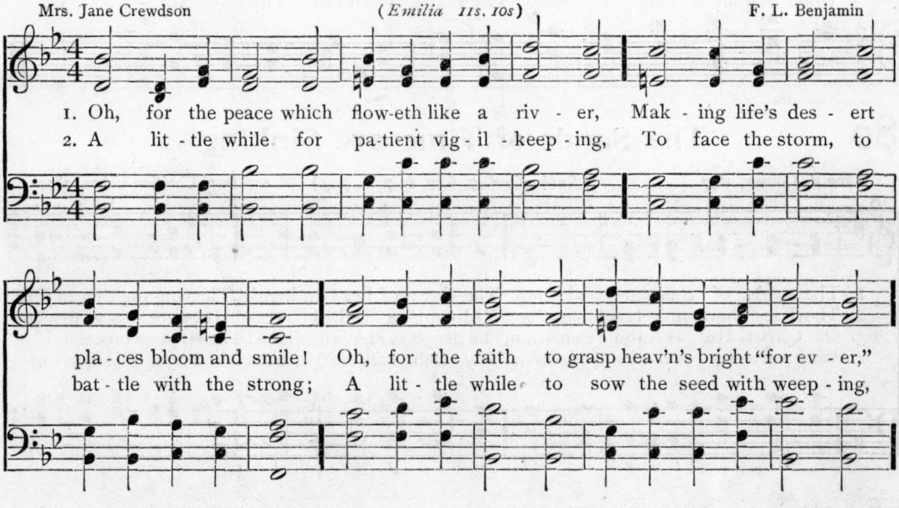
1. Oh, for the peace which flow-eth like a riv-er, Mak-ing life's des-ert pla-ces bloom and smile! Oh, for the faith to grasp heav'n's bright "for ev-er,"
2. A lit-tle while for pa-tient vig-il keep-ing, To face the storm, to bat-tle with the strong; A lit-tle while to sow the seed with weep-ing,

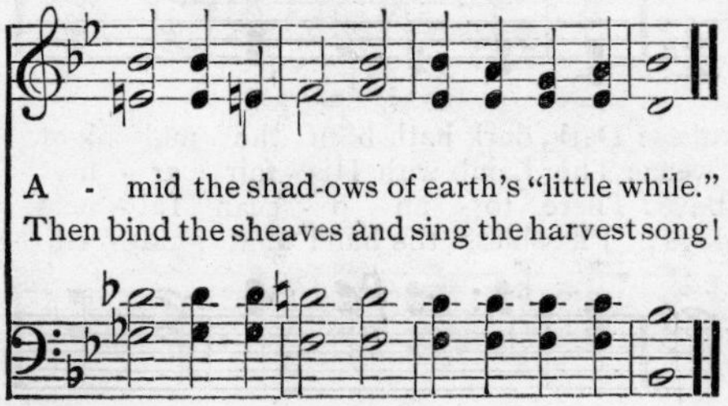
A-mid the shad-ows of earth's "little while."
Then bind the sheaves and sing the harvest song!

3 A little while to keep the oil from failing,
A little while faith's flickering lamp to trim;
And then, the Bridegroom's coming footsteps hailing,
To haste to meet Him with the bridal hymn!

4 And He who is Himself the gift and giver,—
The future glory and the present smile,—
With the bright promise of the glad "for ever"
Will light the shadows of the "little while!"

79 The King of Love My Shepherd is

Rev. Henry W. Baker (8. 7. 8. 7) J. B. Dykes

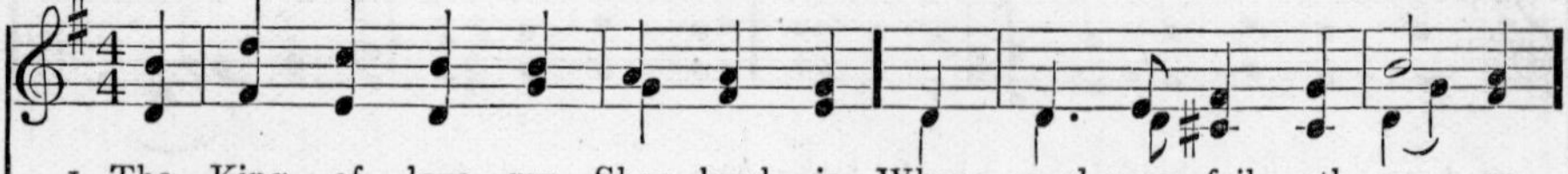

1. The King of love my Shep-herd is, Whose good-ness fail-eth nev-er;
2. Where streams of liv-ing wa-ter flow My ran-somed soul He lead-eth,
3. Per-verse and fool-ish, oft I strayed, But yet in love He sought me,
4. And so through all the length of days Thy good-ness fail-eth nev-er,

I noth-ing lack if I am His, And He is mine for-ev-er.
And, where the ver-dant pas-tures grow, With food ce-les-tial feed-eth.
And on His shoul-der gen-tly laid, And home, re-joi-cing, brought me.
Good Shepherd! may I sing Thy praise With-in Thy house for-ev-er.

80 The Sands of Time are Sinking

Anne R. Cousin, 1857 (*Rutherford* 7. 6. 7. 6. 7. 6. 7. 5) Arr. from Chrétien Urhan, 1834

1. The sands of time are sink-ing, The dawn of heav-en breaks, The sum-mer morn I've
2. The King there in His beau-ty With-out a veil is seen; It were a well-spent
3. O Christ, He is the Foun-tain, The deep sweet Well of love! The streams on earth I've
4. With mer-cy and with judgment My web of time He wove, And aye the dews of

sighed for, The fair sweet morn a-wakes: Dark, dark hath been the mid-night,
jour-ney, Though sev'n deaths lay be-tween: The Lamb with His fair ar-my
tast-ed More deep I'll drink a-bove: There to an o-cean ful-ness
sor-row Were lus-tered by His love: I'll bless the hand that guid-ed,

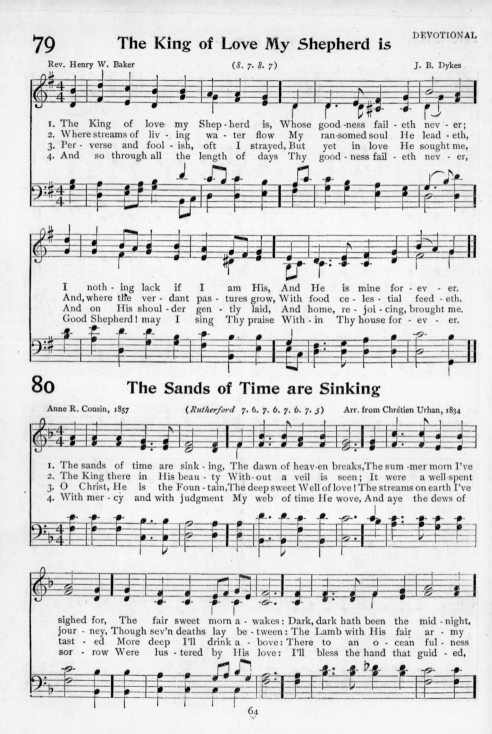

The Sands of Time are Sinking

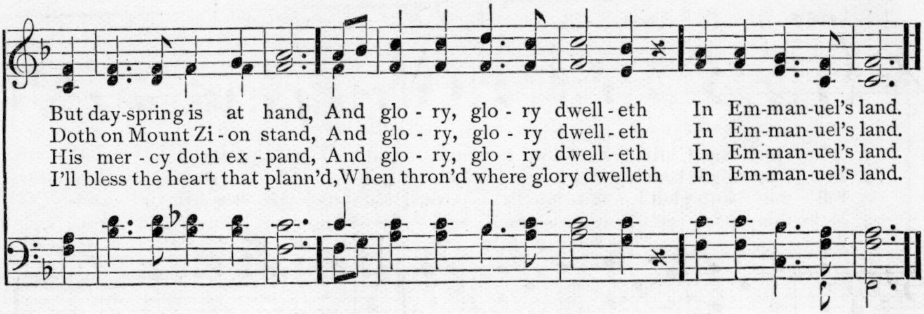

But day-spring is at hand, And glo - ry, glo - ry dwell - eth In Em-man-uel's land.
Doth on Mount Zi - on stand, And glo - ry, glo - ry dwell - eth In Em-man-uel's land.
His mer - cy doth ex - pand, And glo - ry, glo - ry dwell - eth In Em-man-uel's land.
I'll bless the heart that plann'd, When thron'd where glory dwelleth In Em-man-uel's land.

For Me He Careth

81

Horatius Bonar (*Bucroft* 8s. 7s. D.) R. De Witt Mallary

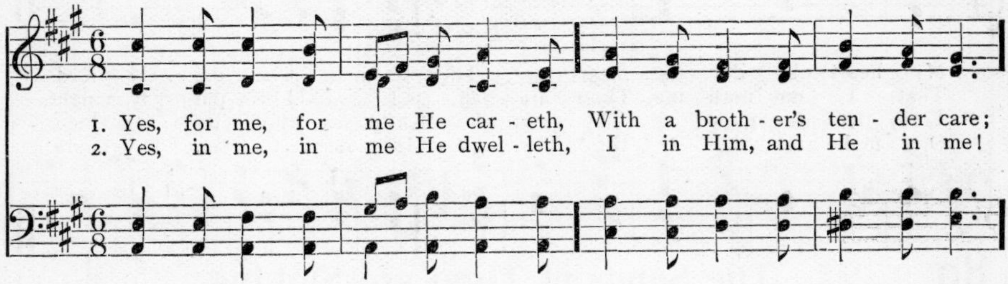

1. Yes, for me, for me He car - eth, With a broth - er's ten - der care;
2. Yes, in me, in me He dwel - leth, I in Him, and He in me!

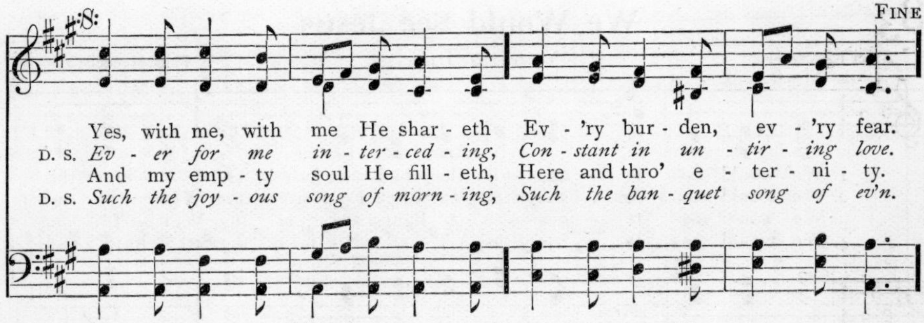

FINE

Yes, with me, with me He shar - eth Ev - 'ry bur - den, ev - 'ry fear.
D. S. *Ev - er for me in - ter - ced - ing, Con - stant in un - tir - ing love.*
And my emp - ty soul He fill - eth, Here and thro' e - ter - ni - ty.
D. S. *Such the joy - ous song of morn - ing, Such the ban - quet song of ev'n.*

D. S.

Yes, for me He stand - eth plead - ing, At the mer - cy - seat a - bove;
Thus I wait for His re - turn - ing, Sing - ing all the way to heav'n;

82 Grow Thou in Me

J. C. Lavater Tr. by H. B. Smith (*Lavater C. M.*) Air harmonized by Nora C. E. Byrne

p
1. O Je - sus Christ, grow Thou in me, And all things else re - cede; .
2. In Thy bright beams which on me fall, Fade ev - 'ry e - vil thought:
3. Fill me with glad - ness from a - bove, Hold me by strength di - vine! .
4. Make this poor self grow less and less, Be Thou my life and aim; .
p
My heart be dai - ly near - er Thee; From sin be dai - ly freed.
That I am noth - ing, Thou art all, I would be dai - ly taught.
Lord, let the glow of Thy great love, Thro' my whole be - ing shine.
O, make me dai - ly thro' Thy grace More meet to bear Thy name!

83 We Would See Jesus

Anna B. Warner (*Raynolds 11s. 10s*) Felix Mendelssohn

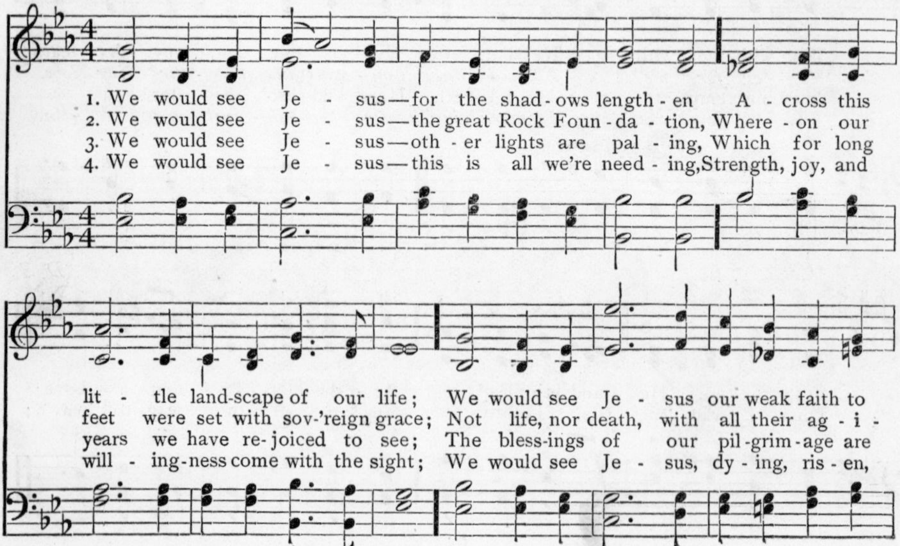
1. We would see Je - sus—for the shad - ows length - en A - cross this
2. We would see Je - sus—the great Rock Foun - da - tion, Where - on our
3. We would see Je - sus—oth - er lights are pal - ing, Which for long
4. We would see Je - sus—this is all we're need - ing, Strength, joy, and
lit - tle land-scape of our life; We would see Je - sus our weak faith to
feet were set with sov-'reign grace; Not life, nor death, with all their ag - i -
years we have re - joiced to see; The bless-ings of our pil - grim - age are
will - ing-ness come with the sight; We would see Je - sus, dy - ing, ris - en,

We Would See Jesus

strength - en, For the last wea - ri - ness—the fi - nal strife.
ta - tion, Can thence re - move us, if we see His face.
fail - ing, We would not mourn them, for we go to Thee.
plead - ing, Then wel - come day, and fare - well mor - tal night!

Lead Us, O Father

84

William H. Burleigh, 1868 (*Longwood 10s*) Sir Joseph Barnby, 1872

1. Lead us, O Fa - ther, in the paths of peace; With - out Thy
2. Lead us, O Fa - ther, in the paths of truth; Un - helped by
3. Lead us, O Fa - ther, in the paths of right; Blind - ly we
4. Lead us, O Fa - ther, to Thy heav'n - ly rest, How - ev - er

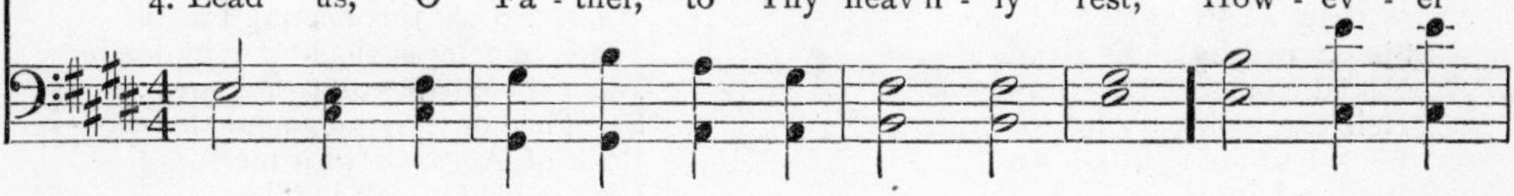

guid - ing hand we go a - stray, And doubts ap - pal, and sor - rows
Thee, in er - ror's maze we grope, While pas - sion stains and fol - ly
stum - ble when we walk a - lone, In - volved in shad - ows of a
rough and steep the path may be; Through joy or sor - row, as Thou

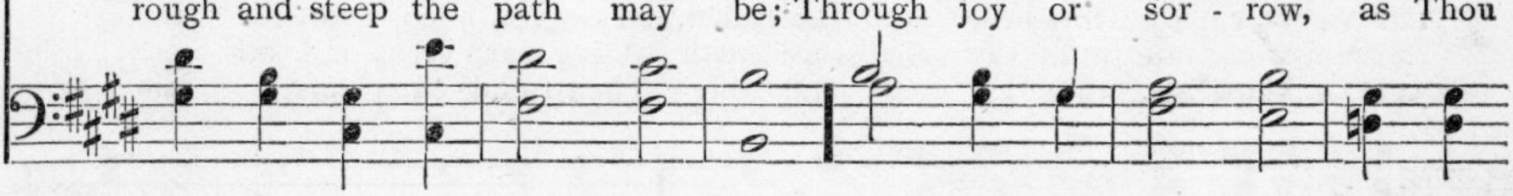

still in - crease: Lead us through Christ, the true and liv - ing Way.
dims our youth, And age comes on un - cheered by faith and hope.
mor - al night; On - ly with Thee we jour - ney safe - ly on.
deem - est best, Un - til our lives are per - fect - ed in Thee.

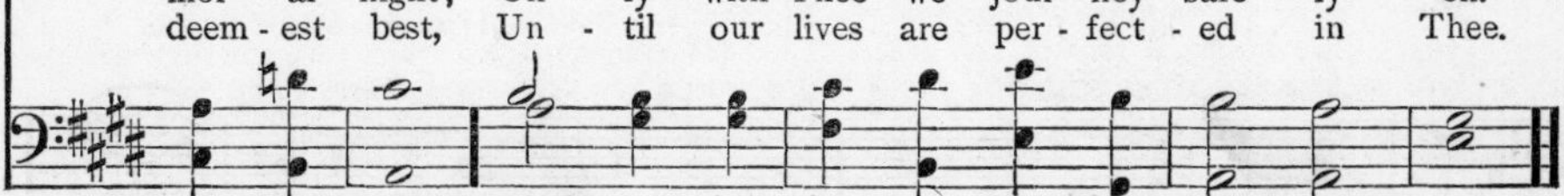

85 Rock of Ages

Rev. A. M. Toplady — (*7s. D.*) — Dr. Thos. Hastings

FINE
1. Rock of A - ges, cleft for me, Let me hide my - self in Thee;
D.C. *Be of sin the dou - ble cure, Save me from its guilt and pow'r.*
2. Not the la - bor of my hands Can ful - fill Thy law's de - mands;
D.C. *All for sin could not a - tone; Thou must save, and Thou a - lone.*
D.C.
Let the wa - ter and the blood, From Thy riv - en side which flowed,
Could my zeal no res - pite know, Could my tears for - ev - er flow,

3 Nothing in my hand I bring,
Simply to Thy cross I cling;
Naked, come to Thee for dress,
Helpless, look to Thee for grace;
Foul, I to the fountain fly,
Wash me, Saviour, or I die.

4 While I draw this fleeting breath,
When mine eyes shall close in death,
When I soar to worlds unknown,
See Thee on Thy judgment throne,—
Rock of Ages, cleft for me,
Let me hide myself in Thee.

86 His Love and Care

J. G. Whittier, 1867 — (*Chester C. M. D.*) — Oratory Hymns, 1868

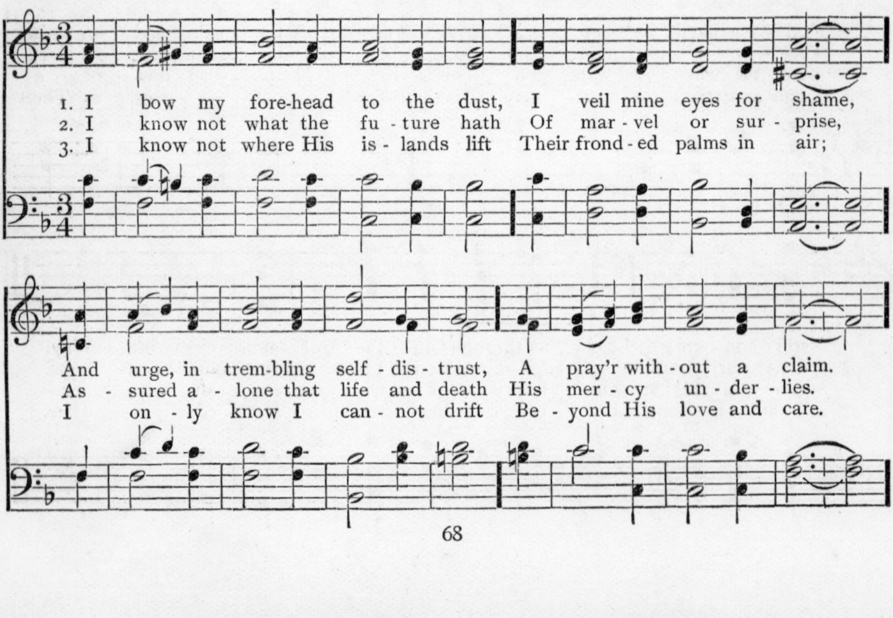
1. I bow my fore-head to the dust, I veil mine eyes for shame,
2. I know not what the fu - ture hath Of mar - vel or sur - prise,
3. I know not where His is - lands lift Their frond - ed palms in air;
And urge, in trem-bling self - dis - trust, A pray'r with - out a claim.
As - sured a - lone that life and death His mer - cy un - der - lies.
I on - ly know I can - not drift Be - yond His love and care.

His Love and Care

No off - 'ring of mine own I have, Nor works my faith to prove;
And so be - side the si - lent sea I wait the muf - fled oar;
And Thou, O Lord, by whom are seen Thy crea - tures as they be,
I can but give the gifts He gave, And plead His love for love.
No harm from Him can come to me On o - cean or on shore.
For - give me if too close I lean My hu - man heart on Thee.

Master, No Offering

87

E. P. P. (*P. M.*) Rev. E. P. Parker

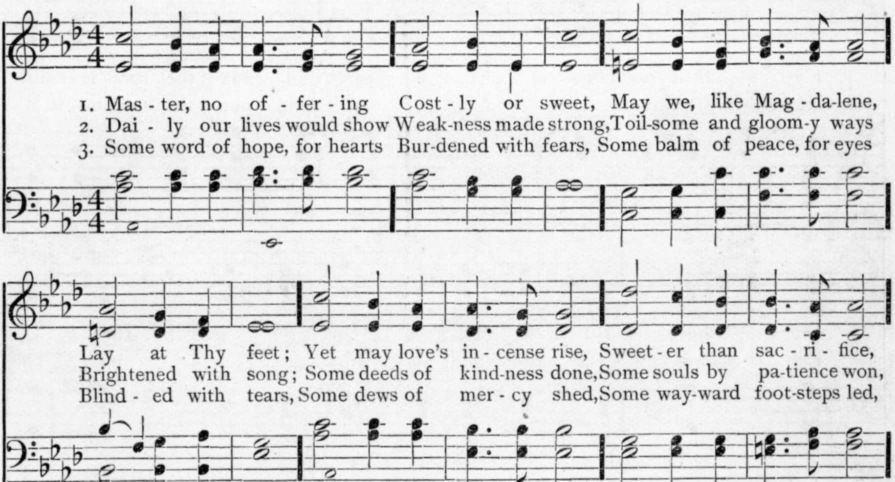
1. Mas - ter, no of - fer - ing Cost - ly or sweet, May we, like Mag - da-lene,
2. Dai - ly our lives would show Weak-ness made strong, Toil-some and gloom-y ways
3. Some word of hope, for hearts Bur-dened with fears, Some balm of peace, for eyes
Lay at Thy feet; Yet may love's in - cense rise, Sweet - er than sac - ri - fice,
Brightened with song; Some deeds of kind-ness done, Some souls by pa-tience won,
Blind - ed with tears, Some dews of mer - cy shed, Some way-ward foot-steps led,

Dear Lord, to Thee, Dear Lord, to Thee.

4 Thus, in Thy service, Lord,
Till eventide
Closes the day of life,
May we abide.
And when earth's labors cease,
Bid us depart in peace,
Dear Lord, to Thee.

88

Flee as a Bird

DEVOTIONAL

Solo or Quartette

Mary S. B. Dana, 1840

Expression
1. Flee as a bird to your moun - tain, Thou who art wea - ry of sin;
2. He will pro-tect thee for - ev - er, Wipe ev - 'ry fall - ing tear;
Go to the clear-flow - ing foun - tain, Where you may wash and be clean;
He will for-sake thee, oh, nev - er, Shel-tered so ten - der - ly there!
f agitato
Fly for th' a-ven - ger is near thee, Call, and the Sav - iour will
Haste then, the hours are fly - ing, Spend not the mo - ments in
a tempo
hear . . thee; He on His bos - om will bear . . thee, O
sigh - ing, Cease from your sor - row and cry - ing, The
rit.
thou, who art wea - ry of sin, O thou, who art wea - ry of sin.
Sav - iour will wipe ev - 'ry tear, The Sav - iour will wipe ev - 'ry tear.

Hark! Hark, My Soul

F. W. Faber

(*Pilgrims* 11. 10. 11. 10. 9. 11)

H. Smart

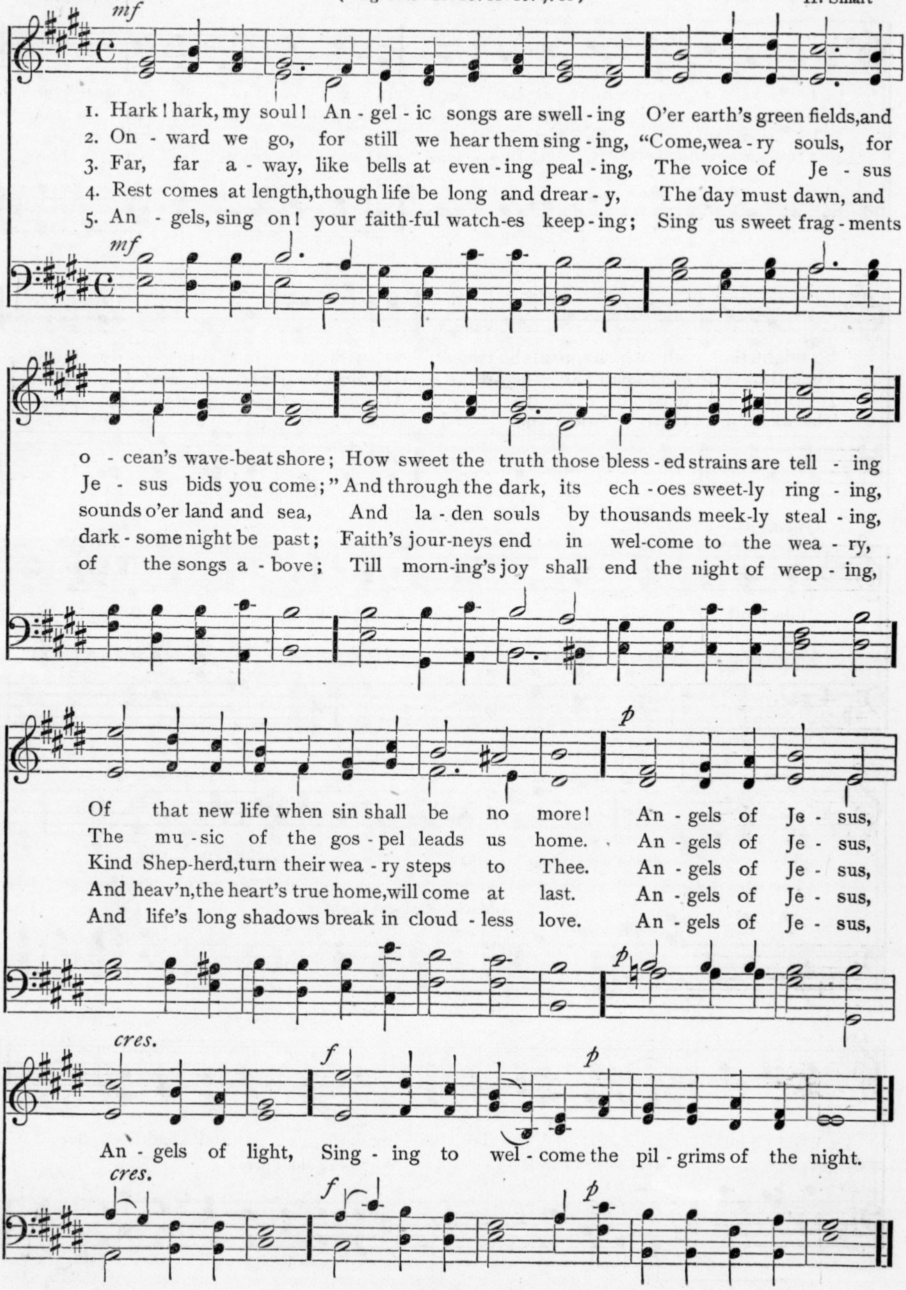
mf
1. Hark! hark, my soul! An - gel - ic songs are swell - ing O'er earth's green fields, and
2. On - ward we go, for still we hear them sing - ing, "Come, wea - ry souls, for
3. Far, far a - way, like bells at even - ing peal - ing, The voice of Je - sus
4. Rest comes at length, though life be long and drear - y, The day must dawn, and
5. An - gels, sing on! your faith-ful watch-es keep - ing; Sing us sweet frag - ments
mf
o - cean's wave-beat shore; How sweet the truth those bless - ed strains are tell - ing
Je - sus bids you come;" And through the dark, its ech - oes sweet-ly ring - ing,
sounds o'er land and sea, And la - den souls by thousands meek-ly steal - ing,
dark - some night be past; Faith's jour-neys end in wel-come to the wea - ry,
of the songs a - bove; Till morn-ing's joy shall end the night of weep - ing,
p
Of that new life when sin shall be no more! An - gels of Je - sus,
The mu - sic of the gos - pel leads us home. An - gels of Je - sus,
Kind Shep-herd, turn their wea - ry steps to Thee. An - gels of Je - sus,
And heav'n, the heart's true home, will come at last. An - gels of Je - sus,
And life's long shadows break in cloud - less love. An - gels of Je - sus,
p
cres.
f
p
An - gels of light, Sing - ing to wel - come the pil - grims of the night.
cres.
f
p

90 The Better Land

DEVOTIONAL

Gurdon Robins, arr. (*8s with Chorus*) Daniel B. Towner

1. There is a land mine eye hath seen In vi-sions of en - rap - tured tho't,
2. A land up - on whose bliss-ful shore There rests no shad - ow, falls no stain;
3. Its skies are not like earth-ly skies, With va-rying hues of shade and light;
4. There sweeps no des - o - la - ting wind A -cross the calm, se - rene a - bode.
So bright, that all which spreads be-tween Is with its ra- diant glo - ries fraught.
There those who meet shall part no more, And those long part - ed meet a - gain.
It hath no need of suns, to rise To dis - si - pate the gloom of night.
The wan-d'rer there a home may find With- in the par - a - dise of God.
CHORUS
Oh, land of love, . of joy and light, . Thy glo - ries
Oh, land of love, of joy and light,
gild . earth's dark-est night; . Thy tran-quil shore, .
Thy glo - ries gild earth's dark - est night;
(earth's dark-est night;)
Thy tran-quil shore,
we, too, shall see, . When day shall break . and shadows flee.
we, too, shall see,
When day shall break

Copyright, 1897, by D. B. Towner. Used by per.

The Lord is My Shepherd

Anon. T. Koschat

Lento. m
1. The Lord is my Shep - herd, no want shall I know, I
2. Thro' the val - ley and shad - ow of death tho' I stray, Since
3. In the midst of af - flic - tion my ta - ble is spread; With
4. Let good - ness and mer - cy, my boun - ti - ful God, Still
feed in green pas - tures, safe fold - ed I rest; He lead - eth my
Thou art my Guar - dian, no e - vil I fear; Thy rod shall de -
bless - ings un - meas - ured my cup run - neth o'er; With per - fume and
fol - low my steps till I meet Thee a - bove. I seek by the
soul where the still wa - ters flow, Re - stores me when wan-d'ring, re -
fend me, Thy staff be my stay; No harm can be - fall, with my
oil Thou a - noint - est my head; Oh, what shall I ask of Thy
path which my fore - fa - thers trod, Thro' the land of their so - journ, Thy
deems when op-press'd, Re - stores me when wan-d'ring, re-deems when op-press'd.
Com - fort - er near, No harm can be - fall, with my Com - fort - er near.
prov - i - dence more? Oh, what shall I ask of Thy prov - i - dence more?
king - dom of love, Thro' the land of their so - journ, Thy king - dom of love.
rit.

92 God's Peace

Anon. *(Kilburn C. M.)* H. G. B. Hunt

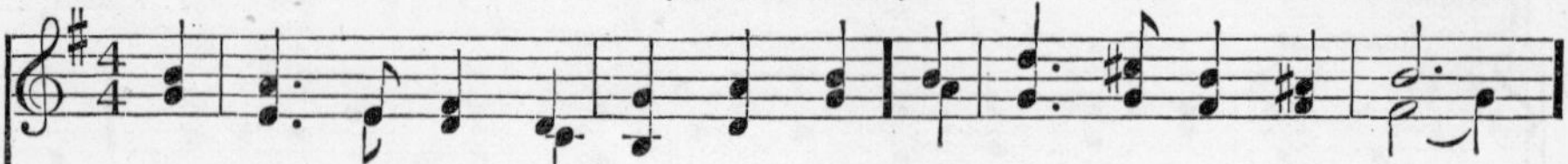

1. We bless Thee for Thy peace, O God! Deep as the sound-less sea, .
2. We ask not, Fa - ther, for re - pose Which comes from out - ward rest, .
3. That peace which suf - fers and is strong, Trusts where it can - not see, .
4. O Fa - ther, give our hearts this peace, What - e'er may out - ward be, .

Which falls like sun - shine on the road Of those who trust in Thee.
If we may have through all life's woes Thy peace with - in our breast; —
Deems not the tri - al - way too long, But leaves the end with Thee.
Till all life's dis - ci - pline shall cease, And we go home to Thee.

93 There is a Green Hill Far Away

Mrs. Cecil Frances Alexander Richard Storrs Willis, 1860

1. There is a green hill far a - way, With - out a cit - y wall,
2. He died that we might be for - given, He died to make us good,
3. O dear - ly, dear - ly has He loved, And we must love Him too,

Where the dear Lord was cru - ci - fied, Who died to save us all.
That we might go at last to heav'n Saved by His pre - cious blood.
And trust in His re - deem - ing blood, And try His works to do.

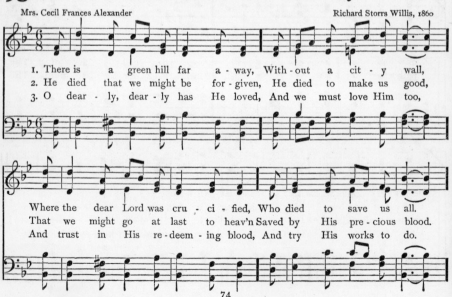

There is a Green Hill Far Away

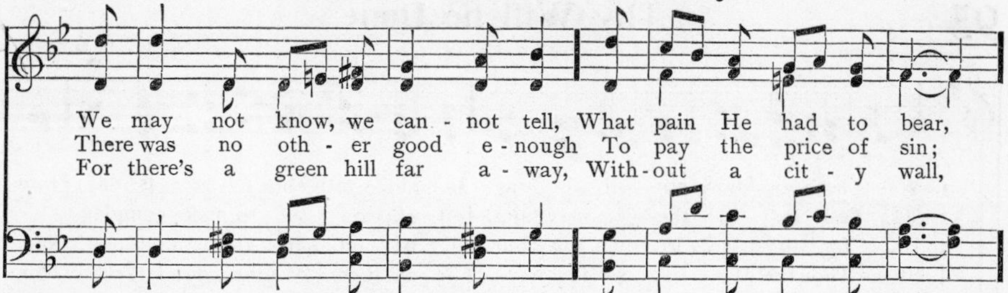
We may not know, we can - not tell, What pain He had to bear,
There was no oth - er good e - nough To pay the price of sin;
For there's a green hill far a - way, With - out a cit - y wall,

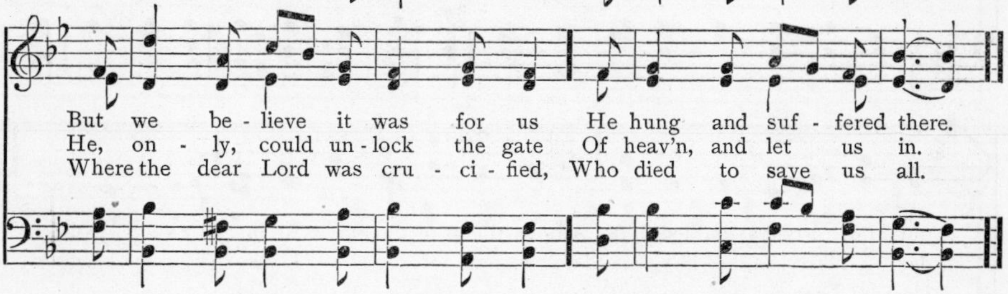
But we be - lieve it was for us He hung and suf - fered there.
He, on - ly, could un - lock the gate Of heav'n, and let us in.
Where the dear Lord was cru - ci - fied, Who died to save us all.

Quiet, Lord, My Froward Heart 94

John Newton

(*Spain* 7s. 6l.)

1. Qui - et, Lord, my fro-ward heart, Make me teach - a - ble and mild; Up - right, sim-ple,
2. What Thou shalt to-day pro - vide, Let me as a child re - ceive; What to-mor-row

free from art; Make me as a lit - tle child, From dis-trust and en - vy free,
may be - tide, Calm - ly to Thy wis - dom leave; 'Tis e-nough that Thou wilt care,

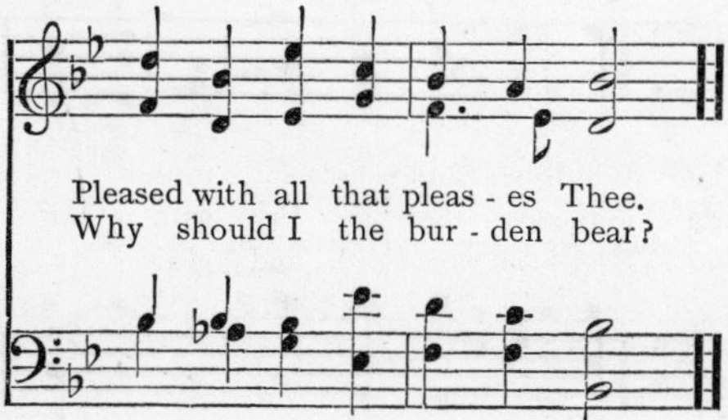
Pleased with all that pleas - es Thee.
Why should I the bur - den bear?

3 As a little child relies
On a care beyond his own;
Knows he's neither strong nor wise;
Fears to stir a step alone;
Let me thus with Thee abide,
As my Father, Guard, and Guide.

4 Thus preserved from Satan's wiles,
Safe from dangers, free from fears,
May I live upon Thy smiles,
Till the promised hour appears,
When the sons of God shall prove
All their Father's boundless love.

95 Thy Will be Done

John G. Whittier (*8. 8. 8. 8. 4*) Mrs. F. H. Jacobs

1. We see not, know not; all the way Is night,—with Thee a - lone is day; From
2. The flesh may fail, the heart may faint, But who are we to make complaint, Or
3. If, for the age to come, this hour Of tri - al hath vi - ca-rious pow'r, And,
4. Strike, Thou the Mas - ter, we Thy keys, The an-them of the des - ti - nies! The

out the torrent's troubled drift, A-bove the storm our pray'rs we lift, Thy will be done.
dare to plead in times like these, The weakness of our love of ease? Thy will be done.
blest by Thee, our pres - ent pain Be lib - er - ty's e - ter - nal gain, Thy will be done.
mi - nor of Thy loft - ier strain, Our hearts shall breathe the old refrain, Thy will be done.

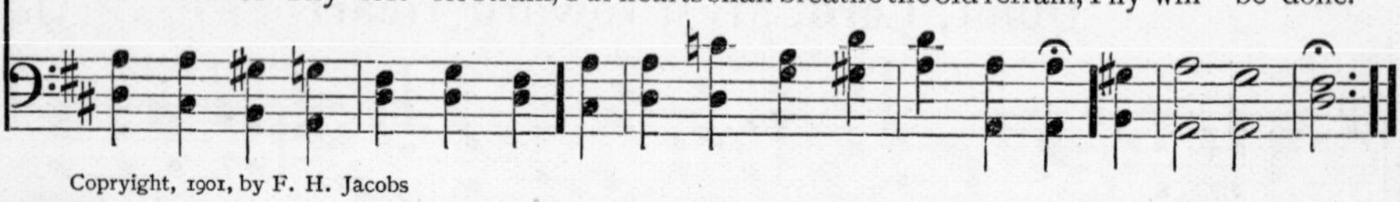

Copyright, 1901, by F. H. Jacobs

96 O Lamb of God, Still Keep Me

J. G. Deck, 1842 (*Davenport 7. 6. 7. 6. D.*) M. D. Babcock, 1896

1. O Lamb of God, still keep me Near to Thy wounded side; 'Tis on - ly there in
2. 'Tis on - ly in Thee hid - ing I feel my life se-cure; On - ly in Thee a -
3. Soon shall mine eyes be - hold Thee, With rapture face to face; One half hath not been

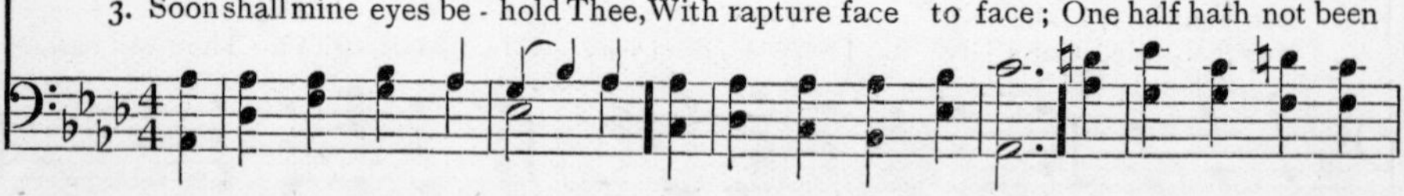

safe - ty And peace I can a - bide. What foes and snares sur - round me!
bid - ing The con - flict can en - dure. Thine arm the vic - t'ry gain - eth
told me Of all Thy pow'r and grace; Thy beau - ty, Lord, and glo - ry,

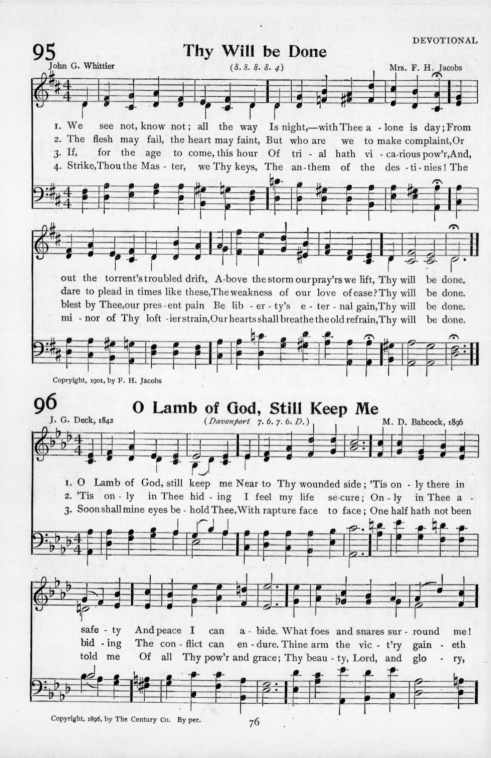

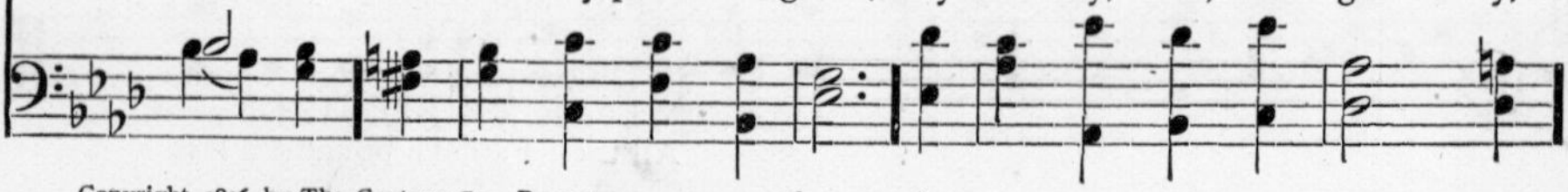

Copyright, 1896, by The Century Co. By per.

O Lamb of God, Still Keep Me

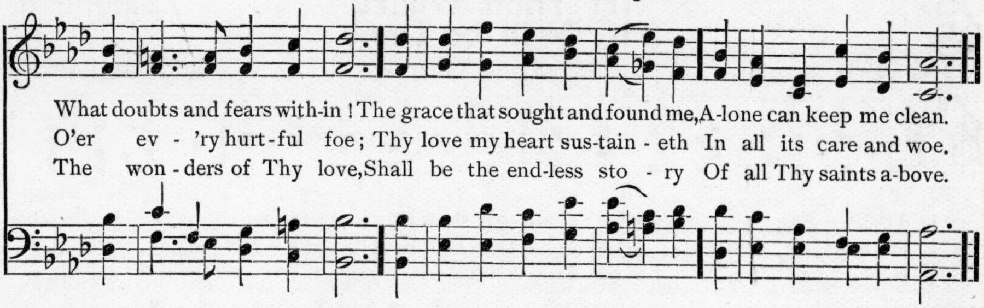
What doubts and fears with-in ! The grace that sought and found me, A-lone can keep me clean.
O'er ev - 'ry hurt-ful foe ; Thy love my heart sus-tain - eth In all its care and woe.
The won - ders of Thy love, Shall be the end-less sto - ry Of all Thy saints a-bove.

Like a River, Glorious 97

Frances R. Havergal

Rev. J. Mountain

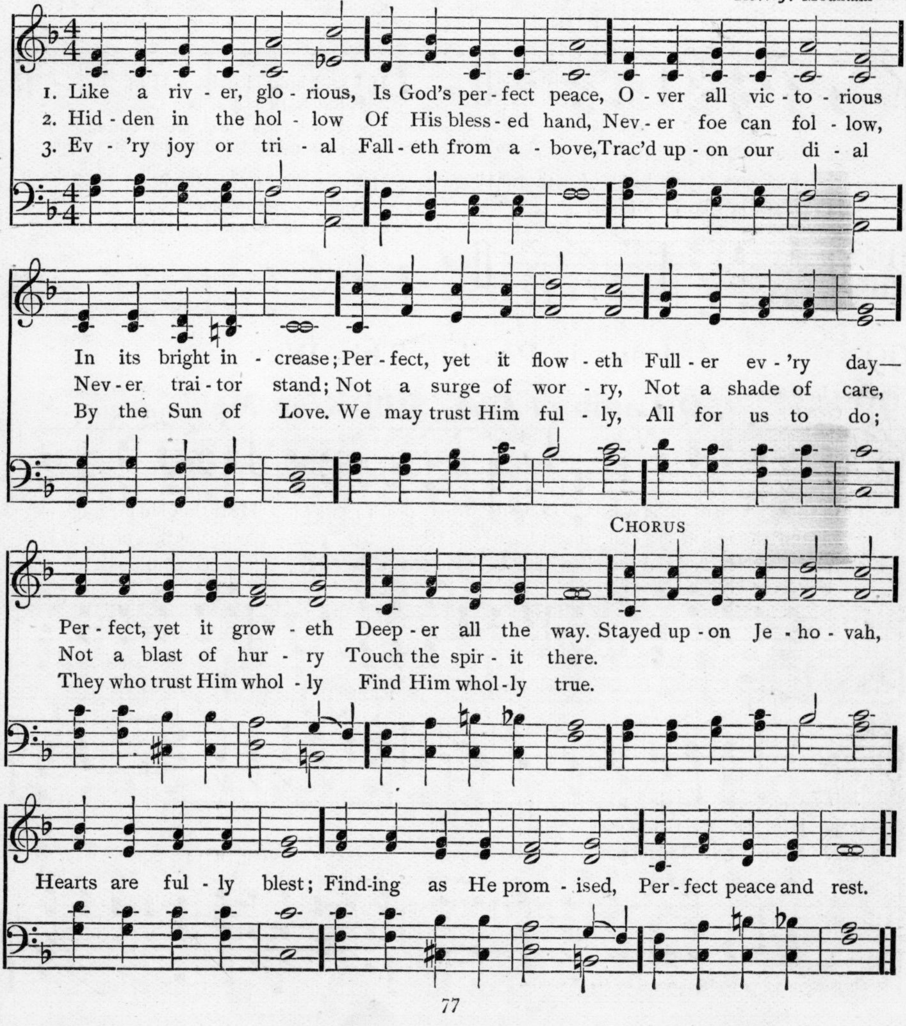
1. Like a riv - er, glo - rious, Is God's per - fect peace, O - ver all vic - to - rious
2. Hid - den in the hol - low Of His bless - ed hand, Nev - er foe can fol - low,
3. Ev - 'ry joy or tri - al Fall - eth from a - bove, Trac'd up - on our di - al
In its bright in - crease; Per - fect, yet it flow - eth Full - er ev - 'ry day—
Nev - er trai - tor stand; Not a surge of wor - ry, Not a shade of care,
By the Sun of Love. We may trust Him ful - ly, All for us to do;
CHORUS
Per - fect, yet it grow - eth Deep - er all the way. Stayed up - on Je - ho - vah,
Not a blast of hur - ry Touch the spir - it there.
They who trust Him whol - ly Find Him whol - ly true.
Hearts are ful - ly blest; Find-ing as He prom - ised, Per - fect peace and rest.

98 Art Thou Weary

Stephen the Sabaite, 8th cent.
Tr. John M. Neale, 1851 (*Stephanos P. M.*) Henry W. Baker, 1861

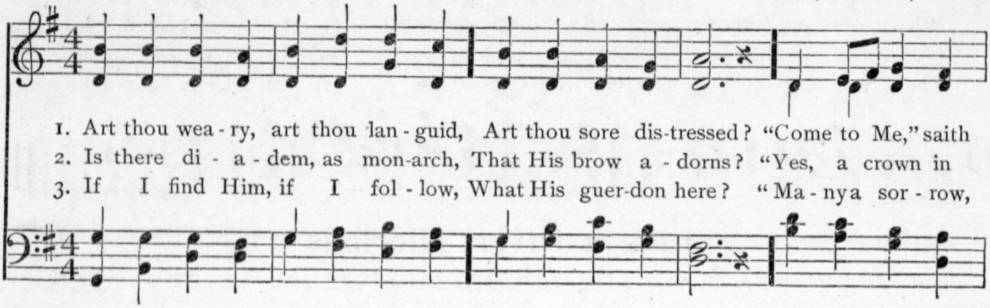

1. Art thou wea - ry, art thou lan - guid, Art thou sore dis-tressed? "Come to Me," saith
2. Is there di - a - dem, as mon-arch, That His brow a - dorns? "Yes, a crown in
3. If I find Him, if I fol - low, What His guer-don here? "Ma - ny a sor - row,

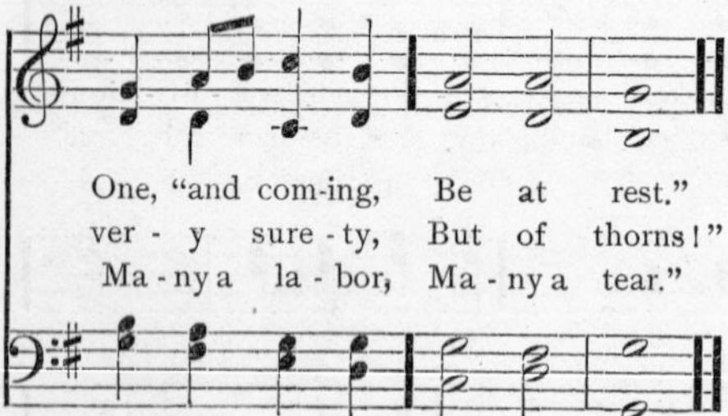

One, "and com-ing, Be at rest."
ver - y sure - ty, But of thorns!"
Ma - ny a la - bor, Ma - ny a tear."

4 If I still hold closely to Him,
What hath He at last?
"Sorrow vanquished, labor ended,
Jordan passed."

5 If I ask Him to receive me,
Will He say me nay?
"Not till earth and not till heaven
Pass away."

99 Jesus is Passing This Way

Annie L. James ("*He was to pass that way.*"—*Luke 19: 4.*) W. H. Doane

Gently

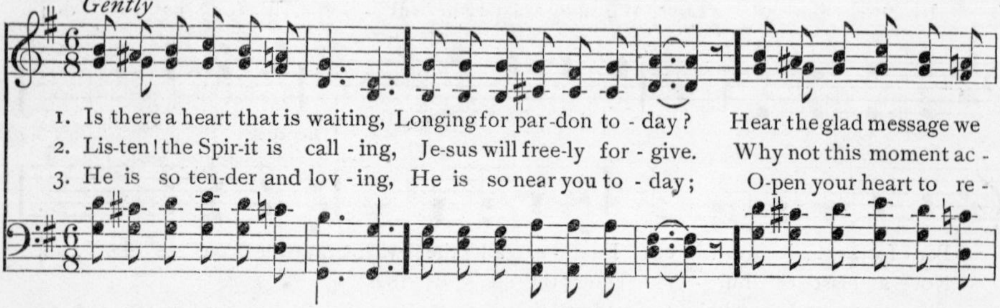

1. Is there a heart that is waiting, Longing for par-don to - day? Hear the glad message we
2. Lis-ten! the Spir-it is call - ing, Je-sus will free-ly for - give. Why not this moment ac -
3. He is so ten-der and lov - ing, He is so near you to - day; O-pen your heart to re -

rit. REFRAIN

bring you, Je - sus is pass - ing this way. Je-sus is passing this way, . . . This
cept Him, Trust in God's mer - cy and live?
ceive Him, While He is pass - ing this way. Je - sus is pass-ing, is pass-ing this way, Is

Copyright, 1895, by W. H. Doane. By per.

Jesus is Passing This Way

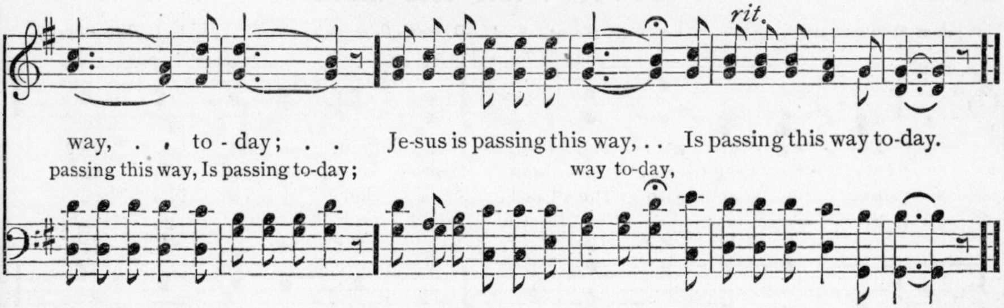
rit.
way, . . to - day; . . Je-sus is passing this way, . . Is passing this way to-day.
passing this way, Is passing to-day; way to-day,

O Fair the Gleams of Glory

100

Charles I. Cameron (*Miriam* 7s. 6s. D.) J. P. Holbrook

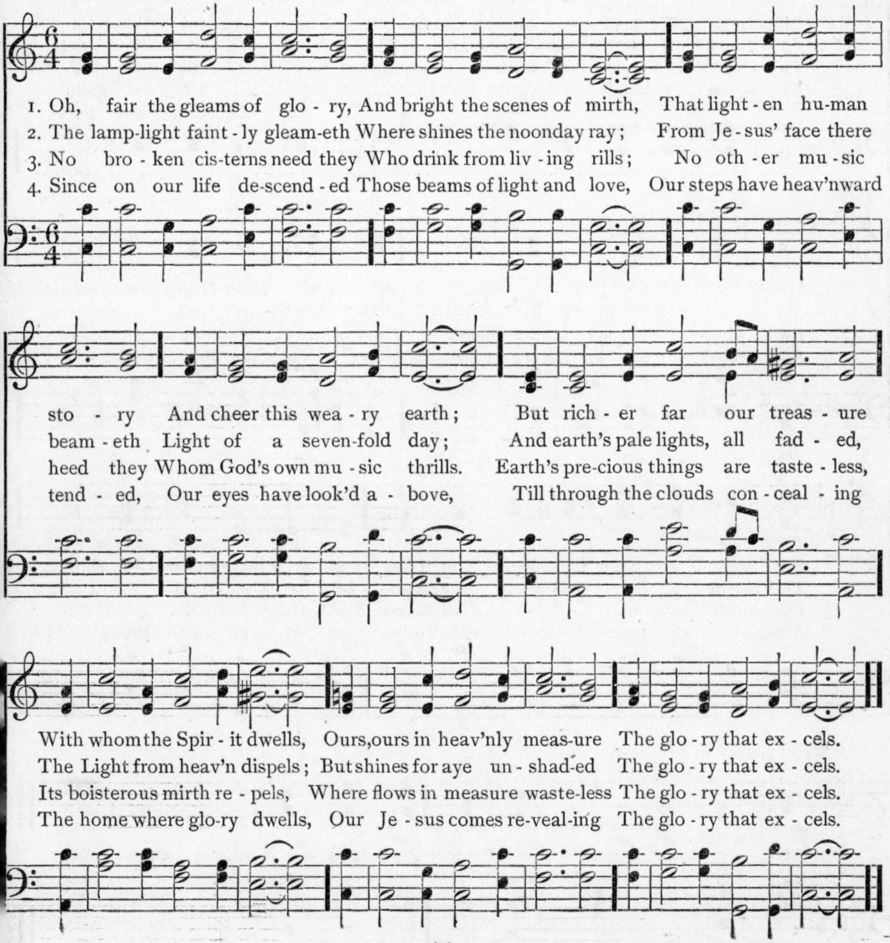
1. Oh, fair the gleams of glo - ry, And bright the scenes of mirth, That light - en hu-man sto - ry And cheer this wea - ry earth; But rich - er far our treas - ure With whom the Spir - it dwells, Ours, ours in heav'nly meas-ure The glo - ry that ex - cels.
2. The lamp-light faint - ly gleam-eth Where shines the noonday ray; From Je - sus' face there beam - eth Light of a seven-fold day; And earth's pale lights, all fad - ed, The Light from heav'n dispels; But shines for aye un - shad-ed The glo - ry that ex - cels.
3. No bro - ken cis-terns need they Who drink from liv - ing rills; No oth - er mu - sic heed they Whom God's own mu - sic thrills. Earth's pre-cious things are taste - less, Its boisterous mirth re - pels, Where flows in measure waste-less The glo - ry that ex - cels.
4. Since on our life de-scend - ed Those beams of light and love, Our steps have heav'nward tend - ed, Our eyes have look'd a - bove, Till through the clouds con - ceal - ing The home where glo-ry dwells, Our Je - sus comes re-veal-ing The glo - ry that ex - cels.

101 Forever with the Lord

James Montgomery (*Nearer Home S. M. D. with Refrain*) I. B. Woodbury

1. For - ev - er with the Lord! A - men, so let it be!
2. My Fa - ther's house on high, Home of my soul, how near
3. For - ev - er with the Lord! Fa - ther, if 'tis Thy will,
4. So when my lat - est breath Shall rend the veil in twain,
Life from the dead is in that word; 'Tis im - mor - tal - i - ty.
At times to faith's fore - see - ing eye, Thy gold - en gates ap - pear!
The prom - ise of that faith - ful word, E'en here to me ful - fill.
By death I shall es - cape from death, And life e - ter - nal gain.
Here in the bod - y pent, Ab - sent from Him I roam;
My thirst - y spir - it faints To reach the land I love,
Be Thou at my right hand, Then can I nev - er fail;
Know - ing as I am known, How shall I love that word!
Yet night - ly pitch my mov - ing tent, A day's march near - er home.
The bright in - her - it - ance of saints — Je - ru - sa - lem a - bove.
Up - hold Thou me, so I shall stand, Fight, and I must pre - vail.
And oft re - peat be - fore the throne, "For - ev - er with the Lord!"
REFRAIN
Near - er home, near - er home, A day's march near - er home.

Lord, Where Thou Wilt

Anon.

(10s. with Refrain)

1. Lord, where Thou wilt — it mat - ters not to me, If Thou art near, and
2. Lord, where Thou wilt — it mat - ters not to me, Though skies may frown, and
3. Lord, where Thou wilt — it mat - ters not to me, If faith's clear eye the
I can cling to Thee; For I am weak, so weak, I am a - fraid
dark my path may be; I am con - tent, since Thou, my Life, my Light,
po - lar star may see; If I can read my ti - tle to a home
REFRAIN
To take one step with - out Thy kind - ly aid. Lead Thou my way, my
Canst pierce the veil that hangs o'er dark - est night.
Where sin and death, and night can nev - er come.
faint - ing heart sus - tain; Lead Thou my way, and make my du - ty plain; Lead Thou my
way, then shall I fear no ill, If Thou, my "Rod and Staff," art with me still.

103 The Crown of Righteousness

Howard B. Grose, 1901 — (8. 8. 8. 8) — F. L. Stone, 1901

1. Sav - iour Di - vine, Thy crown was thorns ; Thy sa-cred brow that crown did press,
2. Hold Thou this crown be - fore our eyes, To give us courage in the strife
3. Hail ! joy - ous hour when Thou shalt say, As we our trust - y arms lay down,

That Thou mightst on Thine own be - stow The glo-rious crown of right - eous-ness !
That we must wage, if we would rise To share in heav'n's im - mor - tal life.
"The faith ye kept ! ye won the day, Come, wear the prize,—a soul-starred crown !"

Copyright, words and music, 1901, by Howard B. Grose.

104 My Refuge

Alice Boise Wood, 1901 — (*Psalm civ. 17. 18*) — M. B. Willis, 1901

1. To the rock flies the co - ny, The stork to her nest, When tem-pests are
2. The nest, whith - er speed - eth The storm-beat - en bird, A - loft, on the
3. The rock where the co - ny Se - cure - ly may hide Is set in the
4. Then blow, thou wild tem - pest, I fear not thy might : Tho' black - ly thou

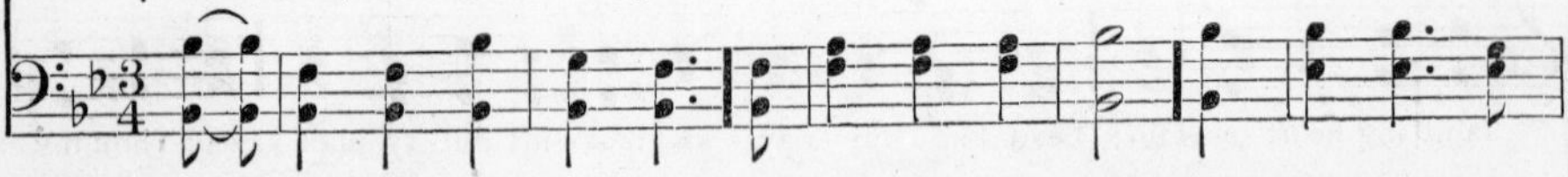

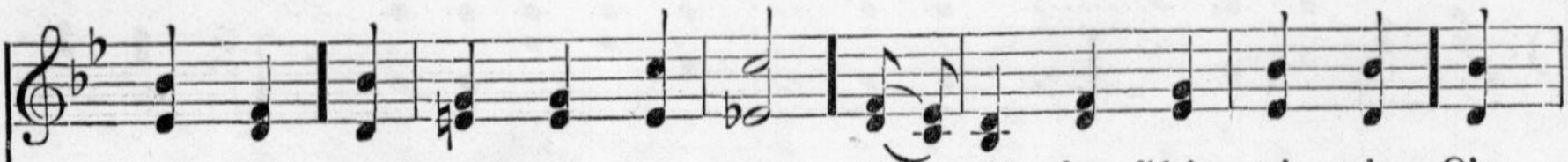

gath - 'ring And black is the west ; So swift, by life's tri - als O'er -
fir - top By tem - pests is stirred ; But the nest of my ref - uge No
moun-tain's Cold, pit - i - less side : But the rock of my safe - ty, The
low - 'rest, My pros - pect is bright : Je - ho - vah, my Sav - iour, I

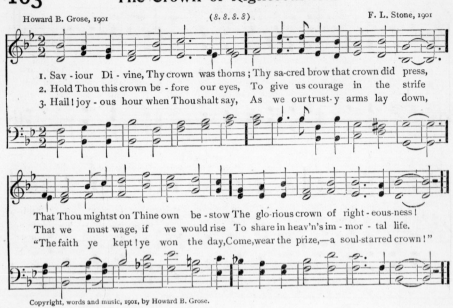

Copyright, 1901, by U. S. C. E.

My Refuge

whelmed and op - pressed, I fly to my ref - uge, Je - ho - vah, my rest!
storm - wind can smite; 'Tis the breast of Je - ho - vah; I'm safe from af - fright.
home of my quest, 'Tis the heart of my Sav - iour, How warm and how blest!
fly to Thy breast: Dear rock of my ref - uge! Dear shel - ter - ing nest!

Jesus, Still Lead On 105

Jane Borthwick, tr. (*Guide P. M.*) U. C. Burnap

1. Je - sus, still lead on, Till our rest be won; And al - tho' the
2. If the way be drear, If the foe be near, Let not faith - less
3. Je - sus, still lead on, Till our rest be won; Heav'nly Lead - er,

way be cheer - less, We will fol - low, calm and fear - less:
fears o'er - take us, Let not faith and hope for - sake us;
still di - rect us, Still sup - port, con - sole, pro - tect us,

Guide us by Thy hand To our Fa - ther - land, To our Fa - ther - land.
For thro' many a foe, To our home we go, To our home we go.
Till we safe - ly stand In our Fa - ther - land, In our Fa - ther - land.

106 He Cares for Me

(*8. 6. 8. 6. D. Chorus*)

Fanny Crosby

Victor H. Benke

1. I have a pre - cious, faith - ful Guide, A firm, a - bid - ing Friend, Who
2. The fra - grant li - lies of the field, He clothes in beau - ty rare, And
3. The birds that nei - ther sow nor reap, By Him are dai - ly fed, Who
in His word the prom - ise gives, To help me to the end. I cast on Him my
tho' they nei - ther toil nor spin, He makes them still His care. No king on earth, how -
num - bers with un - er - ring glance, The hairs up - on my head. With - in His ev - er -
ev - 'ry care, Whose eye my heart can see, . Though oft I wan - der from His love, I
ev - er great, Like them ar - rayed can be, . And so I learn to trust my Lord, And
last - ing arms My soul at peace shall be, . I can - not doubt, be - cause I know My
CHORUS
know He cares for me. He cares for e - ven me, . And this my joy shall
know He cares for me.
Sav - iour cares for me.
be, . . That if He marks the spar - row's fall, I know He cares for me.

Copyright, 1898, by M. E. Upham

Heaven is My Home 107

Rev. Thomas R. Taylor, 1836 (6. 4. 6. 4. 6. 6. 6. 4) Sir Arthur Sullivan, 1872

1. I'm but a stran-ger here, Heav'n is my home; Earth is a des-ert drear,
2. What tho' the tem-pest rage, Heav'n is my home; Short is my pil-grim-age,
3. There, at my Sav-iour's side, Heav'n is my home; I shall be glo-ri-fied,
4. There-fore I mur-mur not, Heav'n is my home; What-e'er my earth-ly lot,
Heav'n is my home. Dan-ger and sor-row stand Round me on ev-'ry hand;
Heav'n is my home: And time's wild win-try blast Soon shall be o-ver-past;
Heav'n is my home. There are the good and blest, Those I love most and best;
Heav'n is my home: And I shall sure-ly stand There at my Lord's right hand;
Heav'n is my fa-ther-land, Heav'n is my home.
I shall reach home at last, Heav'n is my home.
And there I too shall rest, Heav'n is my home.
Heav'n is my fa-ther-land, Heav'n is my home.
A-MEN.

Fade, Fade, Each Earthly Joy 108

1 Fade, fade each earthly joy,
Jesus is mine!
Break every tender tie,
Jesus is mine!
Dark is the wilderness,
Earth has no resting place,
Jesus alone can bless,
Jesus is mine!

2 Tempt not my soul away,
Jesus is mine!
Here would I ever stay,
Jesus is mine!
Perishing things of clay,
Born but for one brief day,
Pass from my heart away,
Jesus is mine!

3 Farewell, ye dreams of night,
Jesus is mine!
Lost in this dawning light,
Jesus is mine!
All that my soul has tried,
Left but a dismal void,
Jesus has satisfied,
Jesus is mine!

4 Farewell, mortality,
Jesus is mine!
Welcome eternity,
Jesus is mine!
Welcome, O loved and blest,
Welcome, sweet scenes of rest,
Welcome, my Saviour's breast,
Jesus is mine!

Mrs. Catherine J. Bonar, 1843

109 Shadow of a Mighty Rock

John Samuel Bewley Monsell, 1862 (*Gottschalk* 7s) Arr. by E. P. Parker

1. Shad - ow of a might - y rock, Stretch - ing o'er a wea - ry land,
2. When Thy pres - ence, O my God, Bright - er is than eye can see,
3. When life's pas - sions o'er me break, Like a storm a - gainst the wall,
4. Out of Thee are shades of death, Wea - ry ways, and hours un - blest;
5. Till the race of life be run, Till my soul in rest be laid,

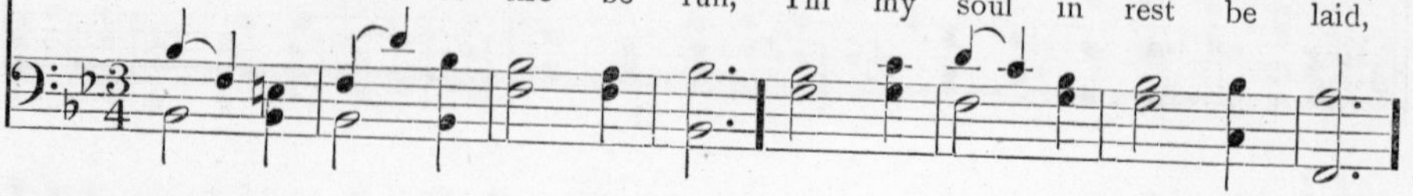

Hide me from the tem - pest's shock, Let me in Thy shel - ter stand.
Shad - ow on the heav'n - ward road, Let me find my shade in Thee.
Let me find for mer - cy's sake Shel - ter where Thy shad - ows fall.
Shad - ow of the rock, be - neath Thee a - lone are joy and rest.
God of gods, Thou art my sun; Son of God, be Thou my shade!

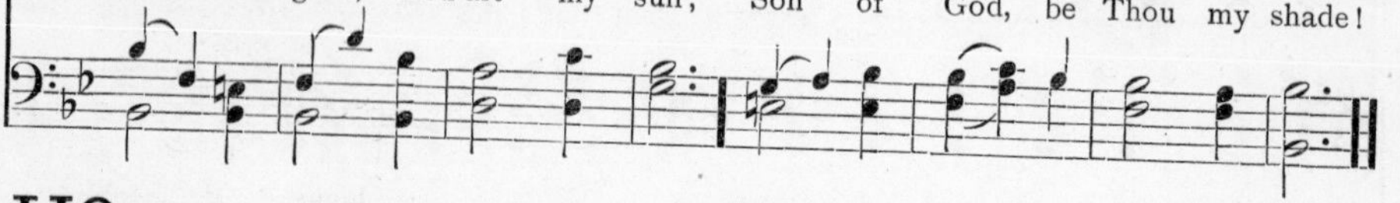

110 Sometimes a Light Surprises

William Cowper, 1779 (*Bentley* 7. 6. 7. 6. D.) John Hullah, 1867

1. Sometimes a light sur-pris - es The Christian while he sings; It is the Lord, who
2. In ho - ly con - tem - pla - tion We sweet - ly then pur - sue The theme of God's sal-
3. It can bring with it noth - ing But He will bear us thro'; Who gives the lil - ies
4. Tho' vine nor fig - tree nei - ther Their wont - ed fruit shall bear, Tho' all the field should

ris - es With heal - ing in His wings: When com - forts are de - clin - ing, He
va - tion, And find it ev - er new; Set free from pres - ent sor - row, We
cloth - ing Will clothe His peo - ple too: Be - neath the spreading heav - ens No
with - er, Nor flocks nor herds be there; Yet God the same a - bid - ing, His

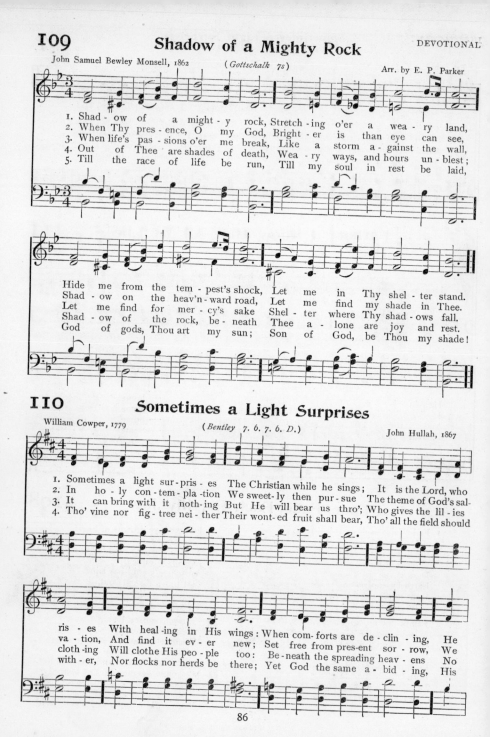

Sometimes a Light Surprises

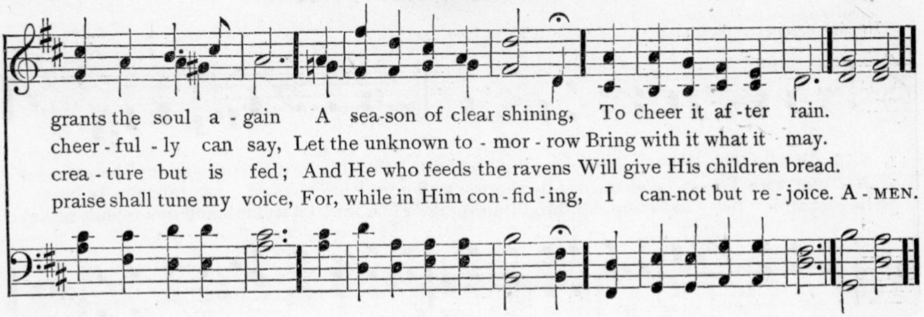
grants the soul a - gain A sea-son of clear shining, To cheer it af - ter rain.
cheer - ful - ly can say, Let the unknown to - mor - row Bring with it what it may.
crea - ture but is fed; And He who feeds the ravens Will give His children bread.
praise shall tune my voice, For, while in Him con - fid - ing, I can-not but re - joice. A - MEN.

Father! I Know that All My Life 111

Anna L. Waring (*Spohr* 8. 6. 6*l*.) Arr. from Spohr

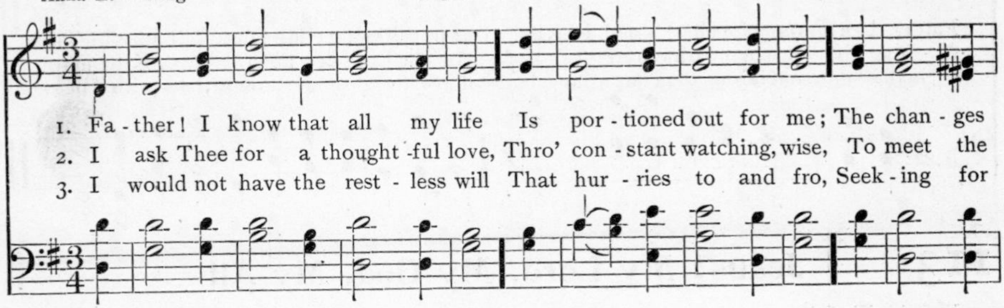
1. Fa - ther! I know that all my life Is por - tioned out for me; The chan - ges
2. I ask Thee for a thought -ful love, Thro' con - stant watching, wise, To meet the
3. I would not have the rest - less will That hur - ries to and fro, Seek - ing for

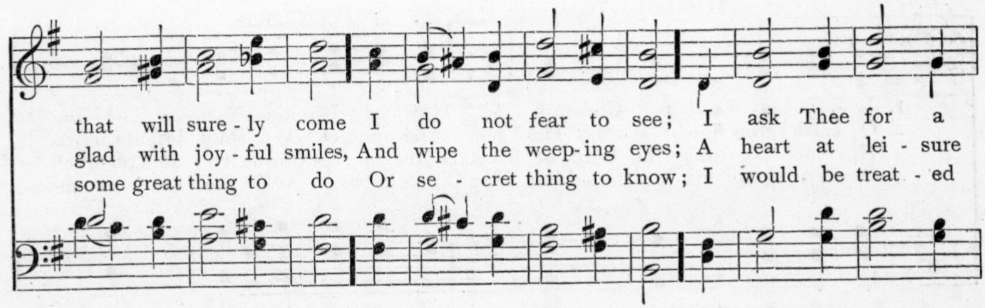
that will sure - ly come I do not fear to see; I ask Thee for a
glad with joy - ful smiles, And wipe the weep - ing eyes; A heart at lei - sure
some great thing to do Or se - cret thing to know; I would be treat - ed

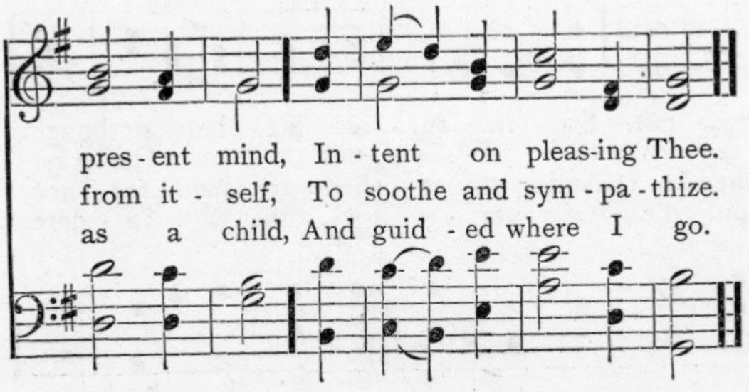
pres - ent mind, In - tent on pleas-ing Thee.
from it - self, To soothe and sym - pa - thize.
as a child, And guid - ed where I go.

4 Wherever in the world I am,
In whatsoe'er estate,
I have a fellowship with hearts
To keep and cultivate;
A work of lowly love to do
For Him on whom I wait.

5 I ask Thee for the daily strength, —
To none that ask denied,
A mind to blend with outward life, —
While keeping at Thy side;
Content to fill a little space,
If Thou be glorified.

112 Still, Still with Thee

Harriet Beecher Stowe, 1835 (*Willingham* 11s. 10s) F. Abt

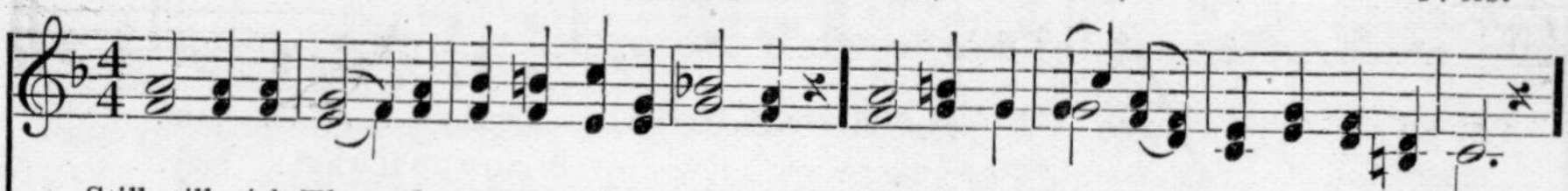

1. Still, still with Thee, when purple morning breaketh, When the bird waketh, and the shadows flee;
2. A - lone with Thee, a - mid the mystic shadows, The solemn hush of na-ture new-ly born;
3. So shall it be at last, in that bright morning, When the soul waketh, and life's shadows flee;

Fair-er than morning, lovelier than the daylight, Dawns the sweet consciousness, I am with Thee.
A - lone with Thee, in breathless ad-o-ra - tion, In the calm dew and freshness of the morn.
O! in that hour, and fair-er than day's dawning, Shall rise the glorious thought, I am with Thee!

113 Jesus! My Lord, My God, My All

Frederick W. Faber, 1814–1863 (*St. Chrysostom* 8s) Sir Joseph Barnby, 1872

1. Je - sus! my Lord, my God, my All! How can I love Thee as I ought?
2. O earth! grow flow'rs be-neath His feet! And thou, O sun, shine bright this day!
3. He comes! He comes! the Lord of Hosts, Borne on His throne tri - um - phant - ly!
4. Our hearts leap up; our trem-bling song Grows faint-er still; we can no more!

And how re - vere this won-drous gift, So far sur - pass - ing hope or thought?
He comes! He comes! O heav'n on earth! Our Je - sus comes up - on His way.
We see Thee, and we know Thee, Lord! And yearn to shed our blood for Thee!
Si - lence! and let us weep—and die Of ver - y love, while we a - dore.

Jesus! My Lord, My God, My All

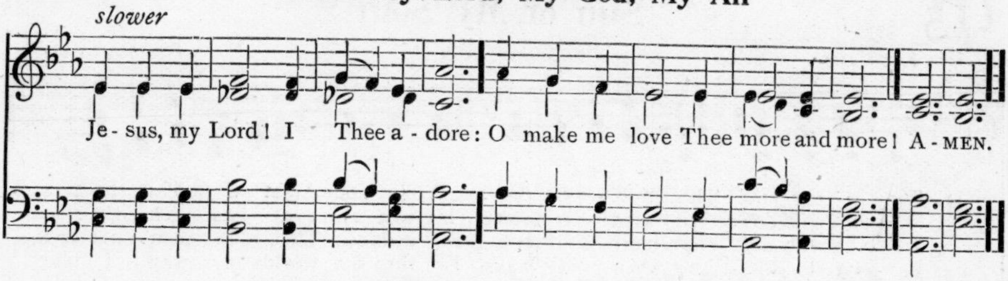
slower
Je - sus, my Lord! I Thee a - dore: O make me love Thee more and more! A - MEN.

Holy Spirit, Faithful Guide

114

M. M. Wells, 1815-1858

Marcus Morris Wells

1. Ho - ly Spir - it, faith - ful Guide, Ev - er near the Christian's side;
2. Ev - er pres - ent, tru - est Friend, Ev - er near Thine aid to lend,
3. When our days of toil shall cease, Wait - ing still for sweet re - lease,
Gen - tly lead us by the hand, Pil - grims in a des - ert land;
Leave us not to doubt and fear, Grop - ing on in dark - ness drear;
Noth - ing left but heav'n and pray'r, Won - d'ring if our names are there;
Wea - ry souls for - e'er re - joice, While they hear that sweet - est voice,
When the storms are ra - ging sore, Hearts grow faint, and hopes give o'er,
Wad - ing deep the dis - mal flood, Plead - ing nought but Je - sus' blood,
Whis - p'ring soft - ly, "Wanderer, come; Fol - low Me, I'll guide thee home."
Whis - per soft - ly, "Wanderer, come; Fol - low Me, I'll guide thee home."
Whis - per soft - ly, "Wanderer, come; Fol - low Me, I'll guide thee home."

115 Sun of My Soul

(*Hursley L. M.*)

John Keble, 1820

Peter Ritter, arr.

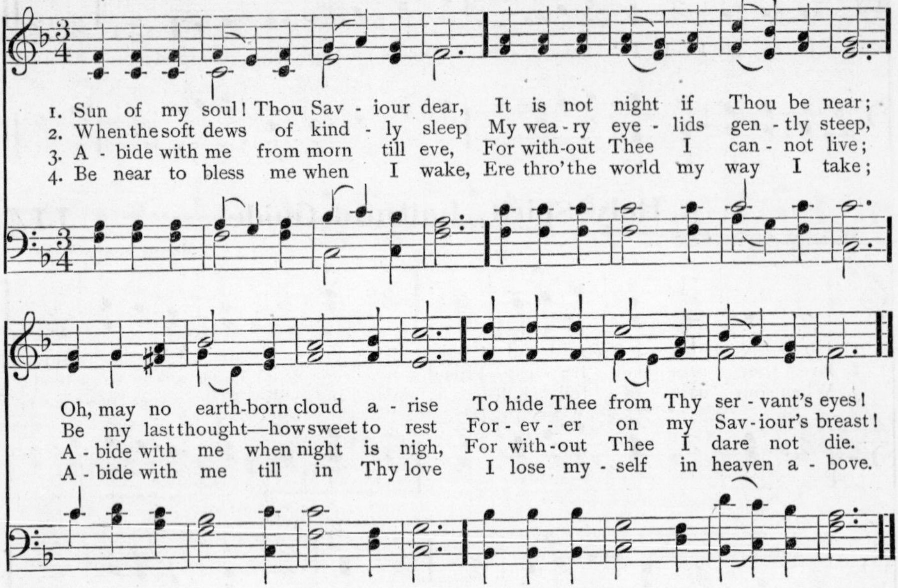
1. Sun of my soul! Thou Sav - iour dear, It is not night if Thou be near;
2. When the soft dews of kind - ly sleep My wea - ry eye - lids gen - tly steep,
3. A - bide with me from morn till eve, For with-out Thee I can - not live;
4. Be near to bless me when I wake, Ere thro' the world my way I take;
Oh, may no earth-born cloud a - rise To hide Thee from Thy ser - vant's eyes!
Be my last thought—how sweet to rest For - ev - er on my Sav - iour's breast!
A - bide with me when night is nigh, For with - out Thee I dare not die.
A - bide with me till in Thy love I lose my - self in heaven a - bove.

116 Purer Yet and Purer

(*St. Mary Magdalene 6s. 5s*)

Johann Wolfgang von Goethe, 1749–1832

J. B. Dykes, 1862

1. Pur - er yet and pur - er I would be in mind, Dear - er yet and
2. Calm - er yet and calm - er In the hours of pain, Sur - er yet and
3. High - er yet and high - er Out of clouds and night, Near - er yet and
4. Swift - er yet and swift - er Ev - er on - ward run, Firm - er yet and
dear - er Ev - 'ry du - ty find; Hop - ing still and trust - ing
sur - er Peace at last to gain; Suf - f'ring still and do - ing,
near - er Ris - ing to the light — Light se - rene and ho - ly,
firm - er Step as I go on; Oft these ear - nest long - ings

Purer Yet and Purer

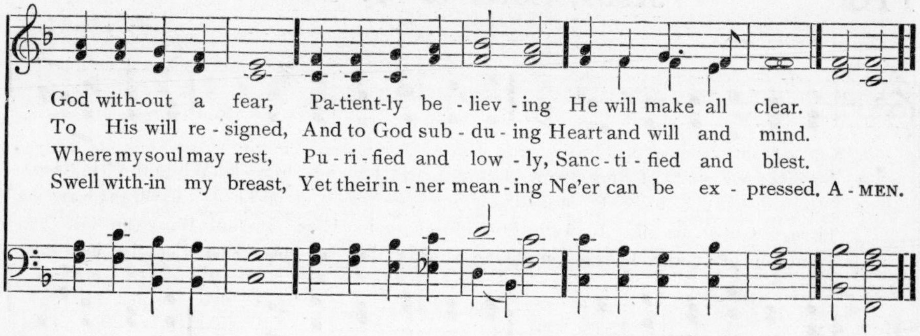
God with-out a fear, Pa-tient-ly be - liev - ing He will make all clear.
To His will re - signed, And to God sub - du - ing Heart and will and mind.
Where my soul may rest, Pu - ri - fied and low - ly, Sanc - ti - fied and blest.
Swell with-in my breast, Yet their in - ner mean - ing Ne'er can be ex - pressed. A - MEN.

I Hear a Sweet Voice Ringing Clear 117

E. Paxton Hood | (*Grassmere P. M.*) | Old Melody, arr.

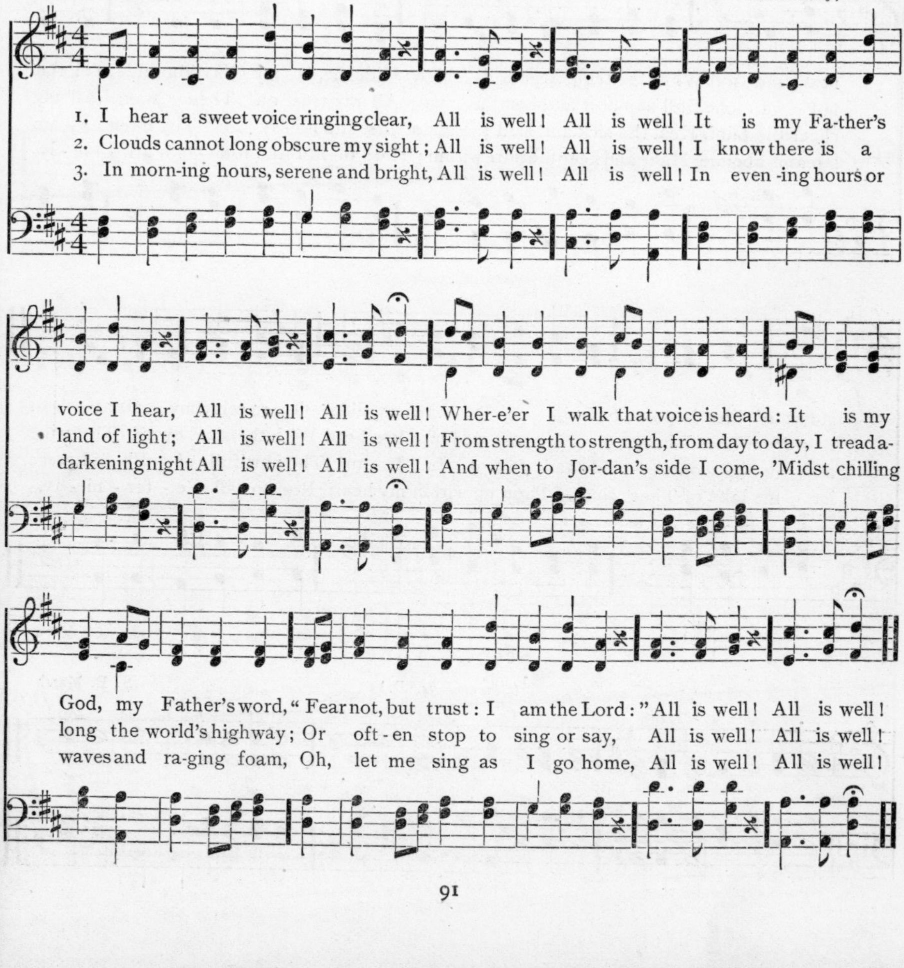
1. I hear a sweet voice ringing clear, All is well! All is well! It is my Fa-ther's
2. Clouds cannot long obscure my sight; All is well! All is well! I know there is a
3. In morn-ing hours, serene and bright, All is well! All is well! In even-ing hours or
voice I hear, All is well! All is well! Wher-e'er I walk that voice is heard: It is my
land of light; All is well! All is well! From strength to strength, from day to day, I tread a-
darkening night All is well! All is well! And when to Jor-dan's side I come, 'Midst chilling
God, my Father's word, "Fear not, but trust: I am the Lord:" All is well! All is well!
long the world's highway; Or oft-en stop to sing or say, All is well! All is well!
waves and ra-ging foam, Oh, let me sing as I go home, All is well! All is well!

118 Jesus, Lover of My Soul

(*Hollingside* 7s. D.)

Charles Wesley, 1740

J. B. Dykes

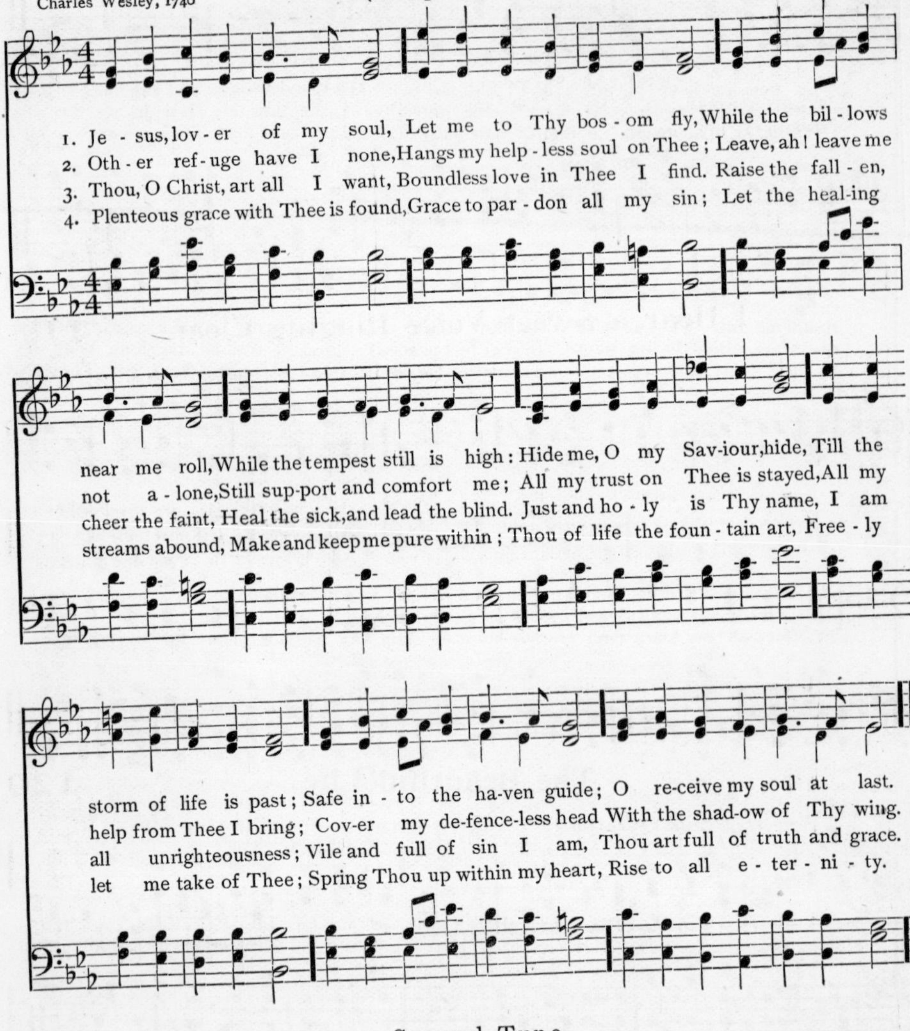
1. Je - sus, lov - er of my soul, Let me to Thy bos - om fly, While the bil - lows
2. Oth - er ref - uge have I none, Hangs my help - less soul on Thee; Leave, ah! leave me
3. Thou, O Christ, art all I want, Boundless love in Thee I find. Raise the fall - en,
4. Plenteous grace with Thee is found, Grace to par - don all my sin; Let the heal-ing
near me roll, While the tempest still is high: Hide me, O my Sav-iour, hide, Till the
not a - lone, Still sup-port and comfort me; All my trust on Thee is stayed, All my
cheer the faint, Heal the sick, and lead the blind. Just and ho - ly is Thy name, I am
streams abound, Make and keep me pure within; Thou of life the foun - tain art, Free - ly
storm of life is past; Safe in - to the ha-ven guide; O re-ceive my soul at last.
help from Thee I bring; Cov-er my de-fence-less head With the shad-ow of Thy wing.
all unrighteousness; Vile and full of sin I am, Thou art full of truth and grace.
let me take of Thee; Spring Thou up within my heart, Rise to all e - ter - ni - ty.

Second Tune

(*Martyn* 7s. D.)

S. B. Marsh

FINE
D.C.

Safe with Jesus

119

(*Refuge* 7s. D.)

J. R. Bispham — Jos. P. Holbrook

1. “Je - sus, lov - er of my soul,” Bids me in His bos-om stay, And tho' bil - lows
2. “Oth - er ref - uge have I none,” He my hab - i - ta - tion is; Here no e - vil
3. “Thou, O Christ, art all I want,” Rest my help-less soul on Thee; Thou wilt nev - er
round me roll, I am safe - ly hid a - way; For He holds me in His arms, Quite be -
can be - fall — I am kept in per-fect peace. I am cov - ered all day long With the
leave a - lone Nor for - get to comfort me. Thou hast sav'd my soul from death, Thou hast
yond the tempest's reach, And He whis-pers in my heart Words unknown to human speech.
shad - ow of His wing; Dwell in safe - ty thro' the night, Wak-ing, this is what I sing.
scat - tered all my fears, And the sun-shine of Thy face Sweet - ly dri - eth all my tears.

The Beautiful Life

120

Charles S. Brown

Smoothly, with expression

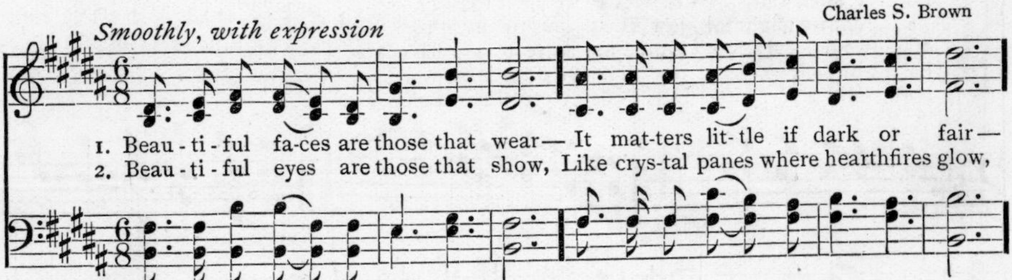
1. Beau - ti - ful fa-ces are those that wear — It mat-ters lit-tle if dark or fair —
2. Beau - ti - ful eyes are those that show, Like crys-tal panes where hearthfires glow,

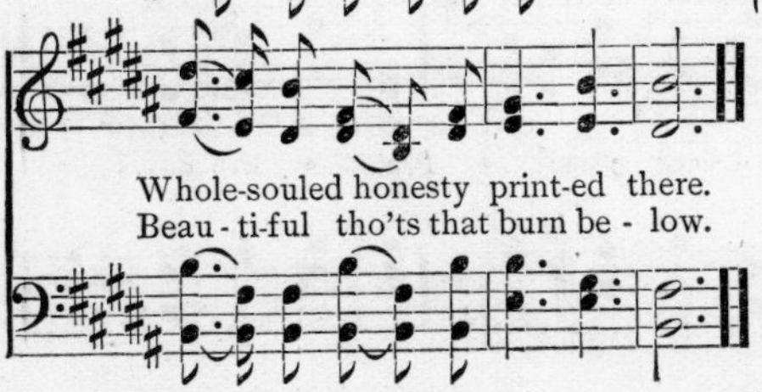
Whole-souled honesty print-ed there.
Beau - ti-ful tho'ts that burn be - low.

3 Beautiful hands are those that do
Work that is earnest and brave and true,
Moment by moment, the long day through.

4 Beautiful lives are those that bless;
Fountains of love and happiness;
Lives that in spirit Christ confess.

Copyright, 1901, by U. S. C. E.

121 Saviour, Blessed Saviour

G. Thring, 1862 (*Bacon 6s. 5s. 8l. With Refrain*) L. C. Jacoby, 1895

1. Sav - iour,blessed Sav - iour, Lis - ten while we sing; Hearts and voi-ces rais - ing
2. Near - er, ev - er near - er, Christ, we draw to Thee, Deep in ad - o - ra - tion
3. Bright-er still and bright-er Glows the west-ern sun, Shed-ding all its glad-ness
4. On - ward,ev - er on -ward, Journeying o'er the road Worn by saints be - fore us,
5. High - er, then, and high - er, Bear the ransomed soul, Earth-ly toils for - get - ting,
Prais - es to our King. All we have we of - fer, All we hope to be, . . .
Bend - ing low the knee: Thou for our re - demp-tion Cam'st on earth to die; . .
O'er our work that's done: Time will soon be o - ver, Toil and sor - row past, . .
Journeying on to God; Leav -ing all be - hind us, May we has - ten on, . . .
Sav - iour, to its goal; Where in joys un-thought of Saints with an - gels sing, . .
All . . . we yield to Thee.
Refrain
Bod - y, soul, and spir - it, All we yield to Thee. Sav-iour,bless-ed Sav - iour,
Thou,that we might fol - low,Hast gone up on high.
May we,blessed Sav - iour, Find a rest at last.
Back-ward nev-er look - ing Till the prize is won.
Nev - er wea - ry, rais - ing Prais-es to their King.
Lis - ten while we sing; Hearts and voi - ces rais - ing Prais - es to our King.

True-hearted, Whole-hearted

122

Frances R. Havergal (*P. M.*) C. E. Kettle

In march time
1. True-heart-ed, whole-heart-ed, faith - ful and loy - al, King of our lives by Thy
2. True-heart-ed, whole-heart-ed, full - est al - le - giance Yield - ing hence-forth to our
3. True-heart-ed, whole-heart-ed, Sav - iour all glo - rious! Take Thy great pow - er and
grace we will be! Un - der the stan - dard ex - alt - ed and roy - al,
glo - ri - ous King; Val - iant en - deav - or and lov - ing o - be - dience,
reign there a - lone, O - ver our wills and af - fec - tions vic - to - rious,
Strong in Thy strength we will bat - tle for Thee.
Free - ly and joy - ous - ly now would we bring.
Free - ly sur - ren - dered and whol - ly Thine own.
ff CHORUS
Peal out the watch-word! and si-lence it nev - er! Song of our spir - its re - joi-cing and free; True-hearted, whole-hearted,
ff
now and for - ev - er, King of our lives, by Thy grace we will be.

Copyright, 1901, by U. S. C. E.

123 Our Lives to Christ We Dedicate

John Pollock — (*C. M. D. and Chorus*) — John Pollock

Marching time

1. Our lives to Christ we ded - i - cate, Who reigns our glo - rious King;
2. Our fa - thers fought her bat - tles oft, And died to set her free;
3. The stains that mar her beau - ty now Shall short - ly dis - ap - pear;
May He re-ceive and con - se - crate The trib - ute that we bring!
And now 'tis ours to bear a - loft Her flag of lib - er - ty.
Soon, in re-mem-brance of His vow, The Bride - groom will be here!
And to His Church we glad - ly give Our ser - vice and our all,
They loved the Mas - ter best of all; His Church they did re - vere,
Then Her di - vi - sions shall be healed, Her tears shall all be dried,
For in her voice we still re - joice To hear His Roy - al call.
They loved the ground where she was found, Her dust to them was dear.
And she shall stand at His right hand, A fault - less, glo - rious bride!
CHORUS
For Christ and the Church!
For Christ, for Christ and the Church of Christ! Be this our fond en - deav - or!

Copyright, 1901, by U. S. C. E.

Our Lives to Christ We Dedicate

For Christ and the Church!
For Christ, for Christ and the Church of Christ! These twain no pow'r can sev - er;
One on earth, one in heav'n,
One on earth, and one in hea - ven, One on earth, and one in hea - ven,
rall.
One on earth, and one in heav'n, For - ev - er and for - ev - er! . .

Scatter Cheering Words

124

Anon. (*Siloam C. M.*) St. Alban's Tune Book

1. Kind, lov - ing words, oh, scat - ter them A - long your earth - ly way, . .
2. Some fam - ish - ing and faint - ing soul Would glad - ly pick them up; . .
3. Soft, ten - der words are like the sea, And as the sum - mer rain . .
As you would strew the blos - soms fair That beau - ti - fy the day. . .
Strong, cheer - ing words may turn a - side The deep and bit - ter cup. . .
That as a ben - e - dic - tion falls, And fall - eth not in vain. .

125 Hark! 'Tis the Clarion

Joseph Brown Morgan | G. Donizetti. Arr. for this work

Vigorously In march style
f
1. Hark! 'tis the clar - ion sound - ing the fight, Turn from each si - ren charm - er.
2. Haste to the res - cue, souls in their need, Loud for re - lief are call - ing;
3. Soon 'twill be o - ver, dan - ger all past; End - ed the march - es drear - y.
Ban - ners are wav - ing, swords gleam - ing bright, Gird on the heav'n - ly ar - mor.
Must they for - ev - er hope - less - ly plead? None hear the cry ap - pall - ing?
Aft - er the war - fare, rest comes at last, Sweet rest for sol - diers wea - ry.
mf
Stern is the con - flict, fierce is the foe; Cow - ards and trai - tors will back - ward go;
Bro - ken in spir - it, wound - ed by sin, Foe - men a - round them, and fear with - in;
Crown aft - er con - flict; ease aft - er pain; Part - ing shall nev - er be known a - gain;
Brave men are want - ed, hearts all a - glow, Want - ed to bat - tle for Je - sus.
Speed ye to help them free - dom to win; Speed with the gos - pel of Je - sus.
Joy ev - er - last - ing all shall ob - tain; All who are faith - ful to Je - sus.
CHORUS
ff
Sol - diers of God, we join you to - day, Join in your grand en - deav - or.

Copyright, 1901, by U. S. C. E.

Hark! 'Tis the Clarion

Sol-diers of God, ad - vance to the fray, For the Truth is tri - um-phant for - ev - er.

Saying "Yes!" to Jesus 126

Edith G. Cherry (*6. 5. 12l.*) Walter H. Cocks

1. Say-ing "Yes!" to Je - sus All our earth-days through; In life's changing mu - sic
2. Say-ing "Yes!" to Je - sus Oh, what rest it brings To the hap-py ser - vants
3. Is the voice of Je - sus Call-ing thee to - day, Bod - y, soul, and spir - it
Keep this key-note true. Sad or glad the life - chords As they rise or fall,
Of the King of kings! From His roy - al er - rands Nev - er hold - ing back,
At His feet to lay? Ah, the life thus yield - ed Shall be found, not lost.
ff
One glad "Yes!" to Je - sus Ring - ing thro' them all. Hints of hea-ven's mu - sic
Go - ing where He sends them, Noth-ing they shall lack! In the Mas-ter's pleas-ure
An-swer "Yes!" to Je - sus, "Yes!" at a - ny cost. His just claim up - on thee,
f
cres.
ff
Bright-est hours shall bless; Dark-est hour shall glad - den, With this key - note "Yes!"
Quick to ac - qui - esce; To the Mas-ter's bid - ding, Quick to an - swer "Yes!"
Soul re-deemed, con - fess; At His feet re - ceiv - ing Strength to an - swer "Yes!"

127 Forward Go

P. H. J. H. F.

1. For - ward, for - ward! For - ward go, for the
2. For - ward, for - ward! For - ward go, for the
Lord is with thee, He is thy life, thy light, thy joy; For - ward,
morn is breaking, Swiftly the shadows fly a - way; For - ward,
for - ward! For - ward go, for the Lord is with thee, Might - y thy foes to de - stroy.
for - ward! For - ward go, for the King in splen - dor Ris - es and conquers the day.
Her - - - - alds of the gos - - pel, Mes - - - sen - gers of
Her - alds of the gos - pel, Her - alds of the gos - pel, Mes - sengers of mer - cy,
mer - - - cy, Chil - - - dren of the king - dom, High the
Mes - sengers of mer - cy, Chil - dren of the king - dom, Chil - dren of the king - dom,

Copyright, 1899, by Fillmore Bros.

Forward Go

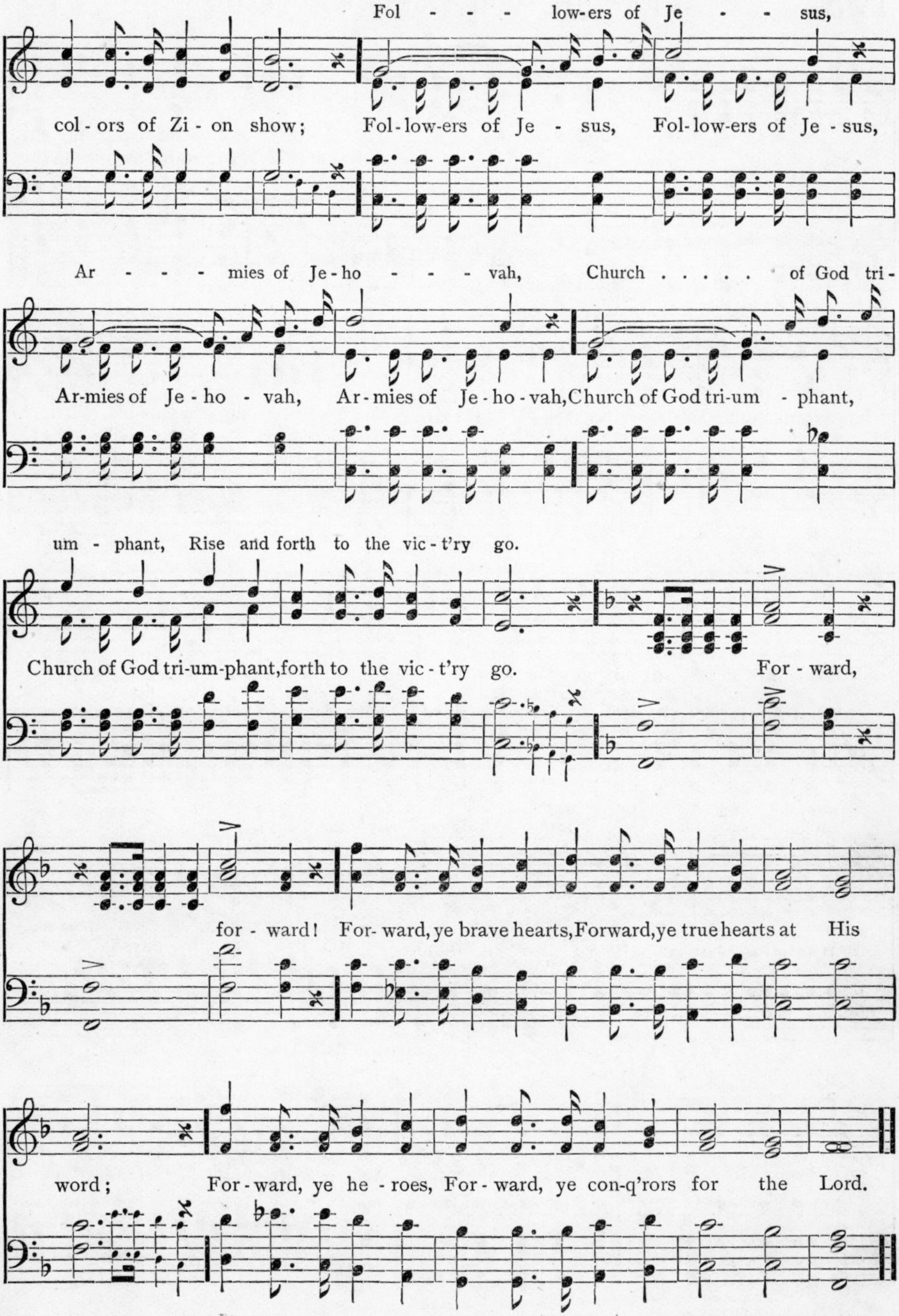
Fol - - - low-ers of Je - - sus,
col-ors of Zi-on show; Fol-low-ers of Je - sus, Fol-low-ers of Je - sus,
Ar - - - mies of Je-ho - - - vah, Church . . . . . of God tri-
Ar-mies of Je-ho - vah, Ar-mies of Je-ho-vah, Church of God tri-um - phant,
um - phant, Rise and forth to the vic-t'ry go.
Church of God tri-um-phant, forth to the vic-t'ry go. For-ward,
for - ward! For-ward, ye brave hearts, Forward, ye true hearts at His
word; For-ward, ye he-roes, For-ward, ye con-q'rors for the Lord.

128 What are You Doing for Jesus

Emily P. Miller | J. Lincoln Hall

1. What are you do - ing for Je - sus, As you jour-ney thro' life?
2. What are you do - ing for Je - sus? Are you striv-ing each day,
3. What are you do - ing for Je - sus? Soon comes set - ting of sun;
Sow - ing the grain for the har - vest, Or scat-ter - ing seeds of strife?
By lit - tle acts of kind - ness, To bright - en some one's way?
Has - ten and tell the glad tid - ings, Lest you leave some work un - done.
CHORUS
What are you do - ing, Do - ing for Je - sus?
What are you do - ing for Je - sus your friend? What are you do - ing for Je - sus to-day?
What are you do - ing, As the days go by? . . . .
What are you do - ing for Je - sus your friend, As the days go by, days go by?
What are you do - ing, Do - ing for Je - sus?
What are you do - ing for Je - sus your friend? What are you do-ing for Je-sus to-day?

Copyright, 1895, by Hall-Mack Co. By per.

What are You Doing for Jesus

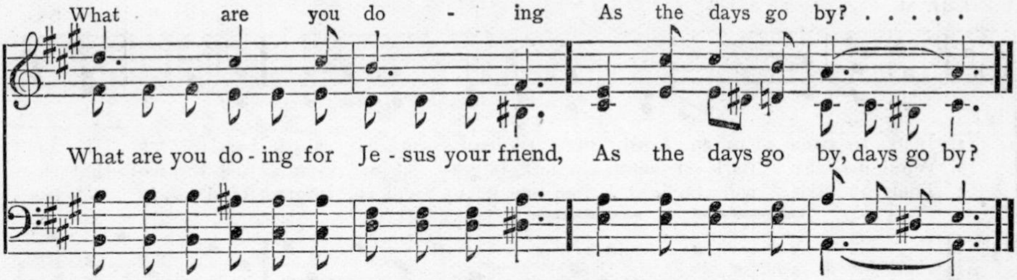
What are you do - ing As the days go by? . . . . .
What are you do - ing for Je - sus your friend, As the days go by, days go by?

On Our Way Rejoicing 129

J. S. B. Monsell (*Fleury 6.5.8l.*) Arr. from Rossini

1. On our way re - joi - cing, As we homeward move, Heark-en to our prais-es,
2. If with hon-est - heart-ed Love for God and man, Day by day Thou find us
3. On our way re - joi - cing, Glad - ly let us go; Con-quer'd hath our Lead-er,
O Thou God of love! Is there grief or sad-ness? Thine it can-not be!
Do - ing what we can, Thou who giv'st the seed-time Wilt give large in-crease,
Van-quish'd is our foe! Christ with-out, our safe - ty, Christ with - in, our joy;
Is our sky be-cloud - ed, Clouds are not from Thee!
Crown the head with bless-ings, Fill the heart with peace.
Who, if we be faith-ful, Can our hope de - stroy?
REFRAIN
On our way re - joi - cing,
As we homeward move, Heark-en to our prais - es, O Thou God of love!

130 Doing His Will

C. H. M — Mrs. C. H. Morris

1. Just to trust in the Lord, just to lean on His word, Just to feel I am His ev-'ry day; Just to walk by His side with His spir-it to guide, Just to fol-low where He leads the way.
2. When my way dark-est seems, when are blight-ed my dreams, Just to feel that the Lord know-eth best; Just to yield to His will, just to trust and be still, Just to lean on His bos-om and rest.
3. Then my heart will be light, then my path will be bright, If I've Je-sus for my dear-est friend; Count-ing all loss but gain, such a friend to ob-tain, True and faith-ful He'll be to the end.
CHORUS
Just to say what He wants me to say, what He wants me to say,
to me; . . . .
pp
And be still when He whis-pers, when He whispers to me; Just to go where He wants me to go, ... where He wants me to go,
Just to be what He wants me to be.

Copyright, 1898, by H. L. Gilmour. By per.

All and Always for the King

131

J. H. K. — Rev. J. H. Keagle

1. We are Christian workers, "all and always for the King;" For His gracious blessings we His praises now would sing; To His glorious service all our talents we will bring, And we'll help to win the world for God.
2. Hear the cry of anguish, "Come and help us ere we die!" To Christ's "Go and teach them," we would answer, "Here am I!" Deeply stirred in soul are we, to aid them we will try, And we'll help to win the world for God.
3. Loyal to our Zion, blessings on her we will pray; Zion of our fathers, take not, Lord, her light away; Keep her in Thy service true until the crowning day, When the world shall all be won to God.
FINE
D.S. talents we will bring, And we'll help to win the world for God.
CHORUS
"All and always, always for the King;" All and always, always for the King;" To His glorious service all our
"All and always, all and always for the King," "All and always, all and always for the King;"
D.S.

Copyright, 1894, by the Hoffman Music Co. Used by per.

132 March On, March On

(*March On P. M.*)

E. S. A.

H. Cohen
Harmonized for this work

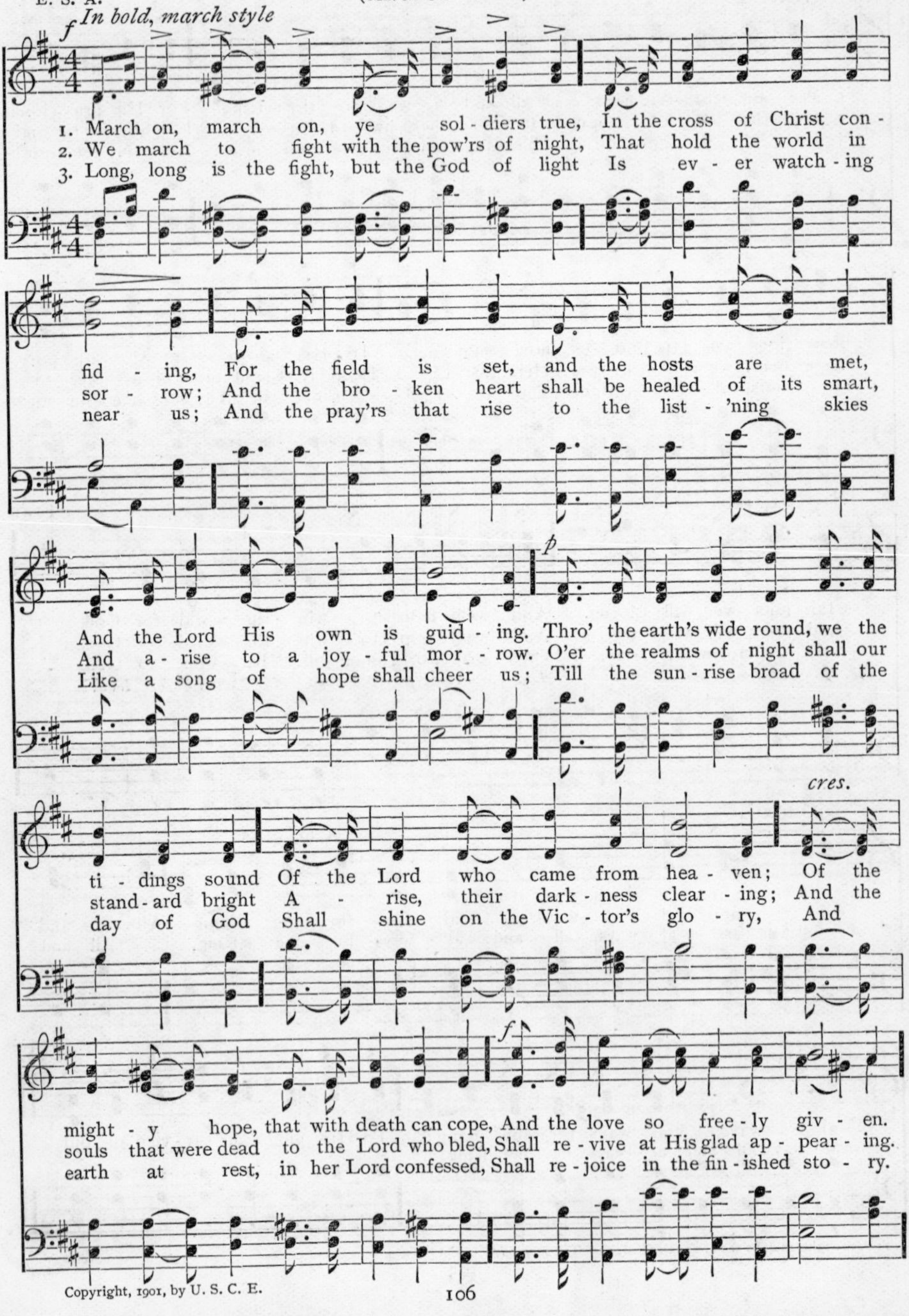
f In bold, march style
1. March on, march on, ye sol-diers true, In the cross of Christ con -
2. We march to fight with the pow'rs of night, That hold the world in
3. Long, long is the fight, but the God of light Is ev - er watch - ing
fid - ing, For the field is set, and the hosts are met,
sor - row; And the bro - ken heart shall be healed of its smart,
near us; And the pray'rs that rise to the list - 'ning skies
p
And the Lord His own is guid - ing. Thro' the earth's wide round, we the
And a - rise to a joy - ful mor - row. O'er the realms of night shall our
Like a song of hope shall cheer us; Till the sun - rise broad of the
cres.
ti - dings sound Of the Lord who came from hea - ven; Of the
stand - ard bright A - rise, their dark - ness clear - ing; And the
day of God Shall shine on the Vic - tor's glo - ry, And
f
might - y hope, that with death can cope, And the love so free - ly giv - en.
souls that were dead to the Lord who bled, Shall re - vive at His glad ap - pear - ing.
earth at rest, in her Lord confessed, Shall re - joice in the fin - ished sto - ry.

Copyright, 1901, by U. S. C. E.

March On, March On

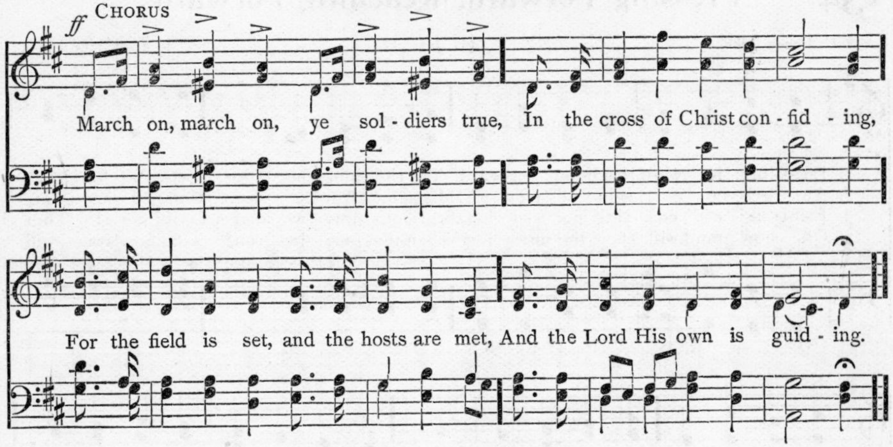
CHORUS
ff
March on, march on, ye sol - diers true, In the cross of Christ con - fid - ing,
For the field is set, and the hosts are met, And the Lord His own is guid - ing.

Have You Not a Word for Jesus 133

Frances R. Havergal (*Love Divine* 8. 7. 8. 7. D.) G. F. Le Jeune

mf
1. Have you not a word for Je - sus? Not a word to say for Him? He is list'ning
2. He has spo-ken words of bless - ing, Par - don, peace, and love to you, Glorious hopes and
3. Yes, we have a word for Je - sus! Liv - ing ech - oes we will be Of Thine own sweet
4. Ma-ny an ef - fort it may cost us, Ma-ny a heart-beat, ma-ny a fear, But Thou knowest,
p
to the cho-rus Of the burn - ing ser - a - phim! He is list'ning; does He hear you Speaking
gracious comfort, Strong and tender, sweet and true; Does He hear you telling others Something
words of blessing, Of Thy gracious "Come to Me." Je - sus, Master! yes, we love Thee, And to
and wilt strengthen, And Thy help is al-ways near. Give us grace to fol - low ful - ly, Vanquish-
cres.
dim.
of the things of earth, On - ly of its passing pleasure, Self - ish sor - row, emp - ty mirth?
of His love un - told, O - ver - flow - ings of thanksgiving For His mercies man - i - fold?
prove our love, would lay Fruit of lips which Thou wilt o - pen At Thy bless - ed feet to - day.
ing our faithless shame, Feebly it may be, but tru - ly, Wit - ness - ing for Thy dear Name.

134 Pressing Forward, Reaching Forward

S. C. Lowry, 1888 (*8s. 5s*) R. DeW. Mallary

1. Press-ing for-ward, reach-ing for-ward, To the things be - fore; See the church of
2. An - gels at our side at - tend us, Mis-sioned from a - bove; Spir - it - hosts un -
3. Faint - ing oft - en, yet pur - su - ing, Still our way we make, Look - ing to our
4. Oh, how grand will be the meet - ing When the race is run; Oh, how sweet will
God moves on - ward Ev - er more and more; Rough the road and stern the tri - al,
seen be - friend us— Min - is - tries of love; God, our Fa - ther, still pro - tects us;
Head, and do - ing All for Je - sus' sake. Glo - ry, hon - or, wis - dom, bless-ing,
be the greet-ing, "Faith-ful one, well done!" Oh, the tho't of clear - ly see - ing
But the end is sure, Faith can smile at self - de - ni - al, Cour-age can en - dure.
Je - sus is our stay; God, the Ho - ly Ghost, di - rects us, Thro' the life - long way.
Lord, for Thee we claim, Noth-ing hav - ing, yet pos-sess - ing All in Thy dear name.
What we dim - ly see; Oh, the joy, our God, of be - ing Ev - er - more with Thee!
Refrain (*in unison*)
Pressing forward, reaching forward, To the things before; See! the church of God moves onward, Ever more and more.

Copyright, 1901, by U. S. C. E,

Zealous for Service

Howard B. Grose, 1901 — (*11s. 10s. with Chorus*) — Josiah Booth, 1890

1. Zeal - ous for ser - vice are we, gra-cious Mas - ter; Teach us Thy will and give
2. Hard is the task of - ten-times, as Thou know-est; Self - ish - ness tempts, sin al -
3. Souls all a-round us are hun - gry for kind - ness; Help us to speak the words
strength to o - bey; Guid - ed by Thee we shall fear no dis - as - ter, Thy grace shall
lures from the way; On - ly as love, grace and joy Thou be-stow - est, Can we to
lov - ing and true; Mas - ter, for - give us our deaf - ness and blind-ness, O - pen our
cov - er the need of the day.
oth - ers Thy spir - it dis - play.
eyes to the good we may do.
CHORUS
Faith is our watchword, and ser - vice our glo - ry,
Love's in - spi - ra - tion our hearts shall keep true:
No - bly we'll tell out re - demp - tion's glad sto - ry,
Do - ing the work Thou hast set us to do.

136 There are Lonely Hearts

George Cooper (*While the Days are Going by* P. M.) Arr. by W. Harding Bonner

With expression
1. There are lone - ly hearts to cher - ish, While the days are go - ing by;
2. All the lov - ing links that bind us, While the days are go - ing by,
There are wea - ry souls who per - ish, While the days are go - ing by;
One by one we leave be - hind us, While the days are go - ing by;
If a smile we can re - new, As our jour - ney we pur - sue,
But the seeds of good we sow, Both in shade and shine will grow,
If a smile we can re - new, As our jour - ney we pur - sue,
But the seeds of good we sow, Both in shade and shine will grow,
O the good we all may do, While the days are go - ing by.
And will keep our hearts a - glow, While the days are go - ing by.
O the good we all may do,
And will keep our hearts a - glow.

Used by per.

There are Lonely Hearts

CHORUS

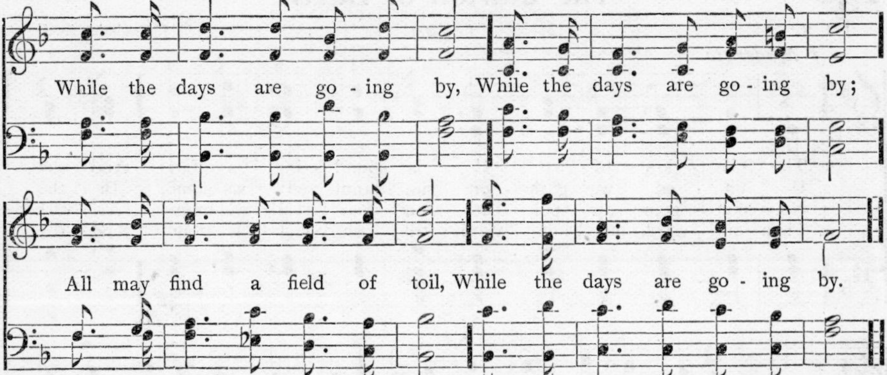
While the days are go - ing by, While the days are go - ing by;
All may find a field of toil, While the days are go - ing by.

O Jesus, I Have Promised 137

John E. Bode, 1869 (*Angel's Story* 7s. 6s. D.) Arthur H. Mann, 1883

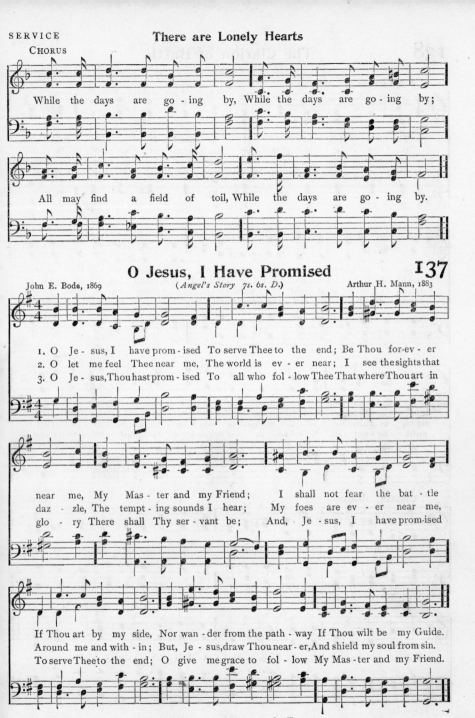

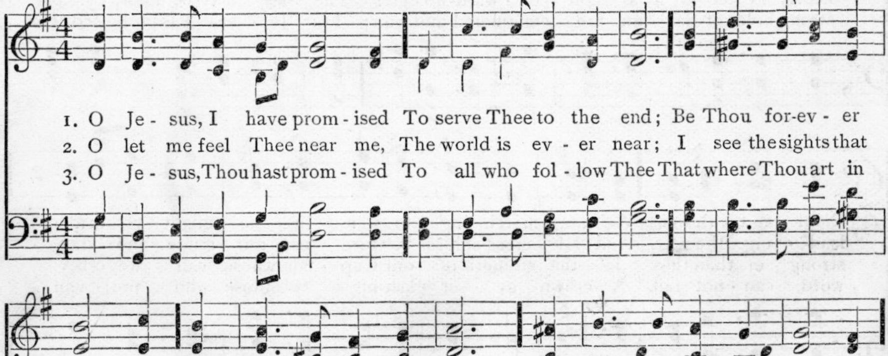
1. O Je - sus, I have prom - ised To serve Thee to the end; Be Thou for-ev - er
2. O let me feel Thee near me, The world is ev - er near; I see the sights that
3. O Je - sus, Thou hast prom - ised To all who fol - low Thee That where Thou art in
near me, My Mas - ter and my Friend; I shall not fear the bat - tle
daz - zle, The tempt - ing sounds I hear; My foes are ev - er near me,
glo - ry There shall Thy ser - vant be; And, Je - sus, I have prom-ised
If Thou art by my side, Nor wan - der from the path - way If Thou wilt be my Guide.
Around me and with - in; But, Je - sus, draw Thou near - er, And shield my soul from sin.
To serve Thee to the end; O give me grace to fol - low My Mas - ter and my Friend.

138 The Clarion of Battle

J. F. S. (*P. M.*) J. Frederick Swift

f Moderato
1. The clar - ion of bat - tle is sound - ing a - far, And the hosts of the Lord they are gath - 'ring for war; With shield and with ban - ner, with shout and with song, We are march - ing to join in the might - y throng.
2. U - nit - ed we gath - er, un - daunt - ed we stand, In the might of a Sav - iour, and led by His hand; His stand - ard tri - um - phant is lead - ing the way, And His cross shines be - fore us, our guide and stay.
3. No dan - gers ap - pal us, no fear shall we know, As with hearts ev - er loy - al right on - ward we go: The foes may be might - y, but strong - er than they Is the strength of our Cap - tain, whose call we o - bey.
4. Then on - ward, march on - ward, till con - flict is done, And the strong-holds of Sa - tan are con-quered and won; For Je - sus has prom-ised, His word can - not fail, A crown ev - er - last-ing to those who pre - vail.
CHORUS *Marcato*
Sol-diers firm and true, stead-fast to pur-sue, Ev - 'ry con-flict thro', the prize to gain,
Till each vic - tor band hails the prom-ised land, At the Lord's right hand with Him to reign.

Anywhere with Jesus 139

Marianne Farningham (*P. M.*)

1. A - ny - where with Je - sus, Says the Chris - tian heart, Let Him take me
2. A - ny - where with Je - sus, Though He lead - eth me Where the path is
3. A - ny - where with Je - sus, For it can - not be Drear - y, dark, or
where He will, So we do not part; Al - ways sit - ting at His feet,
rough and long, Where the dan - gers be. Though He tak - eth from my heart
des - o - late When He is with me. He will love me to the end,
There's no cause for fears; A - ny-where with Je - sus, In this vale of tears.
All I love be - low, A - ny-where with Je - sus, Will I glad - ly go.
Ev - 'ry need sup - ply; A - ny-where with Je - sus, Should I live or die.
CHORUS
A - ny - where with Je - sus, A - ny - where, a - ny - where,
A - ny - where with Je - sus, I'll fol - low a - ny - where.

140 We March to Victory

G. Moultrie, 1867 (*March to Victory P. M.*) J. Barnby, 1869

We march, we march to vic - to - ry, With the cross of the Lord be - fore us,
With His lov - ing eye look-ing down from the sky, And His ho - ly arm spread o'er us,
His ho - ly arm spread o'er us. o'er us.
1 & 2
3
FINE
His arm
1. We come in the might of the Lord of light,
2. Our sword is the Spir - it of God on high,
3. And the choir of an-gels with song a-waits
With ar - mor bright to meet Him; And we put to flight the ar - mies of night,
Our hel - met is His sal - va - tion, Our ban - ner, the cross of Cal - va - ry,
Our march to the gold - en Zi - on, For our Cap - tain has bro - ken the bra - zen gates,
That the sons of the day may greet Him, The sons of the day may greet Him. We
Our watch-word, the In - car - na - tion, Our watch-word, the In - car - na - tion. We
And burst the bars of i - ron, And burst the bars of i - ron. We
D.S.

My Song Shall be of Jesus

141

Fanny J. Crosby (7. 6. 10l.) Ad. from Mendelssohn

mf Brightly
1. My song shall be of Je - sus; His mer - cy crowns my days;
2. My song shall be of Je - sus, When, sit - ting at His feet,
3. My song shall be of Je - sus, While press - ing on my way
He fills my cup with bless - ings, And tunes my heart to praise.
I call to mind His good - ness In med - i - ta - tion sweet.
To reach the bliss - ful re - gion Of pure and per - fect day.
My song shall be of Je - sus, The pre - cious Lamb of God,
My song shall be of Je - sus, What - ev - er ill be - tide;
And when my soul shall en - ter The gate of E - den fair,
f
Who gave Him - self my ran - som, And bought me with His blood.
I'll sing the grace that saves me, And keeps me at His side.
A song of praise to Je - sus I'll sing for - ev - er there.
rit.
Who gave Him - self my ran - som, And bought me with His blood.
I'll sing the grace that saves me, And keeps me at His side.
A song of praise to Je - sus I'll sing for - ev - er there.

142 O Master, Let Me Walk with Thee

Washington Gladden — (*Via Bona L. M.*) — J. B. Dykes

1. O Mas-ter, let me walk with Thee In low-ly paths of ser-vice free;
2. Help me the slow of heart to move By some clear win-ning word of love;
3. Teach me Thy pa-tience! still with Thee In clos-er, dear-er com-pa-ny,
4. In hope that sends a shin-ing ray Far down the fu-ture's broad-'ning way;
Tell me Thy se-cret; help me bear The strain of toil, the fret of care.
Teach me the way-ward feet to stay, And guide them in the home-ward way.
In work that keeps faith sweet and strong, In trust that tri-umphs o-ver wrong.
In peace that on-ly Thou canst give, With Thee, O Mas-ter, let me live!

143 Work, for the Night is Coming

Anna L. Walker — (*Work Song P. M.*) — C. J. Dickenson

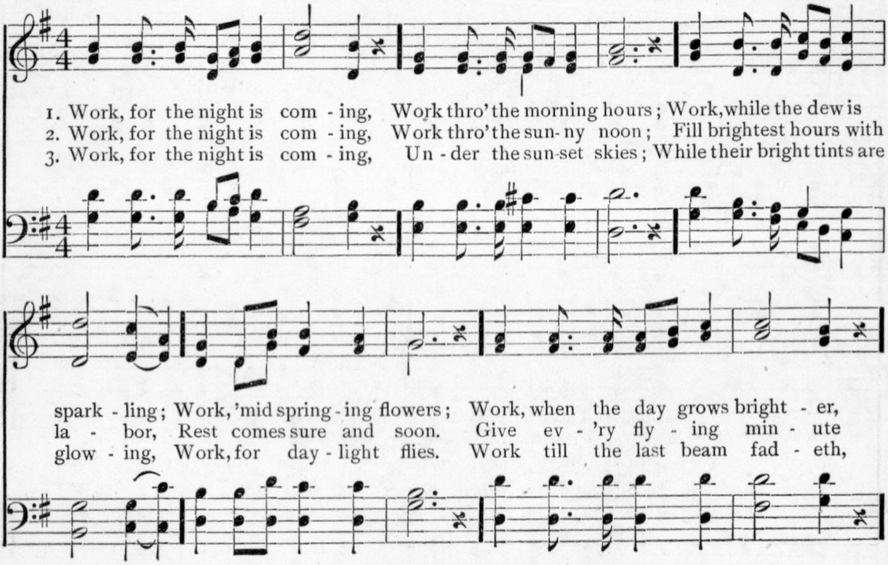
1. Work, for the night is com-ing, Work thro' the morning hours; Work, while the dew is
2. Work, for the night is com-ing, Work thro' the sun-ny noon; Fill brightest hours with
3. Work, for the night is com-ing, Un-der the sun-set skies; While their bright tints are
spark-ling; Work, 'mid spring-ing flowers; Work, when the day grows bright-er,
la-bor, Rest comes sure and soon. Give ev-'ry fly-ing min-ute
glow-ing, Work, for day-light flies. Work till the last beam fad-eth,

Work, for the Night is Coming

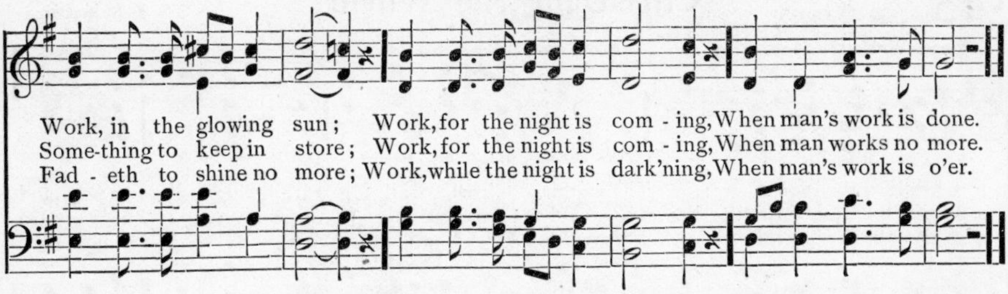
Work, in the glowing sun; Work, for the night is com - ing, When man's work is done.
Some-thing to keep in store; Work, for the night is com - ing, When man works no more.
Fad - eth to shine no more; Work, while the night is dark'ning, When man's work is o'er.

Soldiers of the Cross, Arise 144

W. W. How (*Yerbury* 7s. 8l.) Arthur Berridge

With vigor

1. Sol - diers of the Cross a - rise! Gird you with your ar - mor bright,
2. 'Mid the homes of want and woe, Stran - gers to the liv - ing word,
3. Guard the help - less, seek the strayed, Com - fort trou - bles, ban - ish grief;
Might - y are your en - e - mies, Hard the bat - tle ye must fight.
Let the Sav - iour's her - ald go, Let the voice of hope be heard.
In the might of God ar - rayed, Scat - ter sin and un - be - lief.
O'er a faith - less, fall - en world Raise your ban - ner in the sky;
To the wea - ry and the worn Tell of realms where sor - rows cease;
Be the ban - ner still un - furled, Still un-sheathed the Spir - it's sword,
Let it float there, wide un - furled; Bear it on - ward, lift it high.
To the out - cast and for - lorn Speak of mer - cy and of peace.
Till the king - doms of the world Are the king - dom of the Lord.

145 Christ for the World

Samuel Wolcott (*Italian Hymn* 6s. 4s.) Felice Giardini

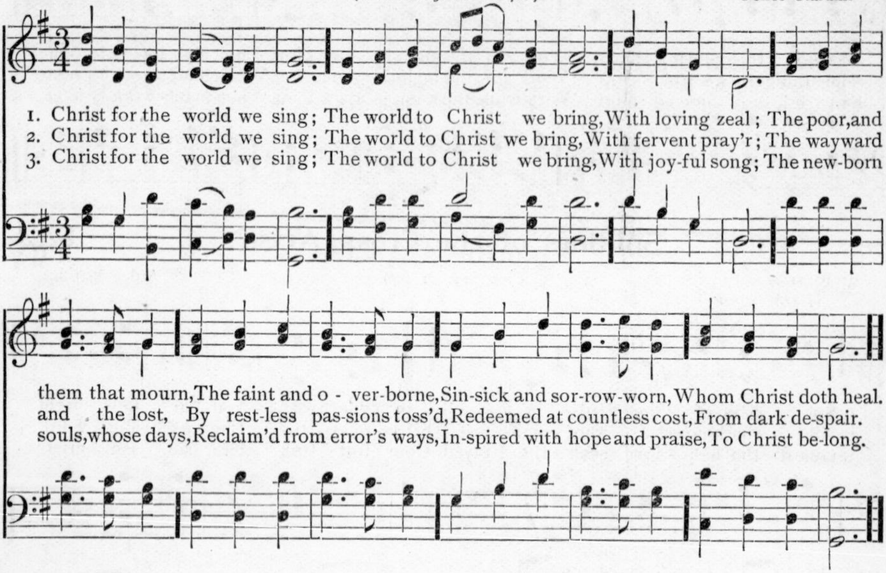
1. Christ for the world we sing; The world to Christ we bring, With loving zeal; The poor, and
2. Christ for the world we sing; The world to Christ we bring, With fervent pray'r; The wayward
3. Christ for the world we sing; The world to Christ we bring, With joy-ful song; The new-born
them that mourn, The faint and o - ver-borne, Sin-sick and sor-row-worn, Whom Christ doth heal.
and the lost, By rest-less pas-sions toss'd, Redeemed at countless cost, From dark de-spair.
souls, whose days, Reclaim'd from error's ways, In-spired with hope and praise, To Christ be-long.

146 Go Forward, Christian Soldier

Lawrence Tuttiet, 1866 (*Farmer* 7s. 6s. D.) J. Farmer

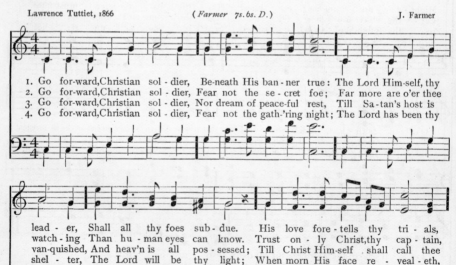

1. Go for-ward, Christian sol - dier, Be-neath His ban - ner true: The Lord Him-self, thy
2. Go for-ward, Christian sol - dier, Fear not the se - cret foe; Far more are o'er thee
3. Go for-ward, Christian sol - dier, Nor dream of peace-ful rest, Till Sa-tan's host is
4. Go for-ward, Christian sol - dier, Fear not the gath-'ring night; The Lord has been thy
lead - er, Shall all thy foes sub - due. His love fore - tells thy tri - als,
watch - ing Than hu - man eyes can know. Trust on - ly Christ, thy cap - tain,
van-quished, And heav'n is all pos - sessed; Till Christ Him-self shall call thee
shel - ter, The Lord will be thy light; When morn His face re - veal - eth,

Go Forward, Christian Soldier

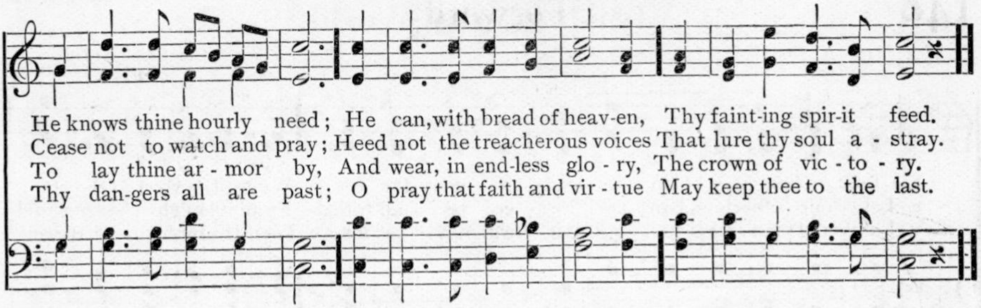
He knows thine hourly need; He can, with bread of heav-en, Thy faint-ing spir-it feed.
Cease not to watch and pray; Heed not the treacherous voices That lure thy soul a - stray.
To lay thine ar - mor by, And wear, in end-less glo - ry, The crown of vic - to - ry.
Thy dan-gers all are past; O pray that faith and vir - tue May keep thee to the last.

Looking Upward

147

Anon. Percy S. Foster

1. Look-ing up-ward ev - 'ry day, Sun - shine on our fa - ces,
2. Walk-ing ev - 'ry day more close To our Eld - er Broth - er,
3. Leav - ing ev - 'ry day be - hind, Some-thing which might hin - der,
Press - ing on - ward ev - 'ry day, Toward the heav'n - ly pla - ces.
Grow - ing ev - 'ry day more true Un - to one an - oth - er.
Run - ning swift - er ev - 'ry day, Grow - ing pur - er, kind - er.
REFRAIN
Look - ing up - ward ev - 'ry day, Sun - shine on our fa - ces,
Look - ing up - ward ev - 'ry day, Sun-shine on our fa - ces,
Press - ing on - ward ev - 'ry day, Toward the heav'n-ly pla - ces.
Press-ing on - ward

Copyright, 1901, by Percy S. Foster.

148 Forward

Mrs. Frank A. Breck

Grant Colfax Tullar

Animato
1. Christ, our might - y Cap - tain, leads a - gainst the foe; We will nev - er fal - ter
2. Let our glo - rious ban - ner ev - er be un-furled—From its might - y strong-hold
3. Fierce the bat - tle ra - ges, but 'twill not be long, Then triumphant—shall we
when He bids us go; Though His right - eous pur - pose we may nev - er know
e - vil shall be hurled; Christ, our might - y Cap - tain, o - ver-comes the world,
join the bless - ed throng, Joy - ful - ly u - nit - ing in the vic - tor's song—
CHORUS
Yet we'll fol - low all the way. For-ward! for-ward! 'tis the Lord's command,
And we fol - low all the way.
If we fol - low all the way.
For - ward! for - ward! to the prom - ised land; For - ward! for - ward!
let the cho - rus ring; We are sure to win with Christ our King!
3

Copyright, 1900, by Tullar-Meredith Co. Used by per.

Do the Next Thing

Howard B. Grose, 1901 Arr. from Balfe

Brightly
1. Do the thing that's next you! 'Tis God's work for you. . .
2. Do the thing that's next you! Look not far a - way, . .
3. Do the thing that's next you! Work lies close at hand; . .
Has the near-by vexed you? Is it hard to do? . Still the du - ty
In the dis - tant mor - row Los - ing life's to - day. . Du - ty's in the
Do not miss the sim - ple, Dream-ing of the grand. Filled with love sin -
next you, Which has sore per-plexed you, Must be done by
pres - ent; Pleas - ant or un-pleas - ant, As a faith - ful
cer - est, Touch the soul that's near - est, Meet the need se -
you, if To God you would be true.
ser - vant Christ's call you must o - bey.
ver - est, Ful - fill - ing Christ's com-mand.
CHORUS
Then do the du - ty next you,
If you would be true; 'Tis the Mas-ter's bid - ding, "This for Me ye do."

Words and arr. copyright, 1901 by Howard B. Grose

150 Lord, a Saviour's Love Displaying

E. Hawkins — (*Abendchor* 8s. 7s) — Arr. from Kreutzer, for this work

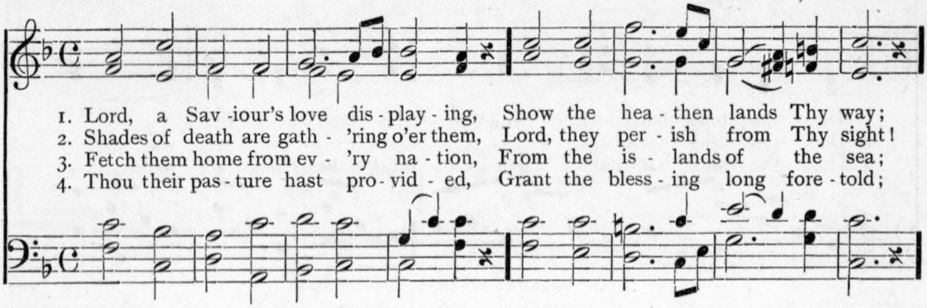
1. Lord, a Sav-iour's love dis-play-ing, Show the hea-then lands Thy way;
2. Shades of death are gath-'ring o'er them, Lord, they per-ish from Thy sight!
3. Fetch them home from ev-'ry na-tion, From the is-lands of the sea;
4. Thou their pas-ture hast pro-vid-ed, Grant the bless-ing long fore-told;

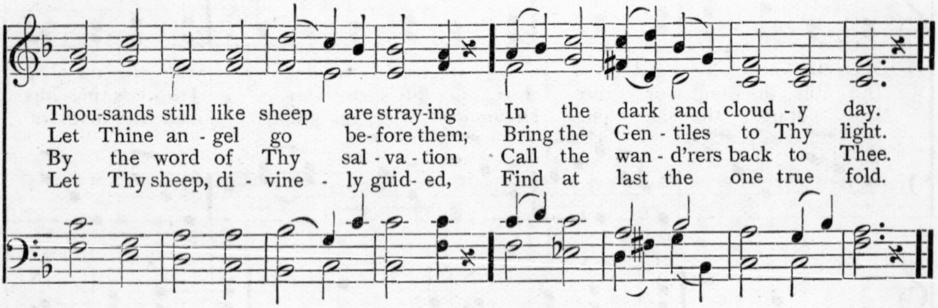
Thou-sands still like sheep are stray-ing In the dark and cloud-y day.
Let Thine an-gel go be-fore them; Bring the Gen-tiles to Thy light.
By the word of Thy sal-va-tion Call the wan-d'rers back to Thee.
Let Thy sheep, di-vine-ly guid-ed, Find at last the one true fold.

151 Haste Not, Rest Not

Goethe — Arr. from Balfe, for this work

Vigorously

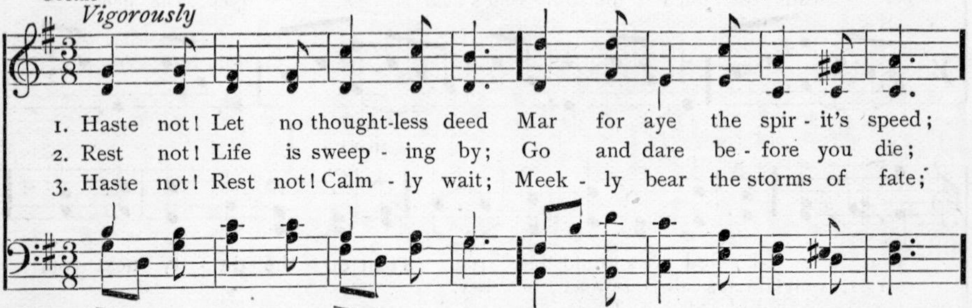
1. Haste not! Let no thought-less deed Mar for aye the spir-it's speed;
2. Rest not! Life is sweep-ing by; Go and dare be-fore you die;
3. Haste not! Rest not! Calm-ly wait; Meek-ly bear the storms of fate;

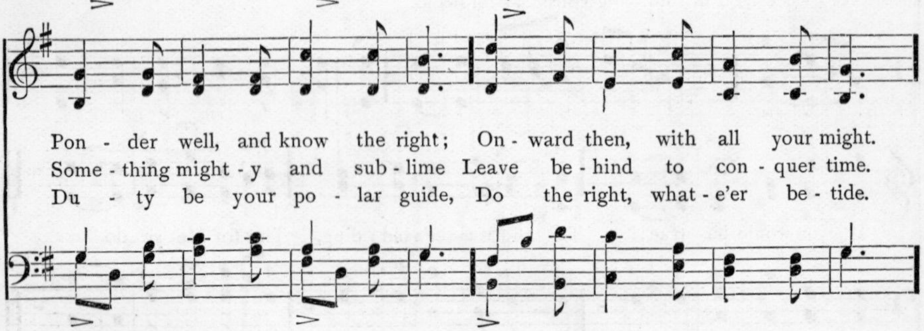
Pon-der well, and know the right; On-ward then, with all your might.
Some-thing might-y and sub-lime Leave be-hind to con-quer time.
Du-ty be your po-lar guide, Do the right, what-e'er be-tide.

Copyright, 1901, by U. S. C. E.

Haste Not, Rest Not

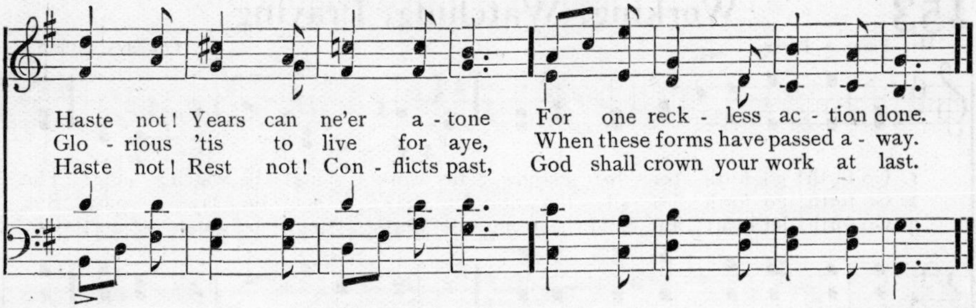
Haste not! Years can ne'er a - tone For one reck - less ac - tion done.
Glo - rious 'tis to live for aye, When these forms have passed a - way.
Haste not! Rest not! Con - flicts past, God shall crown your work at last.

Forward into Service

152

Howard B. Grose, 1901

Frank Leslie Stone, 1901

With animation

1. Thou dost call to ser - vice,— Je-sus, we will heed; . . Lead Thou, we will fol - low,
2. Heav - y hearts a - round us Need our help and cheer, . . Ser-vice calls are sounding,—
3. For - ward in - to ser - vice Joy-ous-ly we go, . . . Know-ing Thou wilt surely
Faith be-get-ting deed. Fill us with Thy spir - it, With Thy love and might,
Make us quick to hear. Grant us clear - er vis - ion Help-ful work to see,
Need - ed strength bestow. Us - ing ev - 'ry tal - ent In Thy blest em - ploy,
Let our whole en-deav - or Be for truth and right.
Read - i - ness to an - swer, "Here am I, send me!"
May we find in ser - vice Ful-ness of Thy joy.
REFRAIN
We are Thy dis - ci - ples,
Loy - al we would be, Keep us in our ser - vice, Mas - ter, true to Thee.

Copyright, words and music, 1901, by Howard B. Grose.

153 Working, Watching, Praying

Mrs. Frank A. Breck — Powell G. Fithian

1. Go forth! go forth for Je - sus now, Be work - ing! be watch - ing! The
2. Go forth! go forth to all the world! Oh, stay not! de - lay not, But
3. Go forth! let heart and hand be strong! Be work - ing! be watch - ing! Oh,
Go forth!
Go forth!
Lord Him-self will teach you how To watch and pray. 'Tis not for thee thy
let Love's ban-ner be un-furled, And grace be told. Oh, let re - deem - ing
stay the might - y pow'r of wrong Wher - e'er ye may. E-quipped with love and
field to choose, No work He gives must thou refuse, Be work-ing! be watch-ing! be pray - ing!
love be sung, A song of joy on ev-'ry tongue! Be working! be watch-ing! be pray - ing!
strength divine, The vic - to - ry is sure-ly thine, Be work-ing! be watch-ing! be pray - ing!
CHORUS
Go forth to work, to watch and pray! 'Tis Je - sus who calls thee,
Go forth!
Go forth!
The har - vest waits for thee to - day, Go bring some sheaves for God.

Copyright, 1901, by Powell G. Fithian. Used by per.

With Steady Pace

(*Better on Before* C. M. D.)

Folksong
Harmonized for this work

With spirit. At good speed
1. With stead-y pace the pil - grim moves On tow'rds the bliss - ful shore,
2. When tempted to for-sake his God, And give the con-test o'er,
3. And when on Jor - dan's bank he stands, And views the ra-diant shore,
bliss-ful shore,
con-test o'er,
ra - diant shore,
And sings with cheer-ful heart and voice, "'Tis bet - ter on be - fore."
He hears a voice which says, "Look up, 'Tis bet - ter on be - fore."
Bright an - gels whis-per, "Come a - way! 'Tis bet - ter on be - fore."
mp
f
rall.
His pas - sage thro' the des - ert lies, Where fu - rious li - ons roar,
When stern af - flic - tion clouds his cheek, And death stands at the door,
And so it is, for high in heav'n They nev - er suf - fer more;
tempo f
rall.
He takes his staff, and, smil - ing, cries, "'Tis bet - ter on be - fore."
Hope cheers him with her hap - piest note "'Tis bet - ter on be - fore."
E - ter - nal calm suc - ceeds the storm — "'Tis bet - ter on be - fore."

Copyright, 1901, by U. S. C. E.

155 Only a Word for the Master

(*Only P. M.*)

John Brash

Slowly and quietly

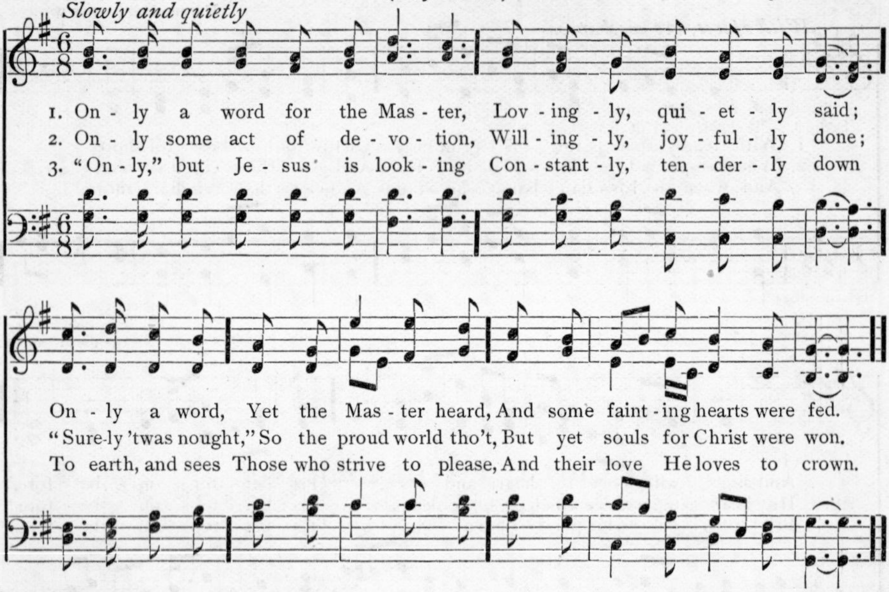

1. On - ly a word for the Mas - ter, Lov - ing - ly, qui - et - ly said;
2. On - ly some act of de - vo - tion, Will - ing - ly, joy - ful - ly done;
3. "On - ly," but Je - sus is look - ing Con - stant - ly, ten - der - ly down
On - ly a word, Yet the Mas - ter heard, And some faint - ing hearts were fed.
"Sure-ly 'twas nought," So the proud world tho't, But yet souls for Christ were won.
To earth, and sees Those who strive to please, And their love He loves to crown.

156 One More Day's Work for Jesus

Miss Anna Warner

Rev. Robert Lowry

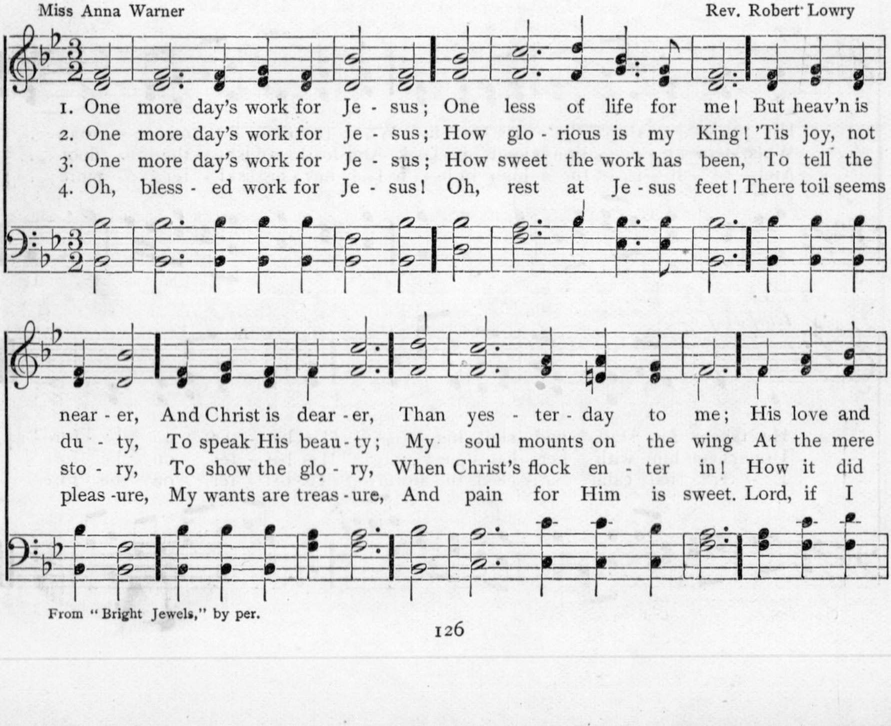

1. One more day's work for Je - sus; One less of life for me! But heav'n is
2. One more day's work for Je - sus; How glo - rious is my King! 'Tis joy, not
3. One more day's work for Je - sus; How sweet the work has been, To tell the
4. Oh, bless - ed work for Je - sus! Oh, rest at Je - sus feet! There toil seems
near - er, And Christ is dear - er, Than yes - ter - day to me; His love and
du - ty, To speak His beau - ty; My soul mounts on the wing At the mere
sto - ry, To show the glo - ry, When Christ's flock en - ter in! How it did
pleas - ure, My wants are treas - ure, And pain for Him is sweet. Lord, if I

From "Bright Jewels," by per.

One More Day's Work for Jesus

CHORUS

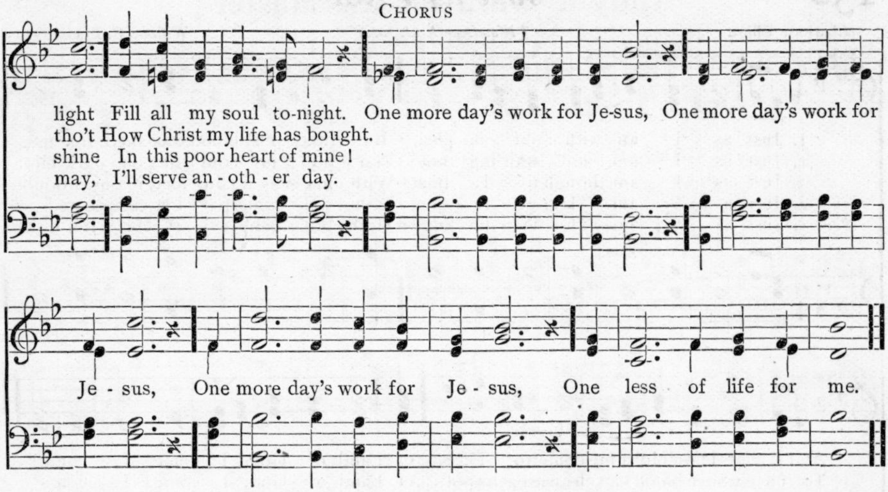
light Fill all my soul to-night. One more day's work for Je-sus, One more day's work for
tho't How Christ my life has bought.
shine In this poor heart of mine!
may, I'll serve an - oth - er day.
Je - sus, One more day's work for Je - sus, One less of life for me.

O Christ, I Will Endeavor **157**

H. T. Mark (*Lymington* 7. 6. 8l.) R. Jackson

1. O Christ, I will en - deav - or To serve Thee day by day; Help me to make Thee
2. Go with me, God my Sav - iour, Go with me ev - 'ry hour; Con - trol my whole be -
3. Why should I not be will - ing To serve Thee with my days, When Thou art ev - er
ev - er My Life, my Truth, my Way. When in my breast Thou burn - est,
hav - ior By Thy full Spir - it's pow'r. Up - lift, and heal, and glad - den,
fill - ing My soul with joy and praise? Why should I not show oth - ers
My thot's grow pure and bright, My words are calm and earn - est, And all seems good and right.
My - self and oth - ers, Lord; May nought that's in me sad - den Those here that love Thy word.
The Light di - vine in Thee? Why should not all my broth - ers See what Thou art to me?

158 Just as I Am

Charlotte Elliott — (*Woodworth L. M.*) — William B. Bradbury

1. Just as I am, with-out one plea, But that Thy blood was shed for me,
2. Just as I am, and wait-ing not To rid my soul of one dark blot,
3. Just as I am, though tossed a-bout With ma-ny a con-flict, ma-ny a doubt,
4. Just as I am—Thou wilt re-ceive, Wilt wel-come, par-don, cleanse, re-lieve;
5. Just as I am—Thy love un-known Hath bro-ken ev-'ry bar-rier down;

And that Thou bid'st me come to Thee, O Lamb of God, I come! I come!
To Thee whose blood can cleanse each spot, O Lamb of God, I come! I come!
Fight-ings with-in, and fears with-out, O Lamb of God, I come! I come!
Be-cause Thy prom-ise I be-lieve, O Lamb of God, I come! I come!
Now, to be Thine, yea, Thine a-lone, O Lamb of God, I come! I come!

159 A Call to Deeds

Charles S. Brown, 1901 — Charles S. Brown

1. If with kind-ly deeds we freighted Moments which to waste we give, Sin and woe would
2. Hear we not a ten-der mes-sage Wafted from that East-ern lake, Where our Lord with

be a-ba-ted, We should learn the way to live. He a-lone knows true en-joy-ment,
lov-ing presage Spake as nev-er mor-tal spake: "As in full un-stint-ed measure

Copyright, 1901, by U. S. C. E.

A Call to Deeds

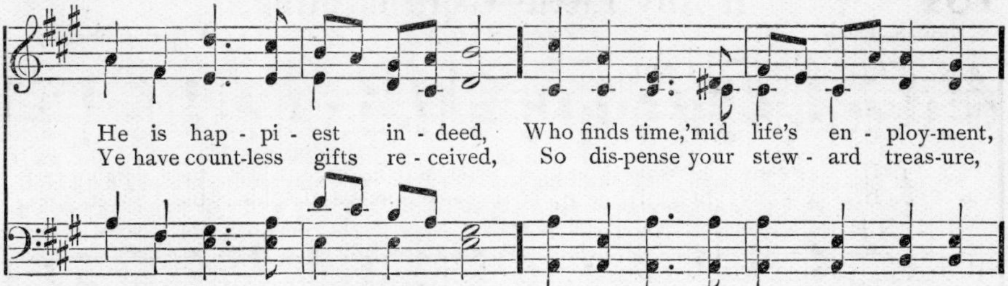
He is hap - pi - est in - deed, Who finds time,'mid life's en - ploy-ment,
Ye have count-less gifts re - ceived, So dis-pense your stew - ard treas-ure,

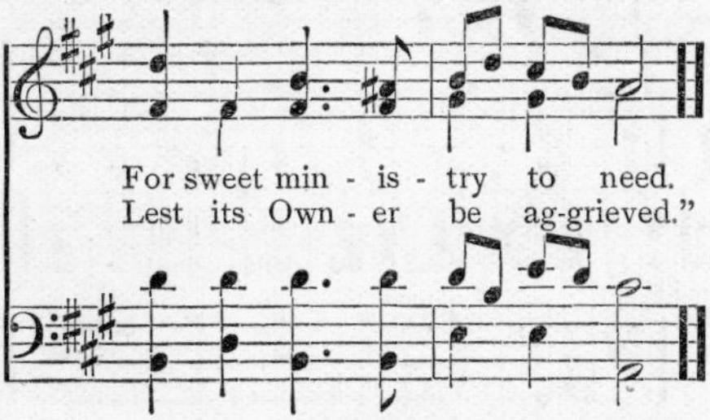
For sweet min - is - try to need.
Lest its Own - er be ag-grieved."

3 Give, and unto you returning
Shall a stream of bounty flow;
They that serve are honors earning
For their Master here below;
Then let each fulfil his mission,
Urged by sympathy and love,
Till endeavor gains fruition
In the perfect rest above.

Hark! 'tis the Watchman's Cry 160

Anon. "The Revival" 1859 (*Bromsgrove P. M.*) F. C. Maker

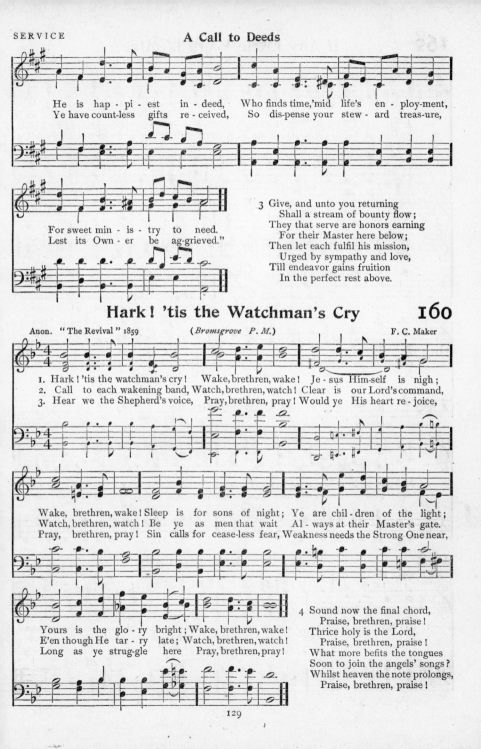

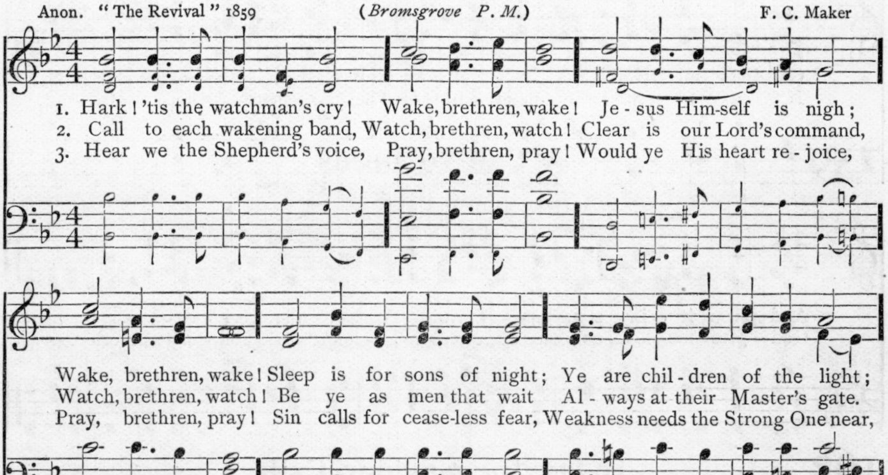
1. Hark! 'tis the watchman's cry! Wake, brethren, wake! Je - sus Him-self is nigh;
2. Call to each wakening band, Watch, brethren, watch! Clear is our Lord's command,
3. Hear we the Shepherd's voice, Pray, brethren, pray! Would ye His heart re - joice,
Wake, brethren, wake! Sleep is for sons of night; Ye are chil - dren of the light;
Watch, brethren, watch! Be ye as men that wait Al - ways at their Master's gate.
Pray, brethren, pray! Sin calls for cease-less fear, Weakness needs the Strong One near,

Yours is the glo - ry bright; Wake, brethren, wake!
E'en though He tar - ry late; Watch, brethren, watch!
Long as ye strug-gle here Pray, brethren, pray!

4 Sound now the final chord,
Praise, brethren, praise!
Thrice holy is the Lord,
Praise, brethren, praise!
What more befits the tongues
Soon to join the angels' songs?
Whilst heaven the note prolongs,
Praise, brethren, praise!

161 If Any Little Word of Mine

(*Bray* 8. 7. 8l.)

Ad. for C. E. Hymnal

162 Today the Saviour Calls

S. F. Smith, 1831

(*Today* 6s. 4s)

Lowell Mason, 1831

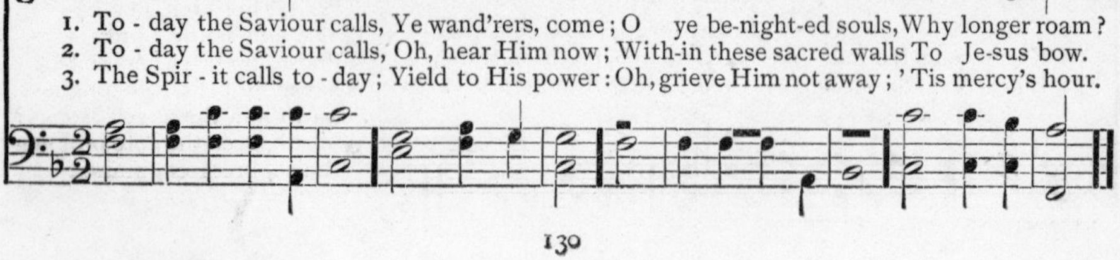

Saved to Serve

163

John D. Morgan (*Saved to Serve P. M.*) Percy S. Foster

1. To daily die to self and sin, and daily to receive
New life from Thee, I pray, O Lord, and more like Thee to live.
2. To daily die to all things past, by spir - it, prayer, and word,
May I in - crease in faith and deed un - to Thy stat - ure, Lord.
3. Tho' dark the way, tho' long the strife, I thro' the Spir - it's might
Shall strive for Thee, Thy king - dom's weal, and for e - ter - nal right;
O saved to serve! by Je - sus' blood from sin and self made free,
O saved to serve! the field is wide; what I can do is small;
Then saved to serve! in heav'n's bright sphere I shall with an - gels sing,
To praise His name, to do His will, thro' - out e - ter - ni - ty. . .
thro' - out, thro' - out e - ter - ni - ty.
With joy - ful heart and hand, O Lord, I give to Thee my all. . .
I give, I give to Thee my all.
And saved by grace be - hold Thy face, my Sav - iour, Lord, and King. .
my Sav - iour, Sav - iour, Lord, and King.

Copyright, 1901, by P. S. Foster. Used by per.

164 Hear the Royal Summons

(6s. 5s)

Anon. — R. DeW. Mallary, 1901

1. Hear the roy-al sum-mons, Gird you for the fight, 'Gainst the pow'rs of darkness, March the sons of light.
2. Armed with Christ's own spirit, Strike at ev'ry wrong; Think not of your weakness, He will make you strong.
3. Hear the roy-al prom-ise, Vic-to-ry is sure; Wrong shall be defeated, Right shall reign secure.

D.S.

Fear not you the con-flict, On to vic-t'ry go, You, with Christ as helper, No de-feat can know.
Shrink not then from danger, Bravely bear the cross; Christ will turn to blessing All your seeming loss.
March we on with cour-age; Help to save the world; Be this conquering banner O'er all lands unfurled.

CHO. *Dare to do your du - ty, Standing for the right; Dare obey the Mas-ter, Walking in His light.*

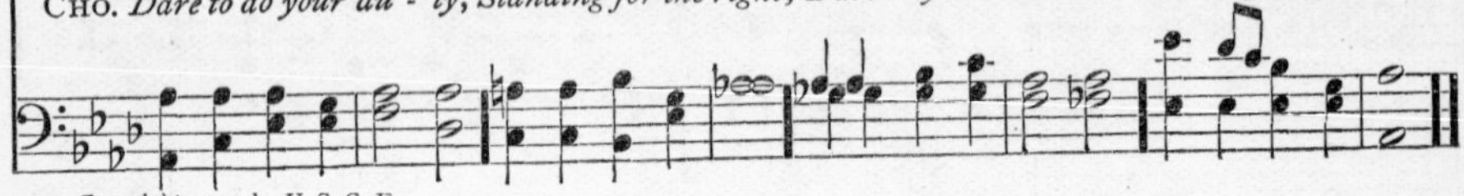

Copyright, 1901, by U. S. C. E.

165 Endeavor and Endure

(C. M. D.)

Charles A. Dickinson — Charles S. Brown

1. While struggling in a maze of doubt, With sore temptations vexed, I seemed to hear our
2. When great af-flictions compassed me And laid my loved ones low, And filled the gar-den
3. "En-deav-or and en-dure, My child, A - long the nar-row way. What tho' the night be

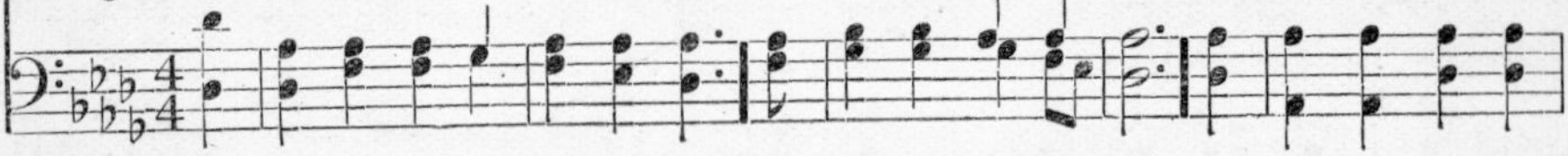

Fa-ther say: "My child, be not perplexed. I'll guide thee with My sleep-less eye; My
of my joys With plants of pain and woe, The Father's voice still cheered my heart: "My
long and dark? It ends in glo-rious day. Go brave-ly on, and trust My love; My

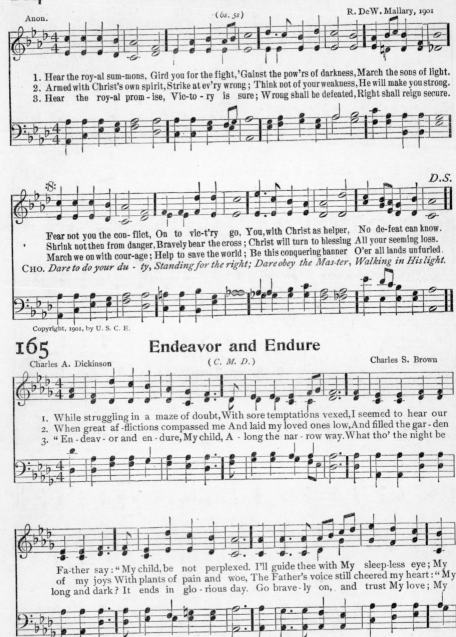

Copyright, 1901, by U. S. C. E.

Endeavor and Endure

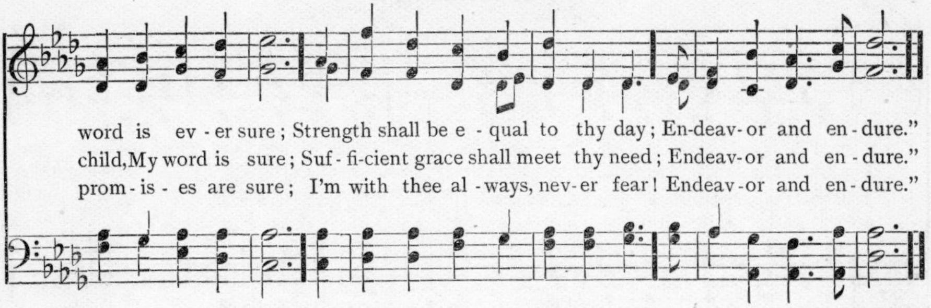
word is ev - er sure ; Strength shall be e - qual to thy day ; En-deav- or and en - dure."
child, My word is sure ; Suf - fi-cient grace shall meet thy need ; Endeav- or and en - dure."
prom - is - es are sure ; I'm with thee al - ways, nev- er fear ! Endeav - or and en - dure."

If You Cannot on the Ocean 166

Ellen H. Gates (*Mission Song* 8s. 7s. D.) P. P. Van Arsdale

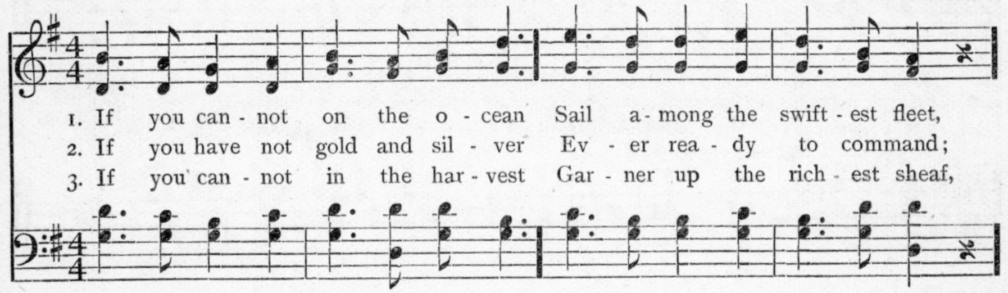
1. If you can - not on the o - cean Sail a - mong the swift - est fleet,
2. If you have not gold and sil - ver Ev - er rea - dy to command ;
3. If you can - not in the har - vest Gar - ner up the rich - est sheaf,

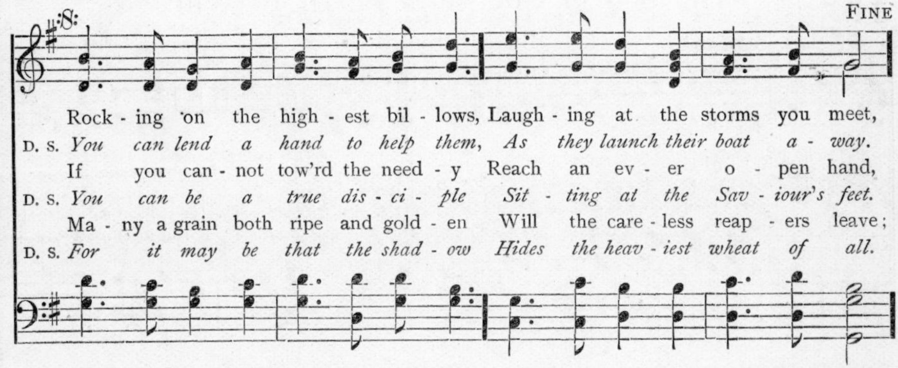
FINE
Rock - ing on the high - est bil - lows, Laugh - ing at the storms you meet,
D. S. *You can lend a hand to help them, As they launch their boat a - way.*
If you can - not tow'rd the need - y Reach an ev - er o - pen hand,
D. S. *You can be a true dis - ci - ple Sit - ting at the Sav - iour's feet.*
Ma - ny a grain both ripe and gold - en Will the care - less reap - ers leave ;
D. S. *For it may be that the shad - ow Hides the heav - iest wheat of all.*

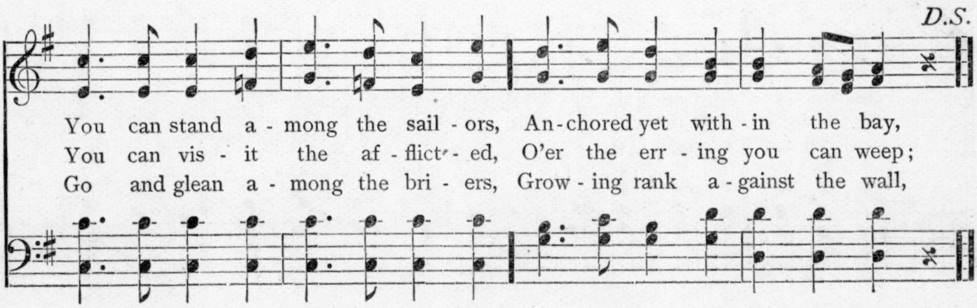
D.S.
You can stand a - mong the sail - ors, An-chored yet with - in the bay,
You can vis - it the af - flict - ed, O'er the err - ing you can weep ;
Go and glean a - mong the bri - ers, Grow - ing rank a - gainst the wall,

167 Daily Work

Ad. from the German *(Vesper 8s. 7s)* Arr. from Flotow

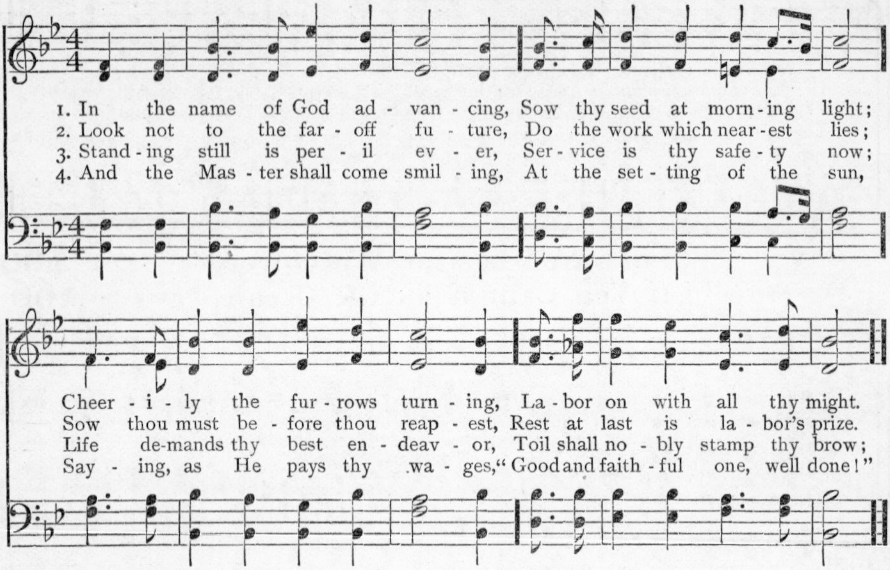
1. In the name of God ad - van - cing, Sow thy seed at morn - ing light;
2. Look not to the far - off fu - ture, Do the work which near - est lies;
3. Stand - ing still is per - il ev - er, Ser - vice is thy safe - ty now;
4. And the Mas - ter shall come smil - ing, At the set - ting of the sun,
Cheer - i - ly the fur - rows turn - ing, La - bor on with all thy might.
Sow thou must be - fore thou reap - est, Rest at last is la - bor's prize.
Life de - mands thy best en - deav - or, Toil shall no - bly stamp thy brow;
Say - ing, as He pays thy wa - ges, "Good and faith - ful one, well done!"

168 The Son of God Goes Forth to War

Bishop Heber, pub. 1827 *(All Saints New C. M. D.)* Henry S. Cutler, 1872

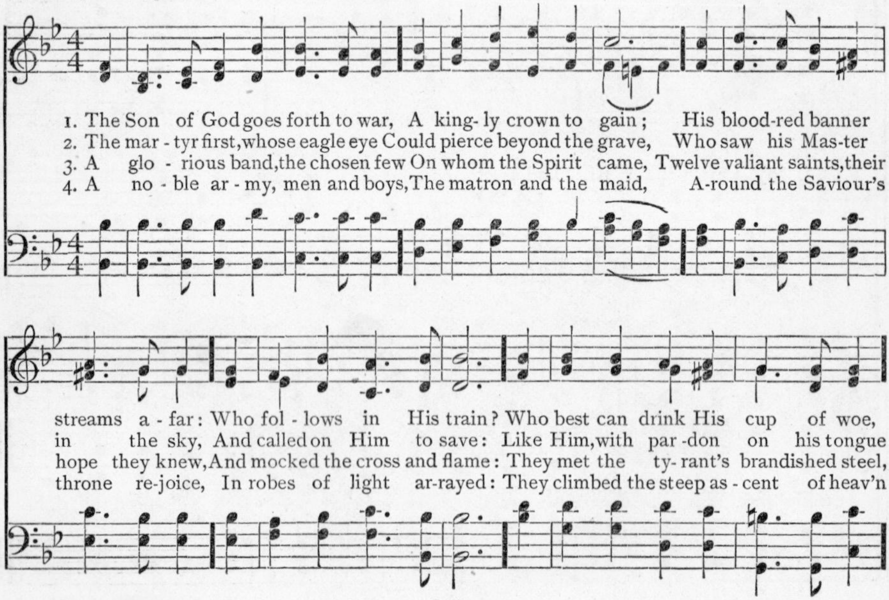
1. The Son of God goes forth to war, A king - ly crown to gain; His blood-red banner
2. The mar - tyr first, whose eagle eye Could pierce beyond the grave, Who saw his Mas - ter
3. A glo - rious band, the chosen few On whom the Spirit came, Twelve valiant saints, their
4. A no - ble ar - my, men and boys, The matron and the maid, A - round the Saviour's
streams a - far: Who fol - lows in His train? Who best can drink His cup of woe,
in the sky, And called on Him to save: Like Him, with par - don on his tongue
hope they knew, And mocked the cross and flame: They met the ty - rant's brandished steel,
throne re - joice, In robes of light ar - rayed: They climbed the steep as - cent of heav'n

The Son of God Goes Forth to War

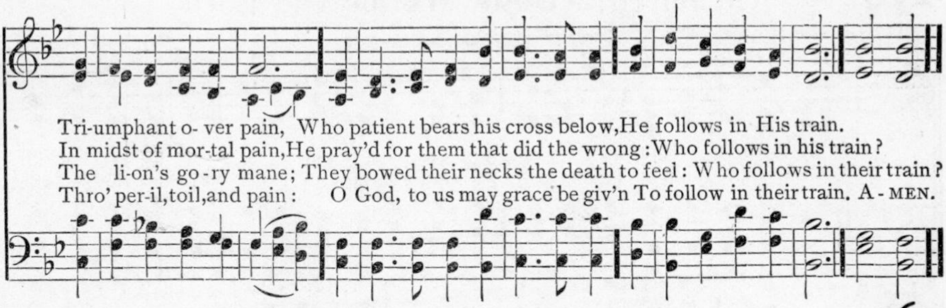
Tri-umphant o- ver pain, Who patient bears his cross below,He follows in His train.
In midst of mor-tal pain,He pray'd for them that did the wrong :Who follows in his train ?
The li-on's go-ry mane; They bowed their necks the death to feel : Who follows in their train ?
Thro' per-il,toil,and pain : O God, to us may grace be giv'n To follow in their train. A - MEN.

Forward ! be Our Watchword 169

Henry Alford, 1865 (*6s. 5s*) Francis J. Haydn, 1797

1. For-ward ! be our watch-word,Steps and voi-ces joined ; Seek the things be - fore us,
2. For-ward out of er - ror,Leave be-hind the night ; For-ward thro' the dark - ness,
3. Far o'er yon ho - ri - zon Rise the cit - y towers, Where our God a - bid - eth ;
Not a look be - hind ; Burns the fi - ery pil - lar, At our ar-my's head,
For-ward in - to light ! Glo-ries up-on glo - ries Hath our God pre - pared,
That fair home is ours ! Thither, on-ward thith - er, In the Spir - it's might,
REFRAIN
Who shall dream of shrink-ing, By our Cap-tain led? For-ward ! in the con - flict,
By the souls that love Him, One day to be shared !
Lov - ers of your coun - try, For-ward in - to light !
Thro' the toil and fight Foes must fall be - fore us, God will speed the right.

170 Go Forth, Ye Sowers for the Lord

F. H. Jacobs — L. M. Biggs

1. Go forth, ye sow-ers for the Lord, With words of life and light; O lin-ger not till
2. Go forth, ye gleaners for the Lord, Your arduous task ful - fil; For in the fields by
set - ting sun Shall kiss the world goodnight. Rich soil and good a - waits the seed, To
reap-ers passed Some souls may lin - ger still. With all your sua - sive ten - derness Com -
dress in liv-ing green The bar-ren hillsides, winding vales, From mountain summits seen.
pel the lost to come, And swell the song the ransomed sing, In yon fair harvest home.

Copyright, 1901, by F. H. Jacobs

171 The Master's Call

Howard B. Grose, 1901 — (*Alpha* 7. 6. 7. 5. D.) — J. H. Leslie

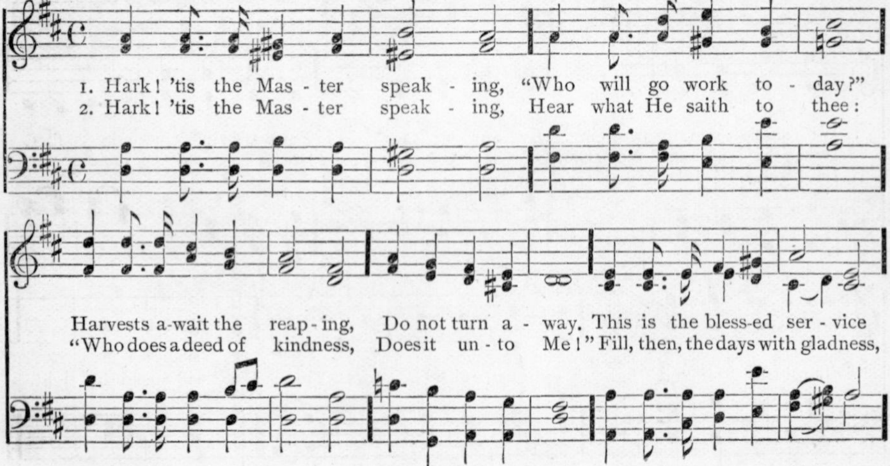
1. Hark! 'tis the Mas - ter speak - ing, "Who will go work to - day?"
2. Hark! 'tis the Mas - ter speak - ing, Hear what He saith to thee:
Harvests a-wait the reap - ing, Do not turn a - way. This is the bless-ed ser - vice
"Who does a deed of kindness, Does it un - to Me!" Fill, then, the days with gladness,

The Master's Call

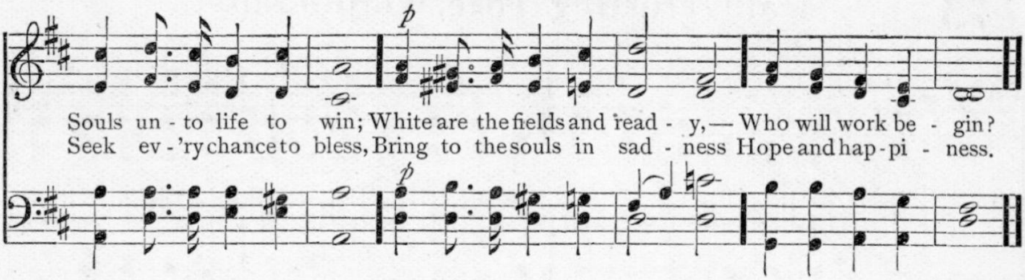
p
Souls un - to life to win; White are the fields and read - y,— Who will work be - gin?
Seek ev - 'ry chance to bless, Bring to the souls in sad - ness Hope and hap - pi - ness.
p

Onward, Christian Soldiers 172

S. Baring Gould (*St. Gertrude 6s. 5s. D.*) Sir Arthur Sullivan

1. On-ward, Chris-tian sol - diers, March-ing as to war, With the cross of Je - sus
2. Like a might - y ar - my, Moves the Church of God; Broth-ers, we are tread - ing
3. On-ward, then, ye peo - ple, Join our hap-py throng; Blend with ours your voi - ces
Go - ing on be - fore. Christ, the roy - al Mas - ter, Leads a-gainst the foe;
Where the saints have trod. We are not di - vid - ed, All one bod - y we;
In the tri - umph-song; Glo - ry, laud, and hon - or, Un - to Christ the King;
CHORUS
For-ward in - to bat - tle, See, His ban-ners go. On-ward, Christian sol - diers,
One in hope and doc - trine, One in char - i - ty.
This thro' countless a - ges, Men and an - gels sing.
Marching as to war, With the cross of Je - sus Go - ing on be - fore.
war, With the cross of Je - sus

173 I am Trusting Thee, Lord Jesus

Frances R. Havergal (8. 5. 8. 3) M. B. Willis, 1901

1. I am trusting Thee, Lord Je - sus, Trust-ing on - ly Thee; Trusting Thee for full sal-
2. I am trusting Thee to guide me; Thou a - lone shalt lead! Ev - 'ry day and hour sup-

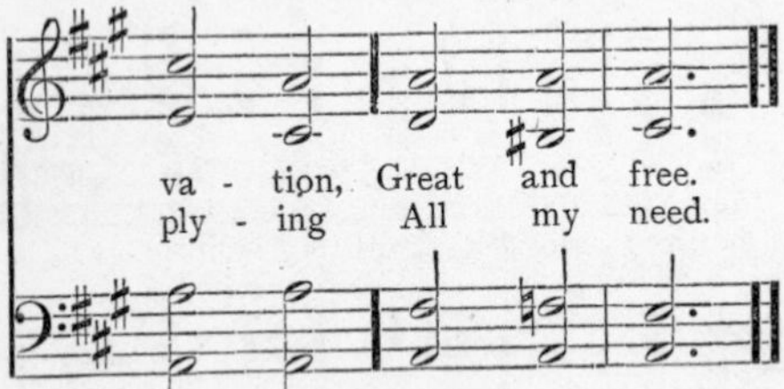
va - tion, Great and free.
ply - ing All my need.

3 I am trusting Thee for power;
Thine can never fail!
Words which Thou Thyself shalt give me
Must prevail.

4 I am trusting Thee, Lord Jesus;
Never let me fall!
I am trusting Thee forever,
And for all.

Copyright, 1901, by U. S. C. E.

174 I Surrender All

J. W. VanDeVenter (8s. 7s. with Refrain) W. S. Weeden

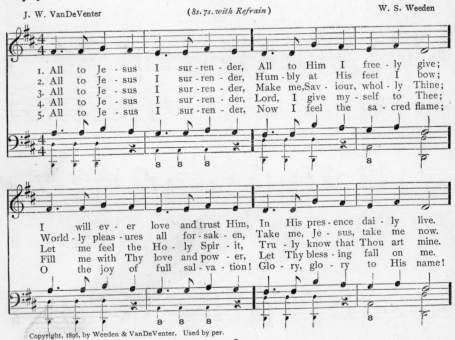

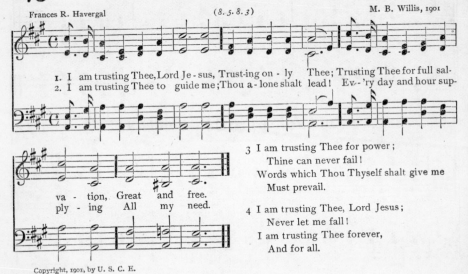

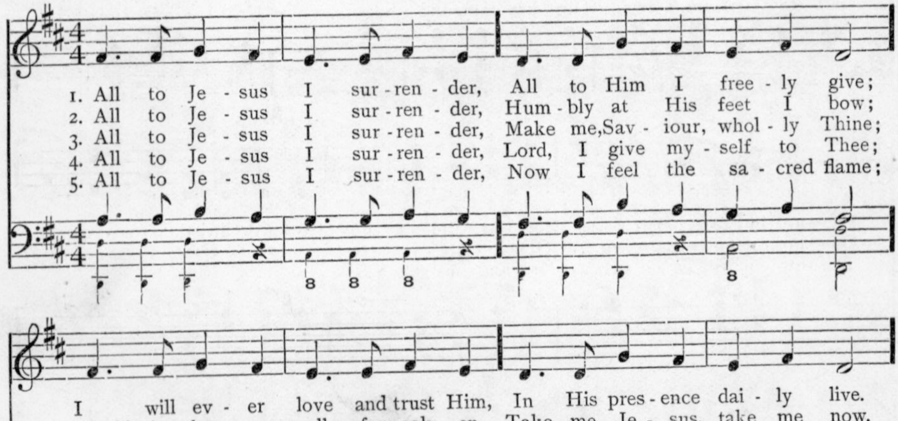
1. All to Je - sus I sur - ren - der, All to Him I free - ly give;
2. All to Je - sus I sur - ren - der, Hum - bly at His feet I bow;
3. All to Je - sus I sur - ren - der, Make me, Sav - iour, whol - ly Thine;
4. All to Je - sus I sur - ren - der, Lord, I give my - self to Thee;
5. All to Je - sus I sur - ren - der, Now I feel the sa - cred flame;
I will ev - er love and trust Him, In His pres - ence dai - ly live.
World - ly pleas - ures all for - sak - en, Take me, Je - sus, take me now.
Let me feel the Ho - ly Spir - it, Tru - ly know that Thou art mine.
Fill me with Thy love and pow - er, Let Thy bless - ing fall on me.
O the joy of full sal - va - tion! Glo - ry, glo - ry to His name!

Copyright, 1896, by Weeden & VanDeVenter. Used by per.

I Surrender All

Refrain
I sur-ren-der all, I sur-ren-der all;
I sur-ren-der all, I sur-ren-der all;
All to Thee, my bless-ed Sav-iour, I sur-ren-der all.

In This Consecration Hour 175

Howard B. Grose, 1901 (*Blumenthal 7s. D.*) J. Blumenthal

1. In this con-se-cra-tion hour, Lord, I lift my soul to Thee; Vis-it me in saving pow'r,
2. As in pen-i-tence I bow, Love di-vine to me re-veal; As I here re-new my vow,
From my-self, oh, set me free. Hear, O God, my earn-est pray'r, For Thy work my
Fill me, Lord, with ho-ly zeal. Hear me, Fa-ther, as I pray; Grace be-stow for
soul pre-pare, In Thy ser-vice give me share, Hearken, Fa-ther, to my plea.
each new day, Keep me near Thee all the way; Hear, O Fa-ther, my ap-peal.

176 The Master's Touch

Anon. — Charles S. Brown, 1901

Smoothly and not too fast

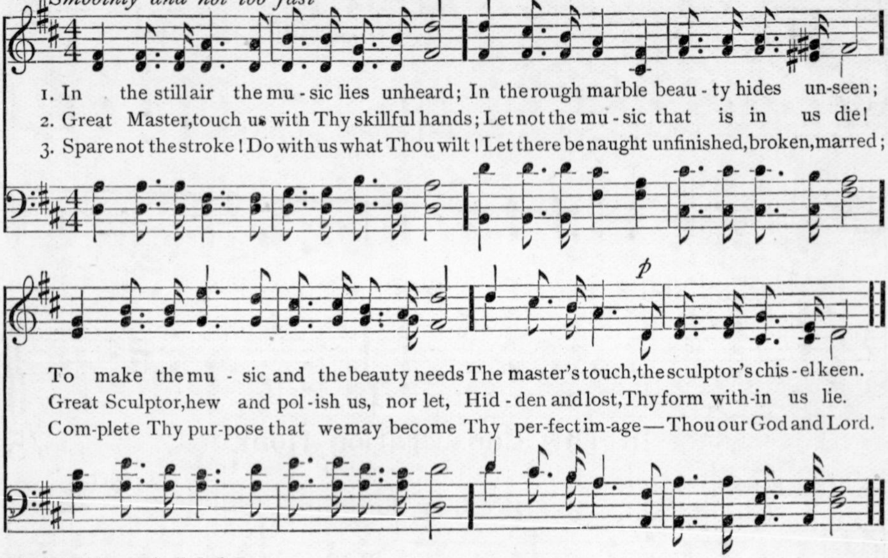
1. In the still air the mu - sic lies unheard; In the rough marble beau - ty hides un-seen;
2. Great Master, touch us with Thy skillful hands; Let not the mu - sic that is in us die!
3. Spare not the stroke! Do with us what Thou wilt! Let there be naught unfinished, broken, marred;
p
To make the mu - sic and the beauty needs The master's touch, the sculptor's chis - el keen.
Great Sculptor, hew and pol - ish us, nor let, Hid - den and lost, Thy form with-in us lie.
Com-plete Thy pur-pose that we may become Thy per-fect im-age — Thou our God and Lord.

Copyright, 1901, by U. S. C. E.

177 The Inner Circle

Flora Kirkland — (8s. 7s. with Refrain) — W. S. Weeden

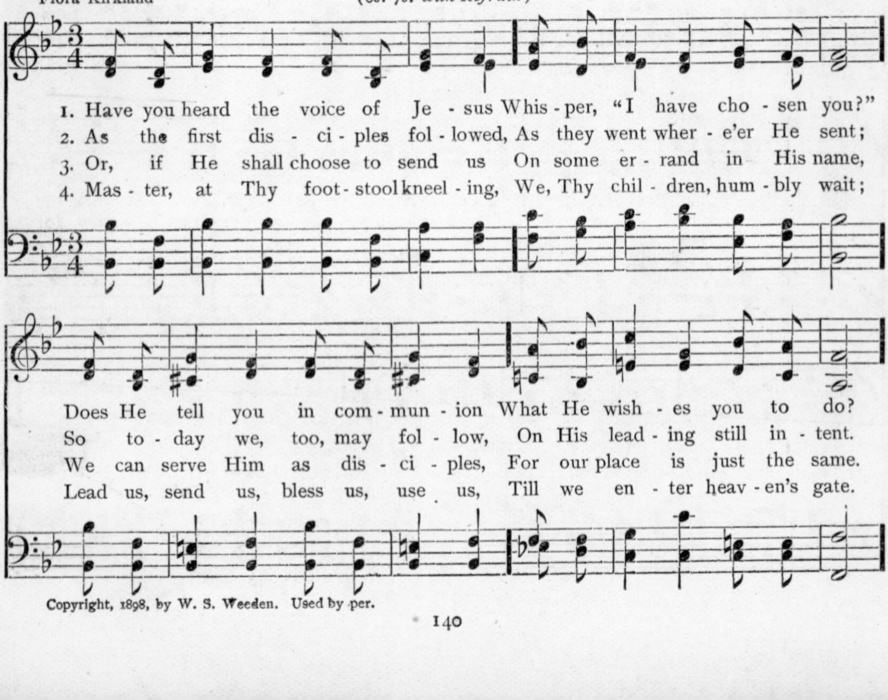
1. Have you heard the voice of Je - sus Whis - per, "I have cho - sen you?"
2. As the first dis - ci - ples fol - lowed, As they went wher - e'er He sent;
3. Or, if He shall choose to send us On some er - rand in His name,
4. Mas - ter, at Thy foot - stool kneel - ing, We, Thy chil - dren, hum - bly wait;
Does He tell you in com - mun - ion What He wish - es you to do?
So to - day we, too, may fol - low, On His lead - ing still in - tent.
We can serve Him as dis - ci - ples, For our place is just the same.
Lead us, send us, bless us, use us, Till we en - ter heav - en's gate.

Copyright, 1898, by W. S. Weeden. Used by per.

The Inner Circle

REFRAIN

Are you in the in - ner cir - cle? Have you heard the Mas - ter's call?
Are you in the in - ner cir - cle? Have you heard the Mas - ter's call?
rit.
Have you giv'n your life to Je - sus? Is He now your All in all?
Have you giv'n your

Take My Life 178

Frances R. Havergal (*Nottingham* 7s) Arr. from Mozart

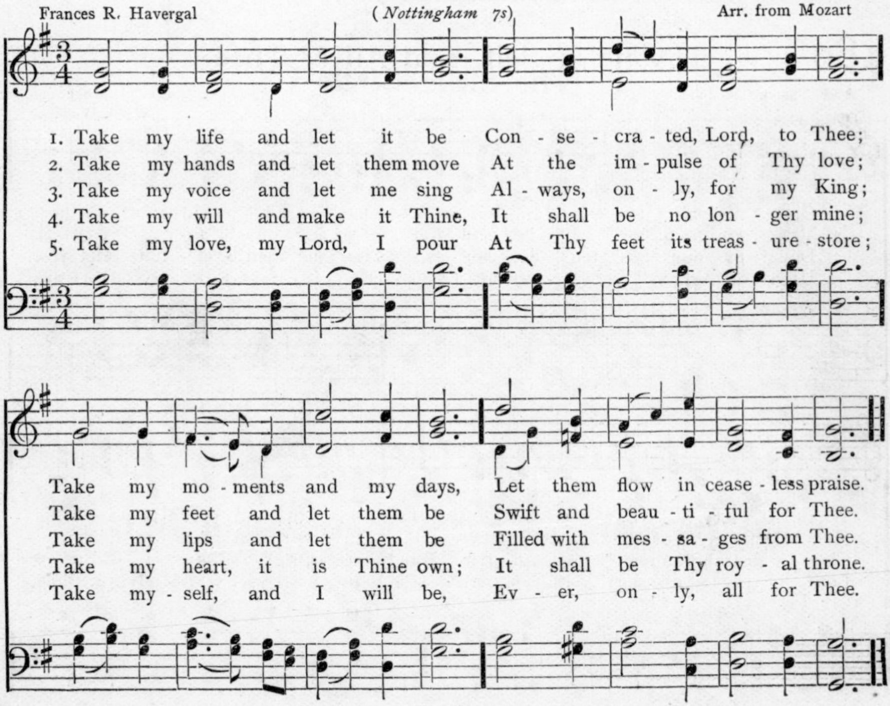
1. Take my life and let it be Con - se - cra - ted, Lord, to Thee;
2. Take my hands and let them move At the im - pulse of Thy love;
3. Take my voice and let me sing Al - ways, on - ly, for my King;
4. Take my will and make it Thine, It shall be no lon - ger mine;
5. Take my love, my Lord, I pour At Thy feet its treas - ure - store;
Take my mo - ments and my days, Let them flow in cease - less praise.
Take my feet and let them be Swift and beau - ti - ful for Thee.
Take my lips and let them be Filled with mes - sa - ges from Thee.
Take my heart, it is Thine own; It shall be Thy roy - al throne.
Take my - self, and I will be, Ev - er, on - ly, all for Thee.

179 Consecration

H. S. B. Harriet S. Brainerd

Softly and slowly

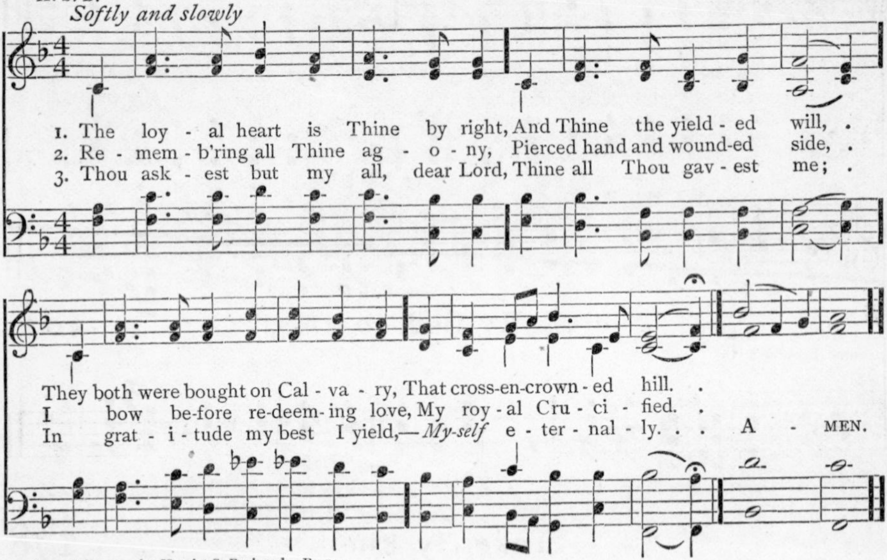
1. The loy - al heart is Thine by right, And Thine the yield - ed will, .
2. Re - mem - b'ring all Thine ag - o - ny, Pierced hand and wound-ed side, .
3. Thou ask - est but my all, dear Lord, Thine all Thou gav - est me; .
They both were bought on Cal - va - ry, That cross-en-crown - ed hill. .
I bow be-fore re-deem - ing love, My roy - al Cru - ci - fied. .
In grat - i - tude my best I yield,—*My-self* e - ter - nal - ly. . . A - MEN.

Copyright, 1899, by Harriet S. Brainerd. By per.

180 None of Self, and All of Thee

Rev. Theodor Monod (*8s. 7s. 6l.*) Rev. J. Mountain

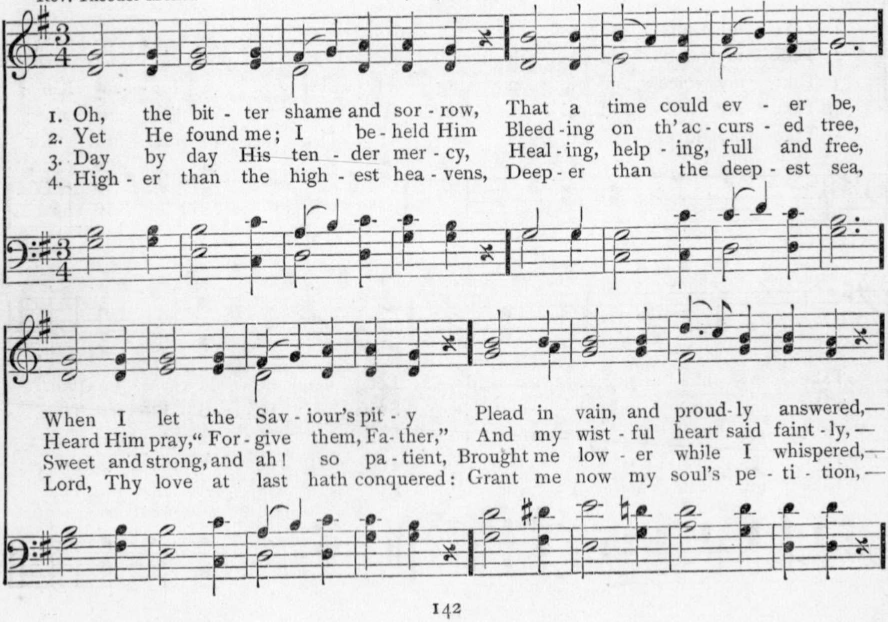
1. Oh, the bit - ter shame and sor - row, That a time could ev - er be,
2. Yet He found me; I be - held Him Bleed - ing on th' ac - curs - ed tree,
3. Day by day His ten - der mer - cy, Heal - ing, help - ing, full and free,
4. High - er than the high - est hea - vens, Deep - er than the deep - est sea,
When I let the Sav - iour's pit - y Plead in vain, and proud - ly answered,—
Heard Him pray, "For - give them, Fa - ther," And my wist - ful heart said faint - ly,—
Sweet and strong, and ah! so pa - tient, Brought me low - er while I whispered,—
Lord, Thy love at last hath conquered: Grant me now my soul's pe - ti - tion,—

None of Self, and All of Thee

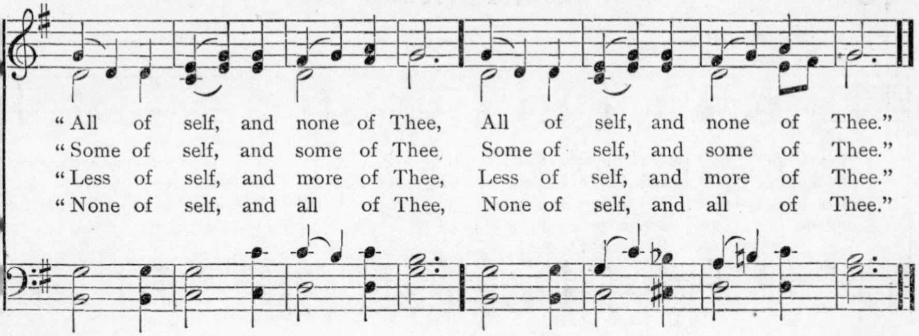
"All of self, and none of Thee, All of self, and none of Thee."
"Some of self, and some of Thee, Some of self, and some of Thee."
"Less of self, and more of Thee, Less of self, and more of Thee."
"None of self, and all of Thee, None of self, and all of Thee."

Nearer, My God, to Thee 181

Sarah F. Adams, 1841 (*Bethany* 6s. 4s.) Lowell Mason, 1856

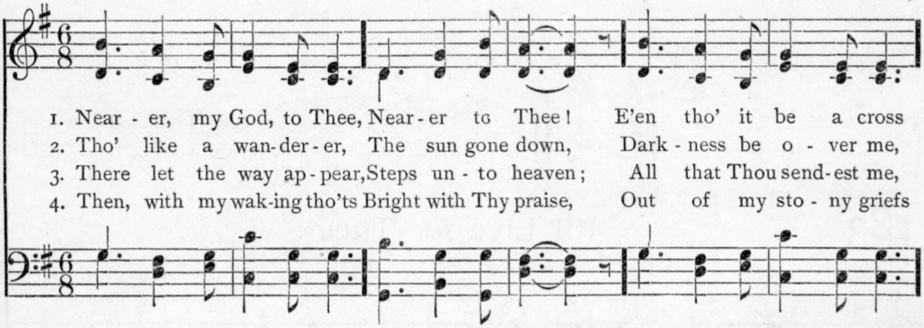
1. Near - er, my God, to Thee, Near - er to Thee! E'en tho' it be a cross
2. Tho' like a wan - der - er, The sun gone down, Dark - ness be o - ver me,
3. There let the way ap - pear, Steps un - to heaven; All that Thou send - est me,
4. Then, with my wak - ing tho'ts Bright with Thy praise, Out of my sto - ny griefs

That rais - eth me; Still all my song shall be, Near - er, my God, to Thee,
My rest a stone, Yet in my dreams I'd be Near - er, my God, to Thee,
In mer - cy given; An - gels to beck - on me Near - er, my God, to Thee,
Beth - el I'll raise; So by my woes to be Near - er, my God, to Thee,

Near - er, my God, to Thee, Near - er to Thee!

5 Or if on joyful wing
Cleaving the sky,
Sun, moon, and stars forgot,
Upward I fly,
Still all my song shall be,
Nearer, my God, to Thee,
Nearer to Thee!

182 Peace, Perfect Peace

E. H. Bickersteth, 1875 (*Pax Tecum*. 10. 10) G. T. Caldbeck, 1877

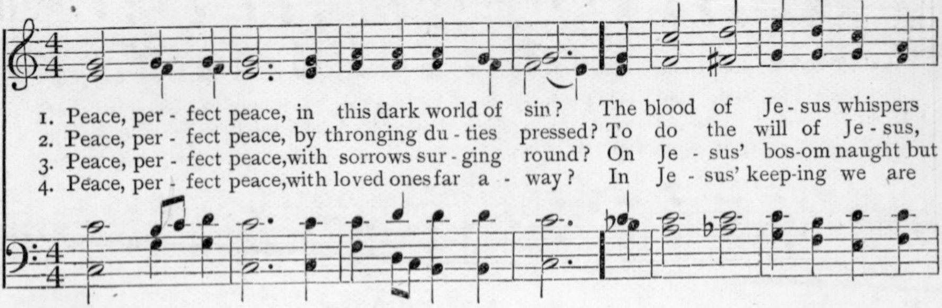
1. Peace, per - fect peace, in this dark world of sin? The blood of Je - sus whispers
2. Peace, per - fect peace, by thronging du - ties pressed? To do the will of Je - sus,
3. Peace, per - fect peace, with sorrows sur - ging round? On Je - sus' bos - om naught but
4. Peace, per - fect peace, with loved ones far a - way? In Je - sus' keep - ing we are

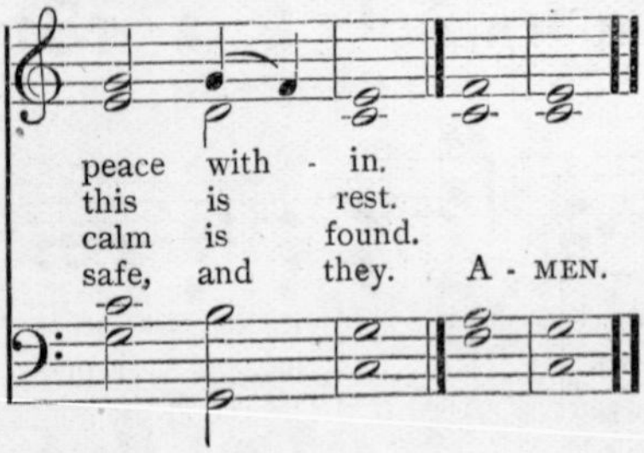
peace with - in.
this is rest.
calm is found.
safe, and they. A - MEN.

5 Peace, perfect peace, our future all unknown?
Jesus we know, and He is on the throne.

6 Peace, perfect peace, death shadowing us and ours?
Jesus has vanquished death and all its powers.

7 It is enough: earth's struggles soon shall cease,
And Jesus call us to heaven's perfect peace.

183 I'll Live for Thee

Ralph E. Hudson Charles R. Dunbar

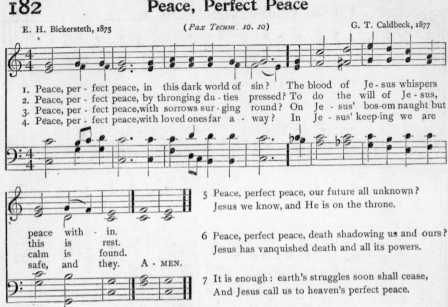

1. My life, my love, I give to Thee, Thou Lamb of God, who died for me;
2. I now be - lieve Thou dost re - ceive, For Thou hast died that I might live;
3. O Thou who died on Cal - va - ry, To save my soul and make me free;
CHO.—*I'll live for Thee, I'll live for Thee, And O how glad my soul should be,*
O may I ev - er faith - ful be, My Sav - iour and my God!
And now hence-forth I'll trust in Thee, My Sav - iour and my God!
I con - se - crate my all to Thee, My Sav - iour and my God!
That Thou didst give Thy - self for me, My Sav - iour and my God!

Copyright, 1882, by R. E. Hudson. Used by per.

I'll Go Where You Want Me to Go 184

Mary Brown (9s. 7s. D. with Refrain) Carrie E. Rounsefell

Andante
1. It may not be on the moun-tain's height, Or o - ver the storm - y sea;
2. Per - haps to - day there are lov - ing words Which Je - sus would have me speak;
3. There's sure - ly some-where a low - ly place, In earth's har-vest fields so wide,
It may not be at the bat - tle's front My Lord will have need of me;
There may be now in the paths of sin, Some wan - d'rer whom I should seek.
Where I may la - bor thro' life's short day For Je - sus the cru - ci - fied.
But if by a still small voice He calls To paths that I do not know,
O Sav - iour, if Thou wilt be my guide, Tho' dark and rugged the way,
So trust - ing my all to Thy ten - der care, And know - ing Thou lov - est me,
FINE
I'll answer, dear Lord, with my hand in Thine, I'll go where you want me to go.
My voice shall ech - o the mes - sage sweet, I'll say what you want me to say.
I'll do Thy will with a heart sin - cere, I'll be what you want me to be.
D.S. I'll say what you want me to say, dear Lord, I'll be what you want me to be.
REFRAIN
D.S.
I'll go where you want me to go, dear Lord, O - ver moun-tain, or plain, or sea;

Copyright, 1894, by C. E. Rounsefell. Used by per.

185 O Golden Day

Charles A. Dickinson | (*Ellacombe C.M.D.*) | Arr. from German Chorale

1. O gold-en day, so long de-sired, Born of a darksome night, The wait-ing earth at
2. The noi-ses of the night shall cease, The storms no lon-ger roar; The fac-tious foes of
3. Sing on, ye cho-rus of the morn, Your grand en-deav-or strain, Till Christian hearts es-
4. O gold-en day, the a-ges crown, A-light with heavenly love, Rare day in proph-e-

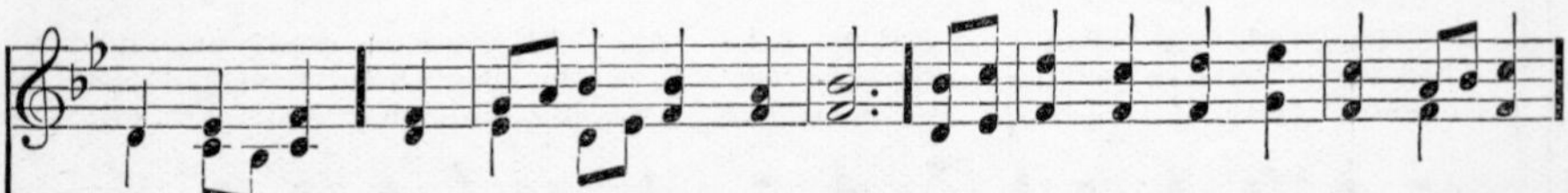

last is fired By Thy re-splen-dent light. And hark! like Memnon's morn-ing chord
God's own peace Shall vex His church no more. A thou-sand thou-sand voi-ces sing
tranged and torn, Blend in the glad re-frain; And all the church, with all its pow'rs,
cy re-nown, On to thy ze-nith move. When all the world, with one ac-cord,

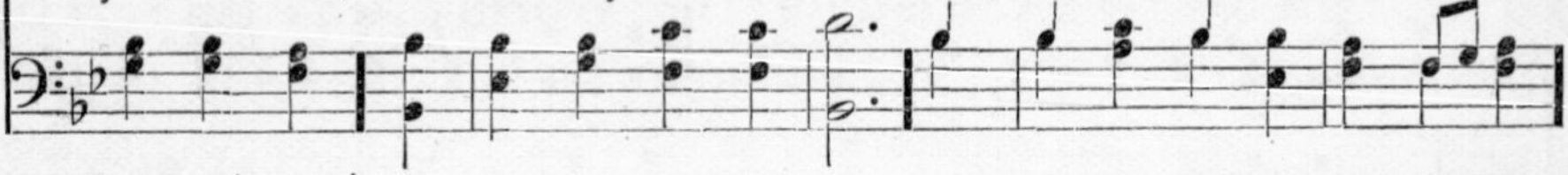

Is heard from sea to sea This song: One Master, Christ the Lord; And brethren all are we.
The surging harmo-ny; One Master, Christ; one Sav-iour-King; And brethren all are we.
In lov-ing loy-al-ty, Shall sing: One Master, Christ, is ours; And brethren all are we.
In full-voiced u-ni-ty, Shall sing: One Master, Christ our Lord; And brethren all are we.

186 How Sweet to Think

H. Whittemore | (*Magi 8.6.8.6.8.8*) | Livesey Carrott

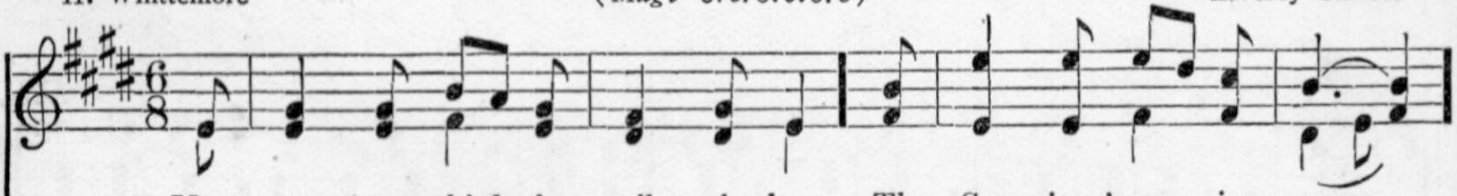

1. How sweet to think that all who love The Sav-iour's pre-cious name,
2. "Our Fa-ther" is the hal-lowed sound, They breathe from day to day;
3. Yes, they are one—tho' some, we know, Have reached the home of love;

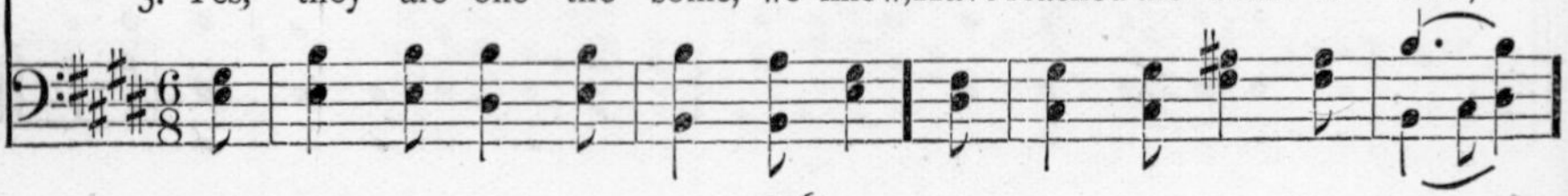

How Sweet to Think

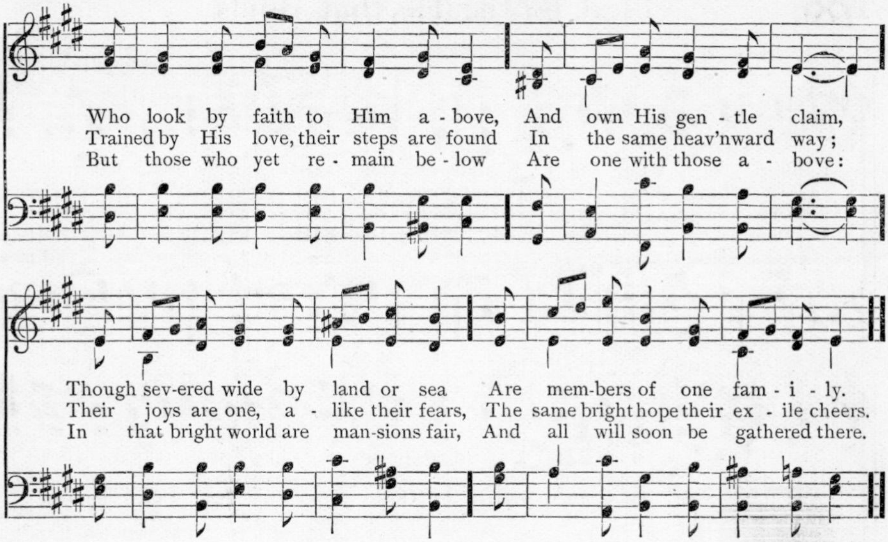
Who look by faith to Him a - bove, And own His gen - tle claim,
Trained by His love, their steps are found In the same heav'nward way;
But those who yet re - main be - low Are one with those a - bove:
Though sev-ered wide by land or sea Are mem-bers of one fam - i - ly.
Their joys are one, a - like their fears, The same bright hope their ex - ile cheers.
In that bright world are man-sions fair, And all will soon be gathered there.

Christ for the World 187

C. G. Clark

With vigor

(*Bethlehem C.M.D.*)

Old Carol

f
1. Christ for the world, the world for Christ, Be this our ral-lying song; With pur-pose true our
2. Christ for the world, the world for Christ, For this our work shall be, Till earth is fill'd with
hosts advance, A brave and conqu'ring throng. An ar - my with a grand re - solve,
right-eous-ness, As wa - ters fill the sea. So shall all na - tions serve the Lord,
And hearts with love a - flame, Will con-quer all the hosts of sin, In their Redeemer's name.
As light to them is giv'n; And then His will be done on earth, As it is done in heav'n.

188 Blest be the Tie that Binds

Rev. John Fawcett (*Dennis S. M.*) H. G. Nageli

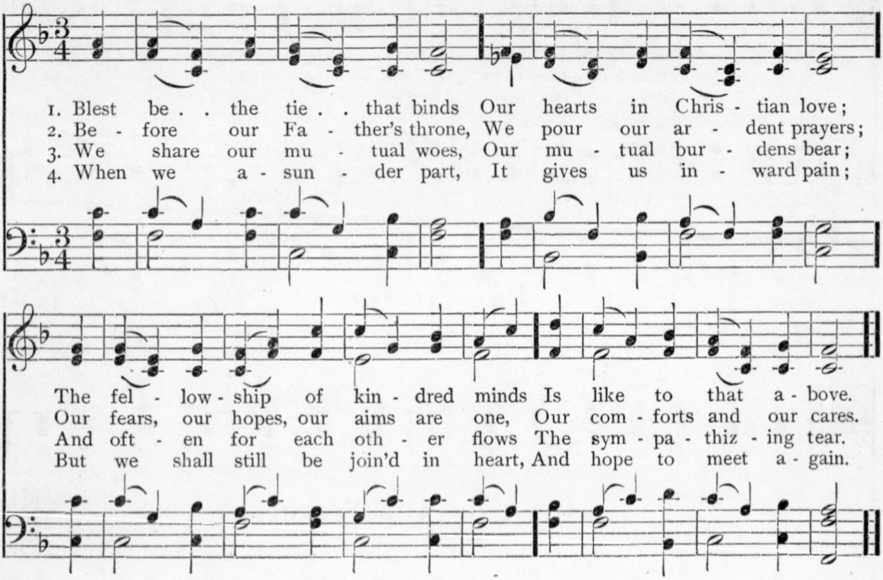
1. Blest be . . the tie . . that binds Our hearts in Chris - tian love;
2. Be - fore our Fa - ther's throne, We pour our ar - dent prayers;
3. We share our mu - tual woes, Our mu - tual bur - dens bear;
4. When we a - sun - der part, It gives us in - ward pain;
The fel - low - ship of kin - dred minds Is like to that a - bove.
Our fears, our hopes, our aims are one, Our com - forts and our cares.
And oft - en for each oth - er flows The sym - pa - thiz - ing tear.
But we shall still be join'd in heart, And hope to meet a - gain.

189 The Church's One Foundation

Samuel J. Stone, 1866 (*Aurelia 7s. 6s. D.*) Samuel S. Wesley, 1864

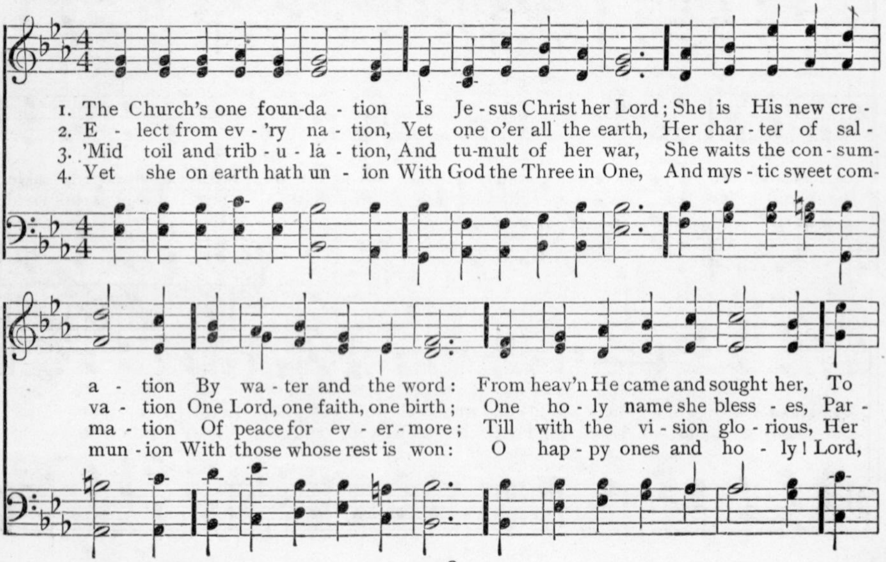
1. The Church's one foun-da - tion Is Je - sus Christ her Lord; She is His new cre -
2. E - lect from ev - 'ry na - tion, Yet one o'er all the earth, Her char - ter of sal -
3. 'Mid toil and trib - u - la - tion, And tu-mult of her war, She waits the con - sum -
4. Yet she on earth hath un - ion With God the Three in One, And mys - tic sweet com -
a - tion By wa - ter and the word: From heav'n He came and sought her, To
va - tion One Lord, one faith, one birth; One ho - ly name she bless - es, Par -
ma - tion Of peace for ev - er - more; Till with the vi - sion glo - rious, Her
mun - ion With those whose rest is won: O hap - py ones and ho - ly! Lord,

The Church's One Foundation

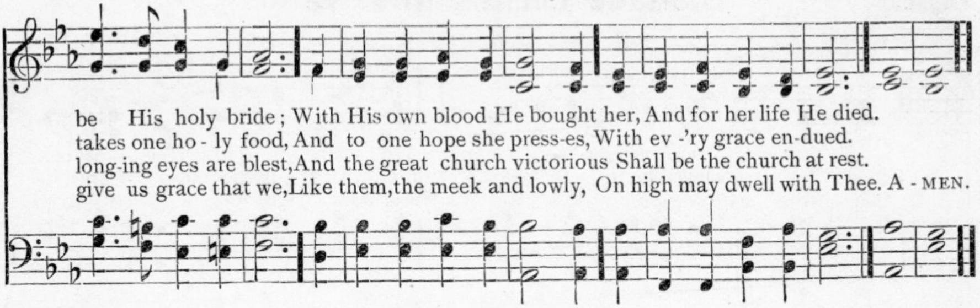
be His holy bride; With His own blood He bought her, And for her life He died.
takes one ho - ly food, And to one hope she press-es, With ev -'ry grace en-dued.
long-ing eyes are blest, And the great church victorious Shall be the church at rest.
give us grace that we, Like them, the meek and lowly, On high may dwell with Thee. A - MEN.

Pass It On

190

Henry Burton — (7.3.7.3.7.7.7.3) — J. Frederick Swift

Moderato

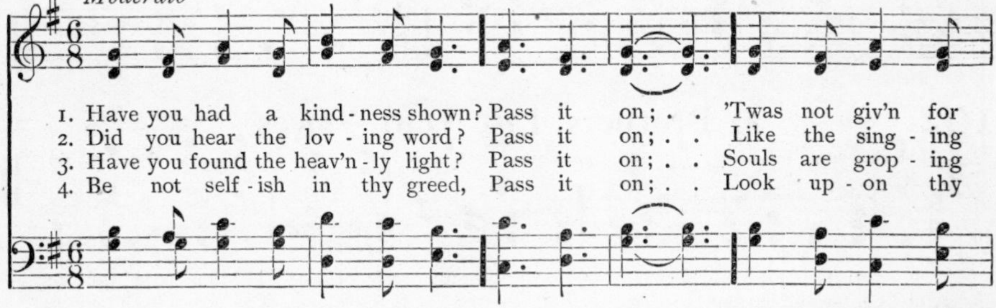
1. Have you had a kind - ness shown? Pass it on; . . 'Twas not giv'n for
2. Did you hear the lov - ing word? Pass it on; . . Like the sing - ing
3. Have you found the heav'n - ly light? Pass it on; . . Souls are grop - ing
4. Be not self - ish in thy greed, Pass it on; . . Look up - on thy

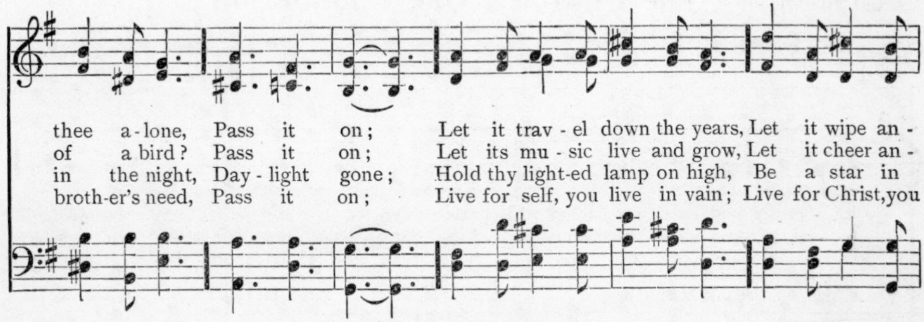
thee a - lone, Pass it on; Let it trav - el down the years, Let it wipe an -
of a bird? Pass it on; Let its mu - sic live and grow, Let it cheer an -
in the night, Day - light gone; Hold thy light-ed lamp on high, Be a star in
broth-er's need, Pass it on; Live for self, you live in vain; Live for Christ, you

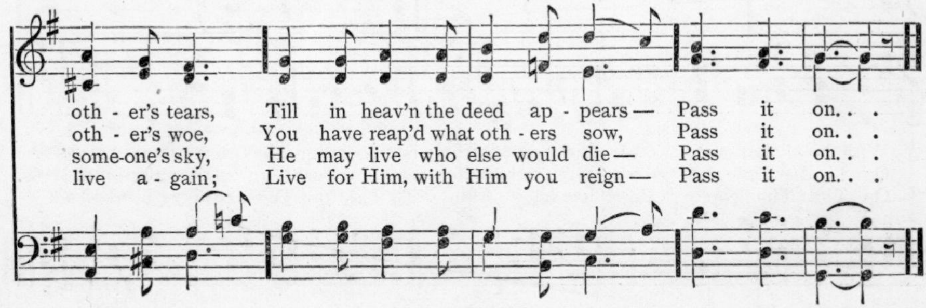
oth - er's tears, Till in heav'n the deed ap - pears — Pass it on. . .
oth - er's woe, You have reap'd what oth - ers sow, Pass it on. . .
some-one's sky, He may live who else would die — Pass it on. . .
live a - gain; Live for Him, with Him you reign — Pass it on. . .

191 Made Perfect in Love

Charles Wesley

(*St. Luke's C. M.*)

Sir Joseph Barnby

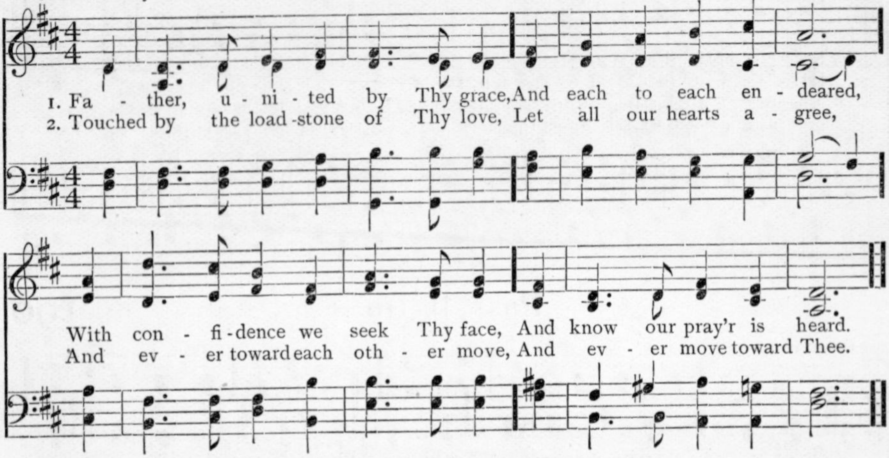
1. Fa - ther, u - ni - ted by Thy grace, And each to each en - deared,
2. Touched by the load - stone of Thy love, Let all our hearts a - gree,
With con - fi - dence we seek Thy face, And know our pray'r is heard.
And ev - er toward each oth - er move, And ev - er move toward Thee.

192 O Brothers, Lift Your Voices

E. H. Bickersteth

(*Bradford 7. 6. 8l.*)

From Haydn

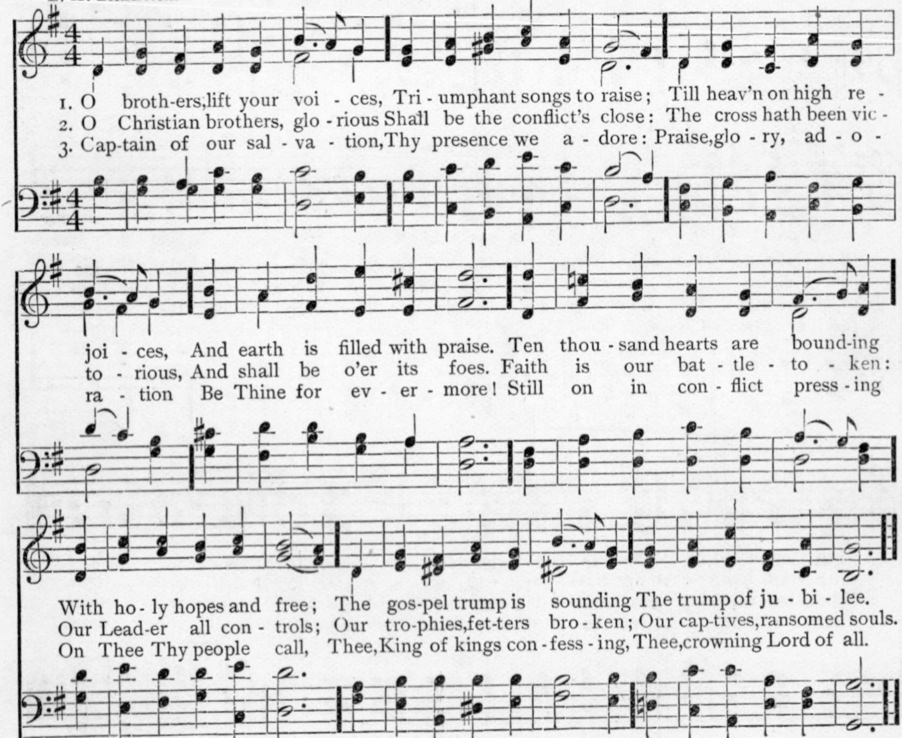
1. O broth-ers, lift your voi - ces, Tri - umphant songs to raise; Till heav'n on high re -
2. O Christian brothers, glo - rious Shall be the conflict's close: The cross hath been vic -
3. Cap-tain of our sal - va - tion, Thy presence we a - dore: Praise, glo - ry, ad - o -
joi - ces, And earth is filled with praise. Ten thou - sand hearts are bound-ing
to - rious, And shall be o'er its foes. Faith is our bat - tle - to - ken:
ra - tion Be Thine for ev - er - more! Still on in con - flict press - ing
With ho - ly hopes and free; The gos-pel trump is sounding The trump of ju - bi - lee.
Our Lead-er all con - trols; Our tro-phies, fet-ters bro - ken; Our cap-tives, ransomed souls.
On Thee Thy people call, Thee, King of kings con - fess - ing, Thee, crowning Lord of all.

I Left It All with Jesus

193

Miss Ellen H. Willis

Miss H. M. Warner

1. I left it all with Je - sus, Long a - go ; All my sins I brought Him
2. I leave it all with Je - sus, For He knows How to steal the bit - ter
3. I leave it all with Je - sus, Day by day ; Faith can firm - ly trust Him
4. Oh, leave it *all* with Je - sus, Drooping soul! Tell not *half* thy sto - ry,

And my woe. When by faith I saw Him On the tree, Heard His small, still
From life's woes ; How to gild the tear - drop With His smile, Make the des - ert
Come what may. Hope has dropped her an - chor, Found her rest In the calm sure
But the whole. Worlds on worlds are hang - ing On His hand, Life and death are

whis - per, " 'Tis for thee," From my heart the bur - den Rolled a - way—
gar - den Bloom a - while: When my weak-ness lean - eth On His might,
ha - ven Of His breast: Love es - teems it heav - en To a - bide
wait - ing His com - mand; Yet His ten - der bos - om Makes *thee* room—

cres.

rit.

Hap - py day! From my heart the bur - den Rolled a - way — Hap - py day!
All seems light. When my weak- ness lean - eth On His might All seems light.
At His side. Love es - teems it heav - en To a - bide At His side.
Oh, come home! Yet His ten - der bos - om, Makes *thee* room — Oh, come home!

194 Saviour and Friend

J. S. B. Monsell (5s. 4s) Arr. from Edouard Batiste

Smoothly, with expression
p
1. Rest of the wea-ry, Joy of the sad, Hope of the drear - y, Light of the glad;
2. Pil - low where ly-ing Love rests its head; Peace of the dy - ing, Life of the dead.
3. When my feet stumble, I'll to Thee cry; Crown of the hum - ble, Cross of the high.
4. Ev - er con-fess - ing Thee, I will raise Un - to Thee bless-ing, Glo - ry, and praise;
p
Home of the stranger, Strength to the end, Ref-uge from dan - ger, Saviour and Friend;
Path of the low - ly, Prize at the end, Breath of the ho - ly, Saviour and Friend;
When my steps wan-der, O - ver me bend, Tru - er and fond - er, Saviour and Friend;
All my en-deav - or, World with-out end, Thine to be ev - er, Saviour and Friend;
dim. e rit.
pp
Ref - uge from dan - ger, Sav - iour and Friend, Sav - iour and Friend.
Breath of the ho - ly, Sav - iour and Friend, Sav - iour and Friend.
Tru - er and fond - er, Sav - iour and Friend, Sav - iour and Friend.
Thine to be ev - er, Sav - iour and Friend, Sav - iour and Friend.

195 Come unto Me

Unknown Mrs. F. H. Jacobs

1. "Come un - to Me, ye wea - ry, And I will give you rest." Oh, bless - ed voice of
2. "Come un - to Me, ye wan-d'rers, And I will give you light." Oh, lov - ing voice of
3. "Come un - to Me, ye faint - ing, And I will give you life." Oh, cheer-ing voice of

Copyright, 1901, by F. H. Jacobs.

Come unto Me

Je - sus, Which comes to hearts op - pressed! It tells of ben - e - dic - tion, Of
Je - sus, Which comes to cheer the night! Our hearts were filled with sad - ness, And
Je - sus, Which comes to aid our strife! The foe is stern and ea - ger, The
par - don, grace, and peace; Of joy that hath no end - ing, Of love which can - not
we had lost our way, But morn - ing brings us glad - ness, And songs the break of
fight is fierce and long; But Thou hast made us might - y, And stronger than the
cease; . . Of joy that hath no end - ing, Of love which can-not cease. . .
day; . . But morn-ing brings us glad - ness, And songs the break of day. . . .
strong; . But Thou hast made us might - y, And strong-er than the strong. . .

Stepping Stones

196

Anon. Geo. J. Ferreira, 1901

1. I would not have my life go on, A lev - el stretch from sun to sun;
2. These rugged paths that wound my feet, These trib - u - la - tions that I meet,
And miss the glo - rious sights I get From Cal-va-ry to Ol - i - vet.
Are stepping stones by which I climb To glo-ries end-less and sub - lime.

Copyright, 1901, by U. S. C. E.

197 Nearer, Still Nearer

C. H. M. Mrs. C. H. Morris

1. Near - er, still near - er, close to Thy heart, Draw me, my Sav - iour, so
2. Near - er, still near - er, noth - ing I bring, Naught as an off - 'ring to
3. Near - er, still near - er, Lord, to be Thine Sin, with its fol - lies, I
4. Near - er, still near - er, while life shall last, Till all its strug - gles and
pre - cious Thou art; Fold me, O fold me close to Thy breast, Shel - ter me
Je - sus my King; On - ly my sin - ful, now con - trite heart, Grant me the
glad - ly re - sign; All of its pleas - ures, pomp and its pride, Give me but
tri - als are past; Then thro' e - ter - nity, ev - er I'll be Near - er, my
safe in that "Ha - ven of Rest," Shel - ter me safe in that "Ha - ven of Rest."
cleans - ing Thy blood doth im - part, Grant me the cleans - ing Thy blood doth im - part.
Je - sus, my Lord cru - ci - fied, Give me but Je - sus, my Lord cru - ci - fied.
Sav - iour, still near - er to Thee, Near - er, my Sav - iour, still near - er to Thee.

Copyright, 1898, by H. L. Gilmour. By per.

198 Walking with God

Wm. Gaskell (*L. M.*) Fr. Curschmann. Arr. by F. L. Stone

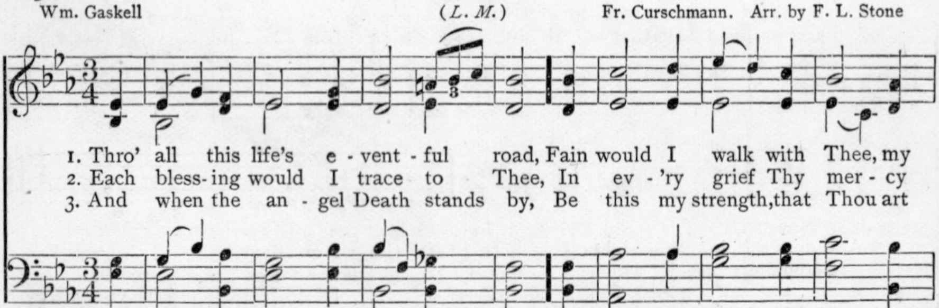
1. Thro' all this life's e - vent - ful road, Fain would I walk with Thee, my
2. Each bless - ing would I trace to Thee, In ev - 'ry grief Thy mer - cy
3. And when the an - gel Death stands by, Be this my strength, that Thou art

Copyright, 1901, by U. S. C. E.

Walking with God

God, And find Thy pres - ence light a - round, And ev - 'ry
see; And thro' the paths of du - ty move, Con - scious of
nigh; And this my joy, that I shall be With those who
step on ho - ly ground, And ev - 'ry step on ho - ly ground.
Thine en - cir - cling love, Con - scious of Thine en - cir - cling love.
dwell in light with Thee, With those who dwell in light with Thee.

Spirit of Love Divine 199

Anon. (*Sweet and Low*) J. Barnby

mf
1. Ho - ly Ghost, Comfort - er, Spir - it of love di - vine, Come dwell in our hearts, Make them
2. Help and bless with Thy peace All who in sor - row mourn; Save, save by Thy love All those
f
ritard
for - ev - er Thine. Hear us while now we seek Thy grace, Show us the brightness of Thy face,
by sin cast down. And when o'erwhelm'd by temptation's pow'r, Then be Thou near in darkest hour,
ff
p
pp
Hear! . . .
Make us to know Thy will. By Thy mercy free, While we pray to Thee, Hear! oh, hear!
Suf - fer us not to fall. Strong deliv'rance bring, O Thou gracious King, Hear! oh, hear!
Hear! . . .

200 Take Time to be Holy

(*St. Luke* 11s)

W. D Longstaff

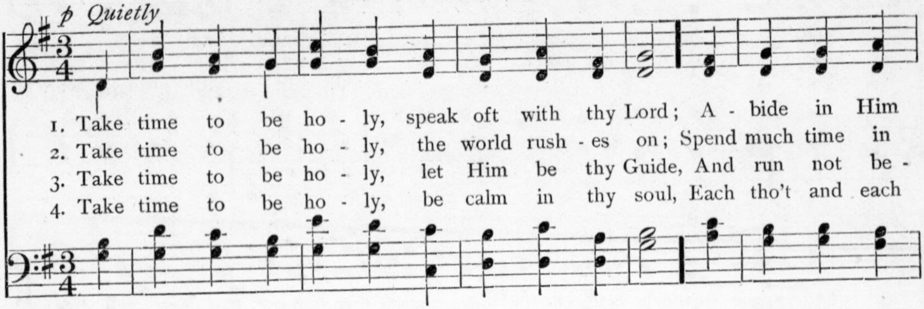
p Quietly
1. Take time to be ho - ly, speak oft with thy Lord; A - bide in Him
2. Take time to be ho - ly, the world rush - es on; Spend much time in
3. Take time to be ho - ly, let Him be thy Guide, And run not be -
4. Take time to be ho - ly, be calm in thy soul, Each tho't and each

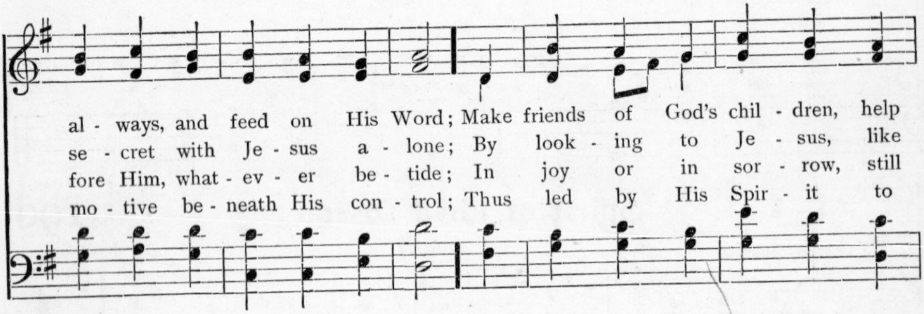
al - ways, and feed on His Word; Make friends of God's chil - dren, help
se - cret with Je - sus a - lone; By look - ing to Je - sus, like
fore Him, what - ev - er be - tide; In joy or in sor - row, still
mo - tive be - neath His con - trol; Thus led by His Spir - it to

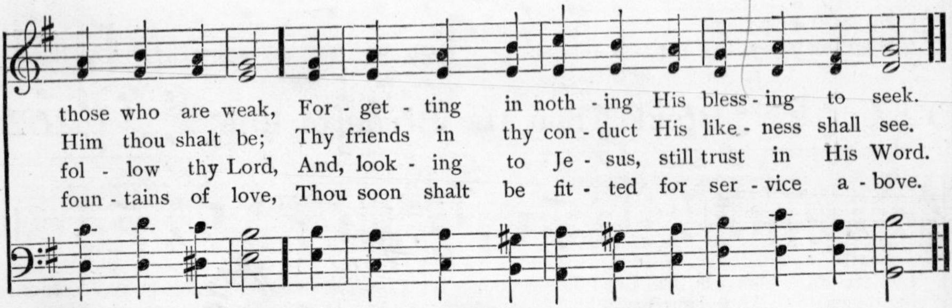
those who are weak, For - get - ting in noth - ing His bless - ing to seek.
Him thou shalt be; Thy friends in thy con - duct His like - ness shall see.
fol - low thy Lord, And, look - ing to Je - sus, still trust in His Word.
foun - tains of love, Thou soon shalt be fit - ted for ser - vice a - bove.

201 Beneath the Cross of Jesus

Elizabeth C. Clephane, 1872 (*St. Christopher* 7. 6. 8. 6. 8. 6. 8. 6) Frederick C. Maker, 1881

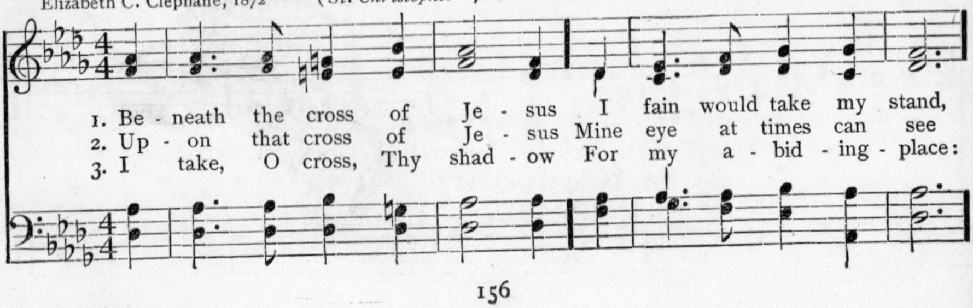
1. Be - neath the cross of Je - sus I fain would take my stand,
2. Up - on that cross of Je - sus Mine eye at times can see
3. I take, O cross, Thy shad - ow For my a - bid - ing - place:

Beneath the Cross of Jesus

The shad - ow of a might - y Rock With - in a wea - ry land;
The ver - y dy - ing form of One Who suf - fered there for me:
I ask no oth - er sun - shine than The sun - shine of His face;
A home with - in the wil - der - ness, A rest up - on the way,
And from my smit - ten heart with tears Two won - ders I con - fess,—
Con - tent to let the world go by, To know no gain nor loss,
From the burn-ing of the noon-tide heat, And the bur - den of the day.
The won - ders of His glo - rious love And my own worthlessness.
My sin - ful self my on - ly shame, My glo - ry all the cross. A - MEN.

Break Thou the Bread of Life 202

Mary A. Lathbury

Wm. F. Sherwin, 1877

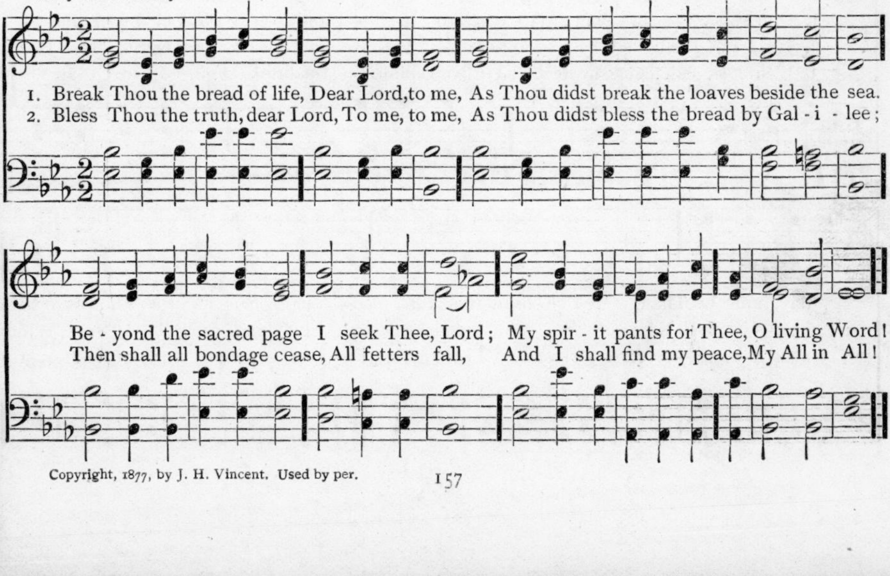
1. Break Thou the bread of life, Dear Lord, to me, As Thou didst break the loaves beside the sea.
2. Bless Thou the truth, dear Lord, To me, to me, As Thou didst bless the bread by Gal - i - lee;
Be - yond the sacred page I seek Thee, Lord; My spir - it pants for Thee, O living Word!
Then shall all bondage cease, All fetters fall, And I shall find my peace, My All in All!

Copyright, 1877, by J. H. Vincent. Used by per.

203 O Teach Me, Lord

Frances R. Havergal (*Nocturn L. M.*) F. H. Burstall

mf

1. O teach me, Lord, that I may teach The pre-cious things Thou dost im - part;
2. O fill me with Thy ful - ness, Lord, Un - til my ver - y heart o'er - flow
3. O use me, Lord, use e - ven me, Just as Thou wilt, and when, and where;

mf

And wing my words, that they may reach The hidden depths of ma - ny a heart.
In kind-ling tho't and glow - ing word, Thy love to tell, Thy praise to show.
Un - til Thy bless - ed face I see, Thy rest, Thy joy, Thy glo - ry share. A - MEN.

204 One Sweetly Solemn Thought

Phoebe Cary, 1852 (*Leominster S. M. D.*) Har. by Sir Arthur Sullivan

Slowly

1. One sweet- ly sol - emn tho't Comes to me o'er and o'er,— Near-er my home, to -
2. Near - er the bound of life, Where bur - dens are laid down; Near-er to leave the
3. E'en now, per-chance, my feet Are slip - ping on the brink, And I, to - day, am

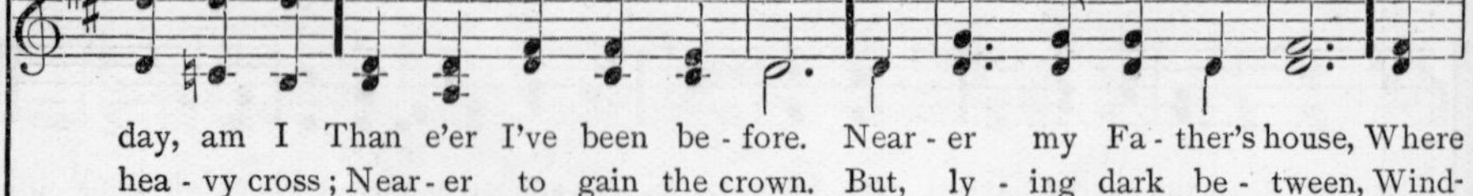

day, am I Than e'er I've been be - fore. Near - er my Fa - ther's house, Where
hea - vy cross; Near - er to gain the crown. But, ly - ing dark be - tween, Wind-
near- er home,— Near-er than now I think. Fa - ther, per - fect my trust; Strength-

One Sweetly Solemn Thought

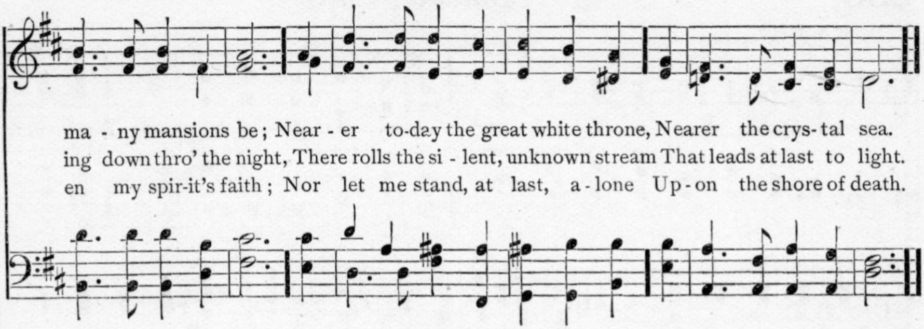
ma - ny mansions be; Near - er to-day the great white throne, Nearer the crys - tal sea.
ing down thro' the night, There rolls the si - lent, unknown stream That leads at last to light.
en my spir-it's faith; Nor let me stand, at last, a - lone Up - on the shore of death.

The Quiet Hour

205

S. B. Pinney — C. W. Jackman

1. The child of God has come and gone, The world is bet - ter now; His joy and hope have spread a - far, To soothe the wea - ry brow.
2. The rush of bu - sy world - ly cares Has oft the light made dim; But in this qui - et hour of trust The soul clings fast to Him.
3. The lit - tle up - per room of old, Where souls may come at will, Is built around the hearth of faith In qui - et cor - ners still.
CHORUS
I love the qui - et hour of trust, With none but Je - sus near; I love to hear the still small voice, It speaks so plain and clear.
p

Copyright, 1901, by U. S. C. E.

206 Solace

Nellie A. Willis

M. B. Willis, 1901

1. When our minds are in a tu - mult, And the world seems go-ing wrong, When our
2. When the tir - ed lit - tle chil - dren Seek their moth-er's close em-brace, And with

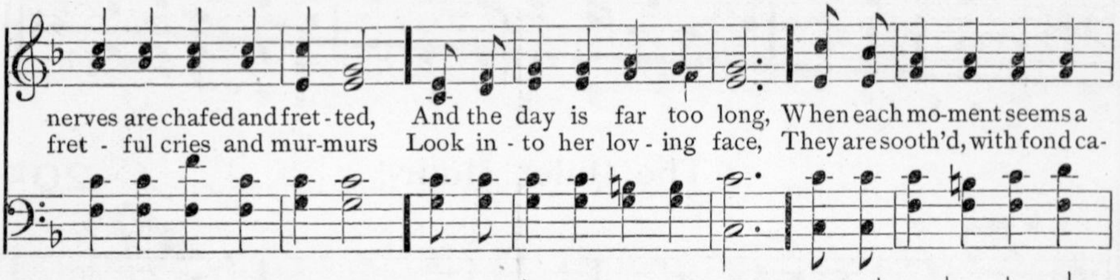
nerves are chafed and fret-ted, And the day is far too long, When each mo-ment seems a
fret - ful cries and mur-murs Look in - to her lov - ing face, They are sooth'd, with fond ca-

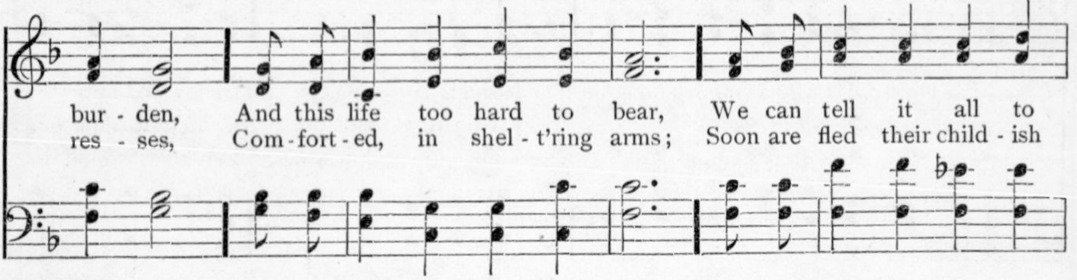
bur - den, And this life too hard to bear, We can tell it all to
res - ses, Com-fort - ed, in shel - t'ring arms; Soon are fled their child - ish

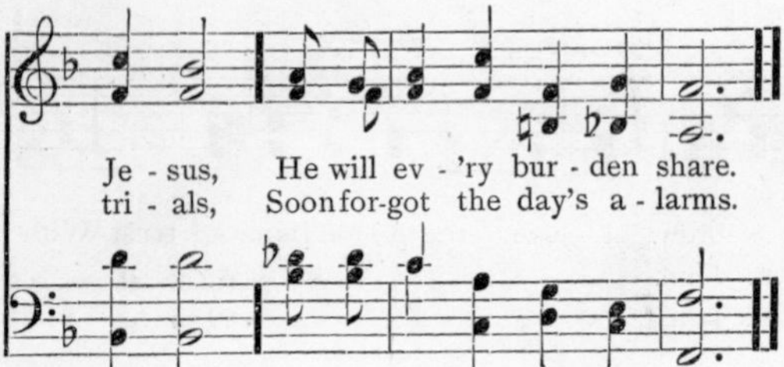
Je - sus, He will ev - 'ry bur - den share.
tri - als, Soon for-got the day's a - larms.

3 Can we not, like little children,
Tell our doubts and fears to Him?
He will lead us through life's mazes
With sight clear, where ours is dim.
Oh! the blessed peace of knowing
We are safe in His dear hands!
All our poor mistakes and failures
We are sure He understands.

Copyright, 1901, by U. S. C. E.

207 I Heard the Voice of Jesus Say

Horatius Bonar, 1846

(*Vox Dilecti C. M. D.*)

J. B. Dykes, 1868

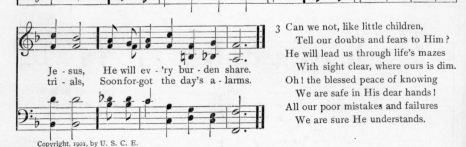

p
mf
1. I heard the voice of Je - sus say, "Come un - to Me and rest;
2. I heard the voice of Je - sus say, "Be - hold, I free - ly give
3. I heard the voice of Je - sus say, "I am this dark world's Light;
p
mf

I Heard the Voice of Jesus Say

cres.
Lay down, thou wea - ry one, lay down Thy head up - on My breast."
The liv - ing wa - ter; thirst - y one, Stoop down and drink, and live."
Look un - to Me, thy morn shall rise, And all thy day be bright."
p
cres.
I came to Je - sus as I was, Wea - ry and worn and sad,
I came to Je - sus and I drank Of that life - giv - ing stream;
I looked to Je - sus, and I found In Him my Star, my Sun;
cres.
f
I found in Him a rest - ing place, And He has made me glad.
My thirst was quenched, my soul re-vived, And now I live in Him.
And in that light of life I'll walk, Till trav'-ling days are done. A - MEN.

Tell Me, My Saviour 208

Charles S. Robinson

(*Lynde P. M.*)

Thuringian Folk-song

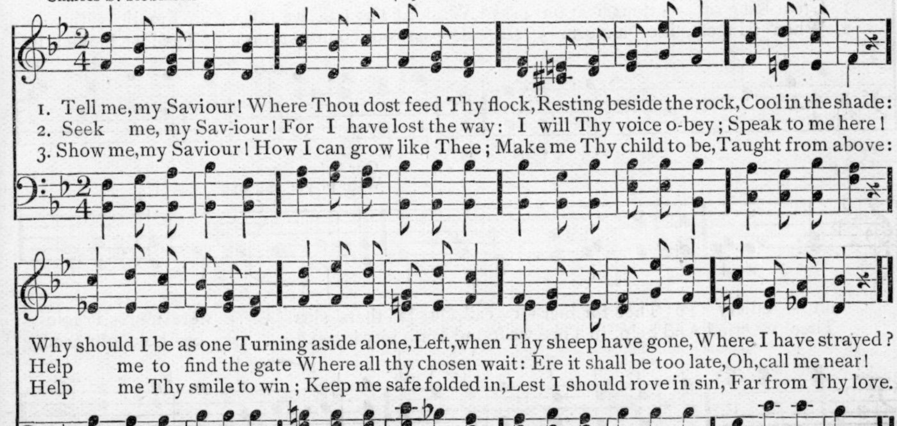
1. Tell me, my Saviour! Where Thou dost feed Thy flock, Resting beside the rock, Cool in the shade:
2. Seek me, my Sav-iour! For I have lost the way: I will Thy voice o-bey; Speak to me here!
3. Show me, my Saviour! How I can grow like Thee; Make me Thy child to be, Taught from above:
Why should I be as one Turning aside alone, Left, when Thy sheep have gone, Where I have strayed?
Help me to find the gate Where all thy chosen wait: Ere it shall be too late, Oh, call me near!
Help me Thy smile to win; Keep me safe folded in, Lest I should rove in sin, Far from Thy love.

209 God the All-Terrible

Henry F. Chorley, 1842 — (*Russian Hymn* 11. 10. 11. 10) — Alexis Lvoff, 1799-1870

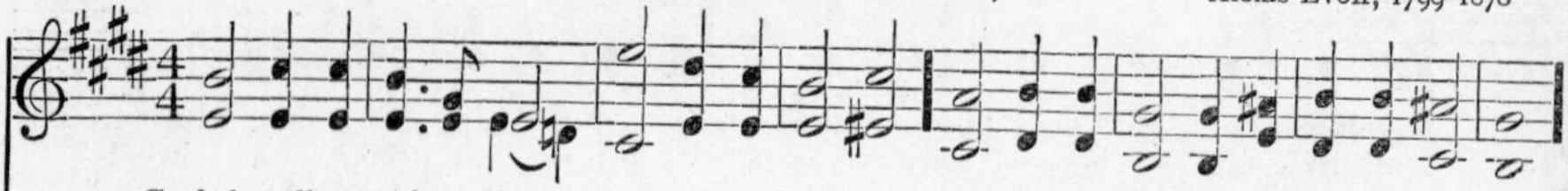

1. God the all-ter-ri-ble! King who ordainest, Great winds Thy clarions, the lightnings Thy sword,
2. God the all-mer-ci-ful! Earth hath for-sak-en Thy way of bless-ed-ness, slighted Thy word;
3. God the all-righteous One! man hath defied Thee, Yet to e-ter-ni-ty standeth Thy word;
4. So shall Thy children, in thankful de-vo-tion, Praise Him who saved them from peril and sword,

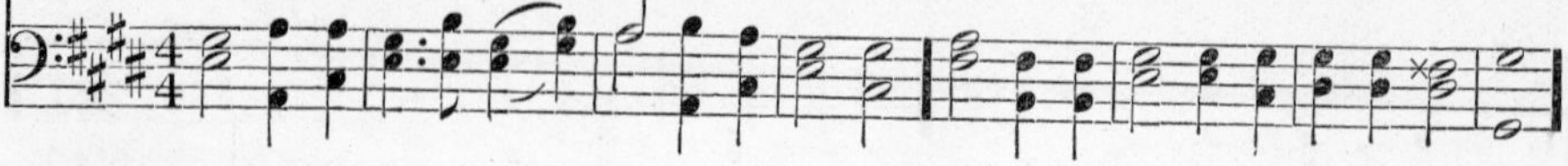

Show forth Thy pit-y on high where Thou reignest, Grant to us peace, O most merci-ful Lord.
Bid not Thy wrath in its ter-rors a-wak-en; Grant to us peace, O most merci-ful Lord.
Falsehood and wrong shall not tarry beside Thee; Grant to us peace, O most merci-ful Lord.
Sing-ing in cho-rus from o-cean to ocean, "Peace to the nations, and praise to the Lord."

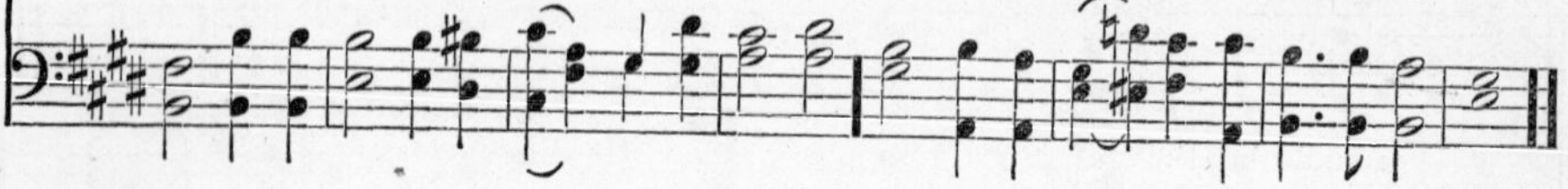

210 Great King of Nations

John Hampden Gurney, 1838 — (*C. M. D.*) — Mendelssohn, Arr. by F. L. Stone

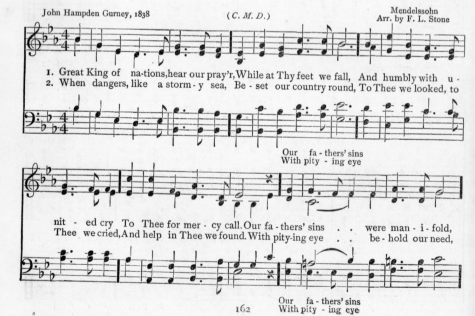

1. Great King of na-tions, hear our pray'r, While at Thy feet we fall, And humbly with u-
2. When dangers, like a storm-y sea, Be-set our country round, To Thee we looked, to

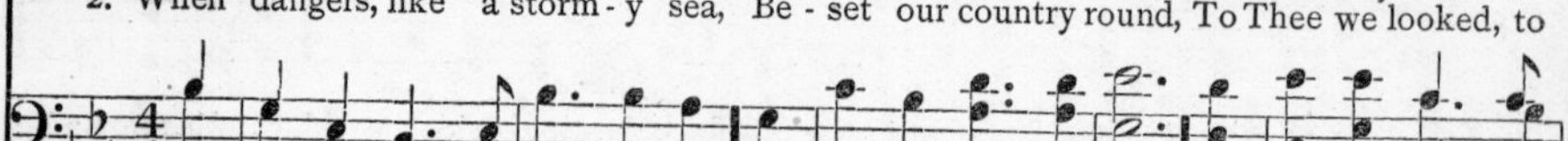

Our fa-thers' sins
With pity-ing eye

nit-ed cry To Thee for mer-cy call. Our fa-thers' sins . . were man-i-fold,
Thee we cried, And help in Thee we found. With pity-ing eye . . be-hold our need,

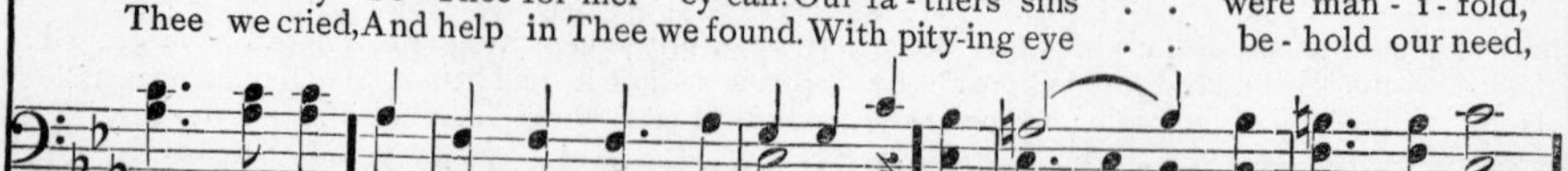

Our fa-thers' sins
With pity-ing eye

Great King of Nations

And ours no less we own; Yet wondrously from age to age Thy goodness hath been shown.
As thus we lift our prayer; Correct us with Thy judgments, Lord, Then let Thy mer-cy spare.

O Lord of Hosts 211

Oliver Wendell Holmes, 1861 (*New Creation L. M.*) Arr. from Haydn

1. O Lord of hosts, al-might - y King, Be - hold the sac - ri - fice we bring;
2. Wake in our breasts the liv - ing fires, The ho - ly faith that warmed our sires:
3. Be Thou a pil-lared flame to show The mid - night snare, the si - lent foe;
4. God of all na-tions, sov - 'reign Lord, In Thy dread name we draw the sword,
5. From treason's rent, from mur - der's stain, Guard Thou its folds till peace shall reign,

To ev - 'ry arm Thy strength im - part; Thy Spir - it shed thro' ev - 'ry heart.
Thy hand hath made our na - tion free; To die for her is serv - ing Thee.
And when the bat - tle thun - ders loud, Still guide us in its mov - ing cloud.
We lift the star - ry flag on high That fills with light our storm - y sky.
Till fort and field, till shore and sea, Join our loud an - them,— praise to Thee.

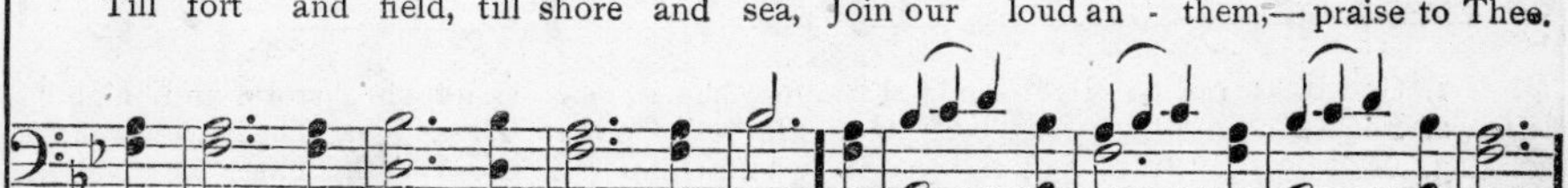

To ev - 'ry arm Thy strength im - part; Thy Spir - it shed thro' ev - 'ry heart.
Thy hand hath made our na - tion free; To die for her is serv - ing Thee.
And when the bat - tle thun - ders loud, Still guide us in its mov - ing cloud.
We lift the star - ry flag on high That fills with light our storm - y sky.
Till fort and field, till shore and sea, Join our loud an - them,— praise to Thee.

212 O Thou, Before Whose Presence

S. J. Stone, 1889 (*Temperance* 7.6.7.6.D.) J. B. Dykes, 1875

1. O Thou, be-fore whose pres-ence Naught e - vil may come in, Yet who dost look in mer - cy Down on this world of sin, O give us no - ble pur - pose To set the sin-bound free, And Christ-like tender pit - y To seek the lost for Thee.
2. Fierce is our sub - tle foe - man: The for - ces at his hand With woes that none can num - ber De - spoil the pleas - ant land; All they who war a - gainst them, In strife so keen and long, Must in their Saviour's ar - mor Be stronger than the strong.

213 God Bless Our Native Land

C. T. Brooks, 1834 (6s.4s) Frank Leslie Stone, 1901

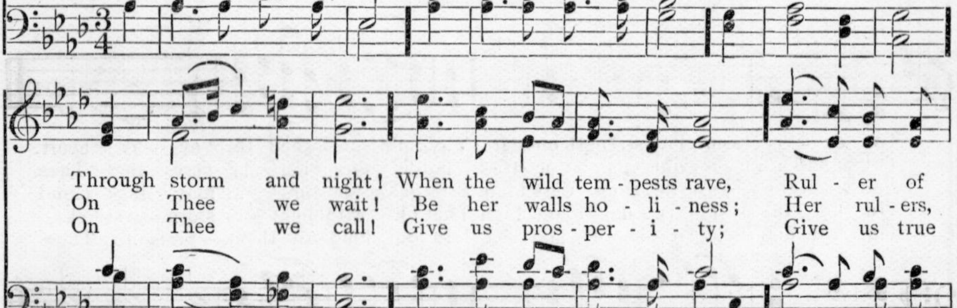
With majesty
1. God bless our na - tive land! Firm may she ev - er stand Thro' storm and night! Through storm and night! When the wild tem - pests rave, Rul - er of
2. For her our pray'rs shall be, Our father's God, to Thee, On Thee we wait! On Thee we wait! Be her walls ho - li - ness; Her rul - ers,
3. Lord of all truth and right, In whom a - lone is might, On Thee we call! On Thee we call! Give us pros - per - i - ty; Give us true

Copyright, 1901, by U. S. C. E.

God Bless Our Native Land

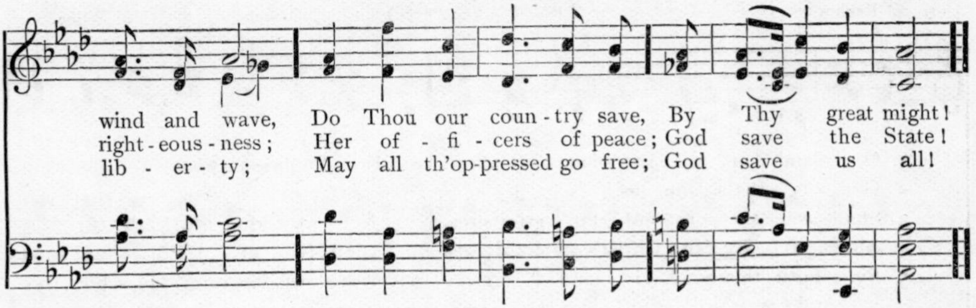
wind and wave, Do Thou our coun-try save, By Thy great might!
right-eous-ness; Her of-fi-cers of peace; God save the State!
lib-er-ty; May all th'op-pressed go free; God save us all!

God of Our Fathers 214

Rudyard Kipling (*Recessional*) Arthur H. Ryder

1. God of our fa-thers, known of old; Lord of our far-flung bat-tle line,
2. The tu-mult and the shout-ing dies; The cap-tains and the kings de-part;
3. If, drunk with sight of power, we loose Wild tongues that have not Thee in awe,
4. For hea-then heart that puts her trust In reek-ing tube and i-ron shard,
Be-neath whose aw-ful hand we hold Do-min-ion o-ver palm and pine;
Still stands Thine an-cient sac-ri-fice, An hum-ble and a con-trite heart.
Such boast-ing as the Gen-tiles use, Or less-er breeds with-out the law;
All val-iant dust that builds on dust, And guard-ing calls not Thee to guard;
Lord God of Hosts, be with us yet, Lest we for-get — lest we for-get.
Lord God of Hosts, be with us yet, Lest we for-get — lest we for-get.
Lord God of Hosts, be with us yet, Lest we for-get — lest we for-get.
For fran-tic boast and fool-ish word, Thy mer-cy on Thy peo-ple, Lord.

215 Fair Freedom's Land

J. E. Rankin (*Watch on the Rhine*) Carl Wilhelm

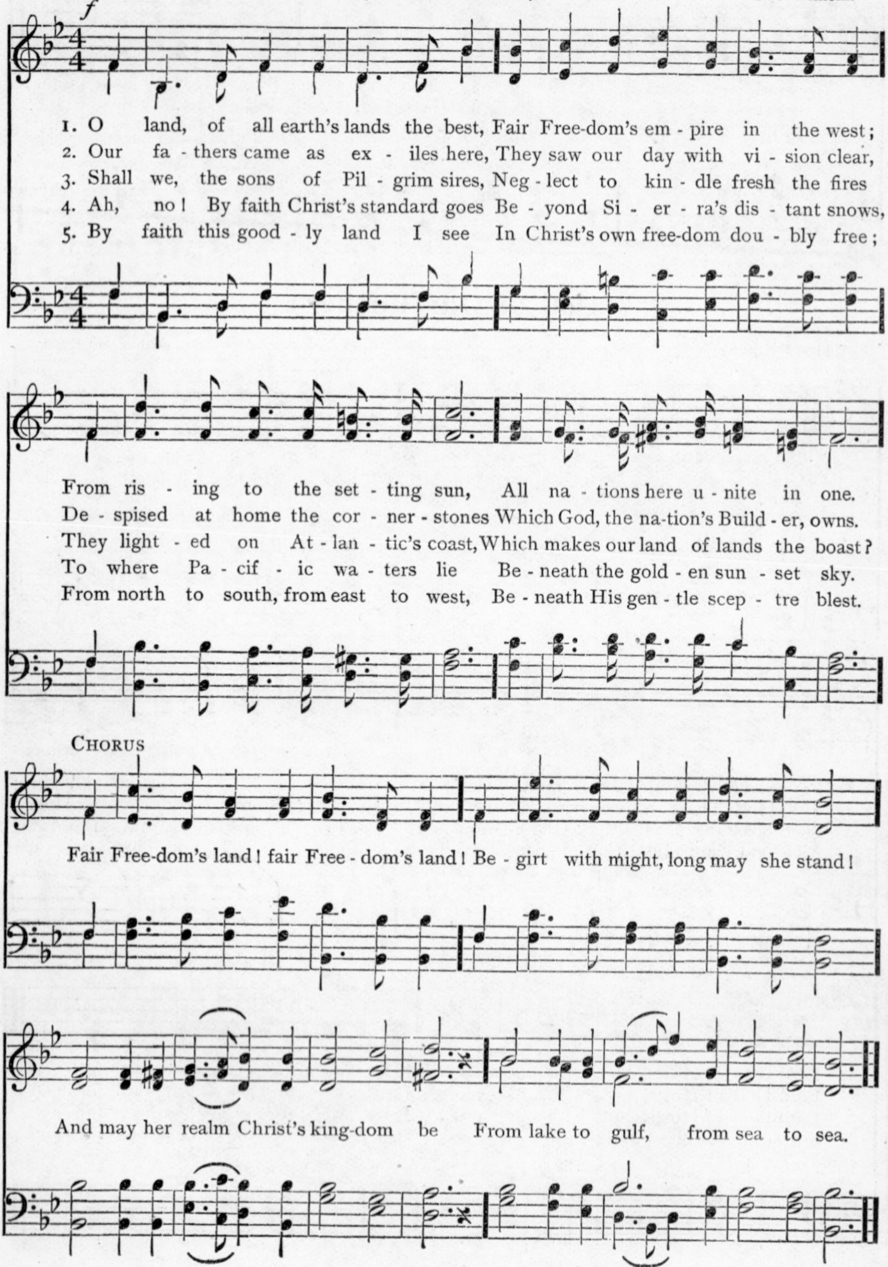
f
1. O land, of all earth's lands the best, Fair Free-dom's em - pire in the west;
2. Our fa - thers came as ex - iles here, They saw our day with vi - sion clear,
3. Shall we, the sons of Pil - grim sires, Neg - lect to kin - dle fresh the fires
4. Ah, no! By faith Christ's standard goes Be - yond Si - er - ra's dis - tant snows,
5. By faith this good - ly land I see In Christ's own free-dom dou - bly free;
From ris - ing to the set - ting sun, All na - tions here u - nite in one.
De - spised at home the cor - ner - stones Which God, the na-tion's Build - er, owns.
They light - ed on At - lan - tic's coast, Which makes our land of lands the boast?
To where Pa - cif - ic wa - ters lie Be - neath the gold - en sun - set sky.
From north to south, from east to west, Be - neath His gen - tle scep - tre blest.
CHORUS
Fair Free-dom's land! fair Free - dom's land! Be - girt with might, long may she stand!
And may her realm Christ's king-dom be From lake to gulf, from sea to sea.

Bless This Our Land

216

John H. Hopkins (*P. M.*) C. O Arnold, 1897

Spirited
ff
1. God of our fa - thers, Bless this our land; O-cean to o - cean
2. Lord God of Sa - ba-oth, Might-y in war, Boundless and num-ber-less
3. Lord God our Sav - iour, Thy love o'er- flows, Mak - ing our wil-der- ness
4. Spir - it of u - ni- ty, Crown of all kings, Find us a rest-ing place
Own - eth Thy hand. Home of all na - tions From far and near,
Thine ar - mies are. Thy right hand conquer - eth All that op -pose;
Bloom as the rose. Thou with true lib - er - ty Mak - est us free,
Un - der Thy wings; By Thine own pres - ence Thy will be done,
Give to u - nite us, Thy faith and fear. God of our fa - thers,
Launch forth Thy thun-der-bolts, Smite down our foes; Lord God of Sa - ba-oth,
Know - ing no mas - ter, No king, but Thee; Lord God our Sav - iour,
Mil - lions of free men Band-ed as one. Lord God al - might - y,
Ben marcato
Fail- ing us nev- er, God of our fa - thers, Be ours for - ev - er.
Fail- ing us nev- er, Lord God of Sa- ba-oth, Fight for us ev - er.
Fail- ing us nev- er, Lord God our Sav - iour, Reign Thou for - ev - er.
Fail- ing us nev- er, Thine be the glo - ry, Now and for - ev - er.

217 Give Courage, Lord

Howard B. Grose, 1901

Ad. from Grieg, for this work

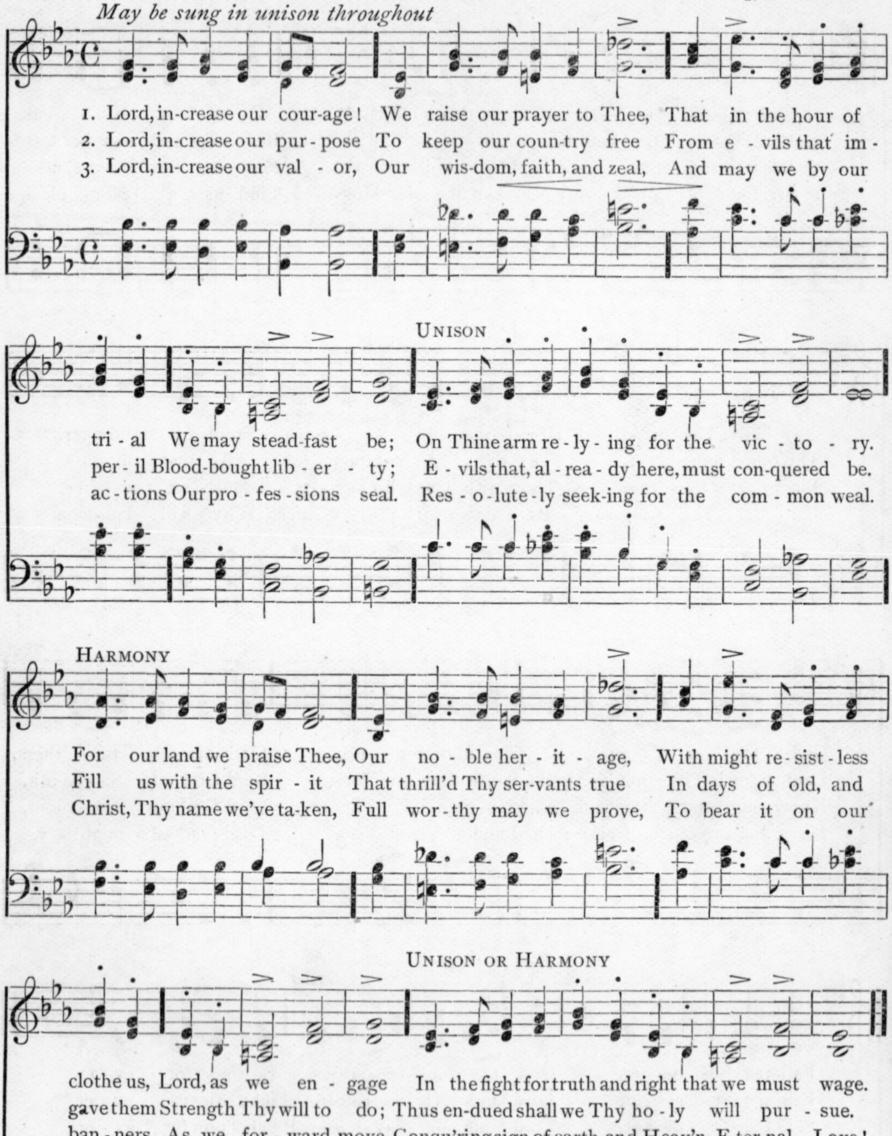
May be sung in unison throughout
1. Lord, in-crease our cour-age! We raise our prayer to Thee, That in the hour of
2. Lord, in-crease our pur-pose To keep our coun-try free From e - vils that im -
3. Lord, in-crease our val - or, Our wis-dom, faith, and zeal, And may we by our
Unison
tri - al We may stead-fast be; On Thine arm re - ly - ing for the vic - to - ry.
per - il Blood-bought lib - er - ty; E - vils that, al - rea - dy here, must con-quered be.
ac - tions Our pro - fes - sions seal. Res - o - lute - ly seek-ing for the com - mon weal.
Harmony
For our land we praise Thee, Our no - ble her - it - age, With might re - sist - less
Fill us with the spir - it That thrill'd Thy ser-vants true In days of old, and
Christ, Thy name we've ta-ken, Full wor - thy may we prove, To bear it on our
Unison or Harmony
clothe us, Lord, as we en - gage In the fight for truth and right that we must wage.
gave them Strength Thy will to do; Thus en-dued shall we Thy ho - ly will pur - sue.
ban - ners, As we for - ward move, Conqu'ring sign of earth and Heav'n, E-ter-nal Love!

Copyright, 1901, words and music, by H. B. Grose

A Mighty Fortress is Our God

218

Tr. F. H. Hedge, 1852 (*Ein' Feste Burg P. M.*) Martin Luther, 1527

1. A mighty - y for - tress is our God, A bul - wark nev- er fail - - ing;
2. Did we in our own strength con - fide, Our striv- ing would be los - - ing;
3. And though this world, with de - mons filled, Should threaten to un - do . . . us,
4. That word a - bove all earth - ly pow'rs, No thanks to them, a - bid - eth;
Our help - er He, a - mid the flood Of mor - tal ills pre - vail - ing.
Were not the right man on our side, The man of God's own choos - ing.
We will not fear, for God hath willed His truth to tri - umph through us.
The Spir - it and the gifts are ours Thro' Him who with us sid - eth.
For still our an- cient foe Doth seek to work us woe; His craft and pow'r are great,
Dost ask who that may be? Christ Je - sus, it is He; Lord Sa -baoth is His name,
The prince of darkness grim, We trem - ble not for him; His rage we can en - dure,
Let goods and kin- dred go, This mor - tal life al - so; The bo - dy they may kill;
And, arm'd with cru - el hate, On earth is not his e - qual.
From age to age the same, And He must win the bat - tle.
For lo! his doom is sure: One lit - tle word shall fell him.
God's truth a - bid - eth still, His king - dom is for - ev - er. A - MEN.

219 Courage, Brother! Do Not Stumble

Norman Macleod, 1857 (*Trusting* 8s. 7s. D.) Sir Arthur Sullivan

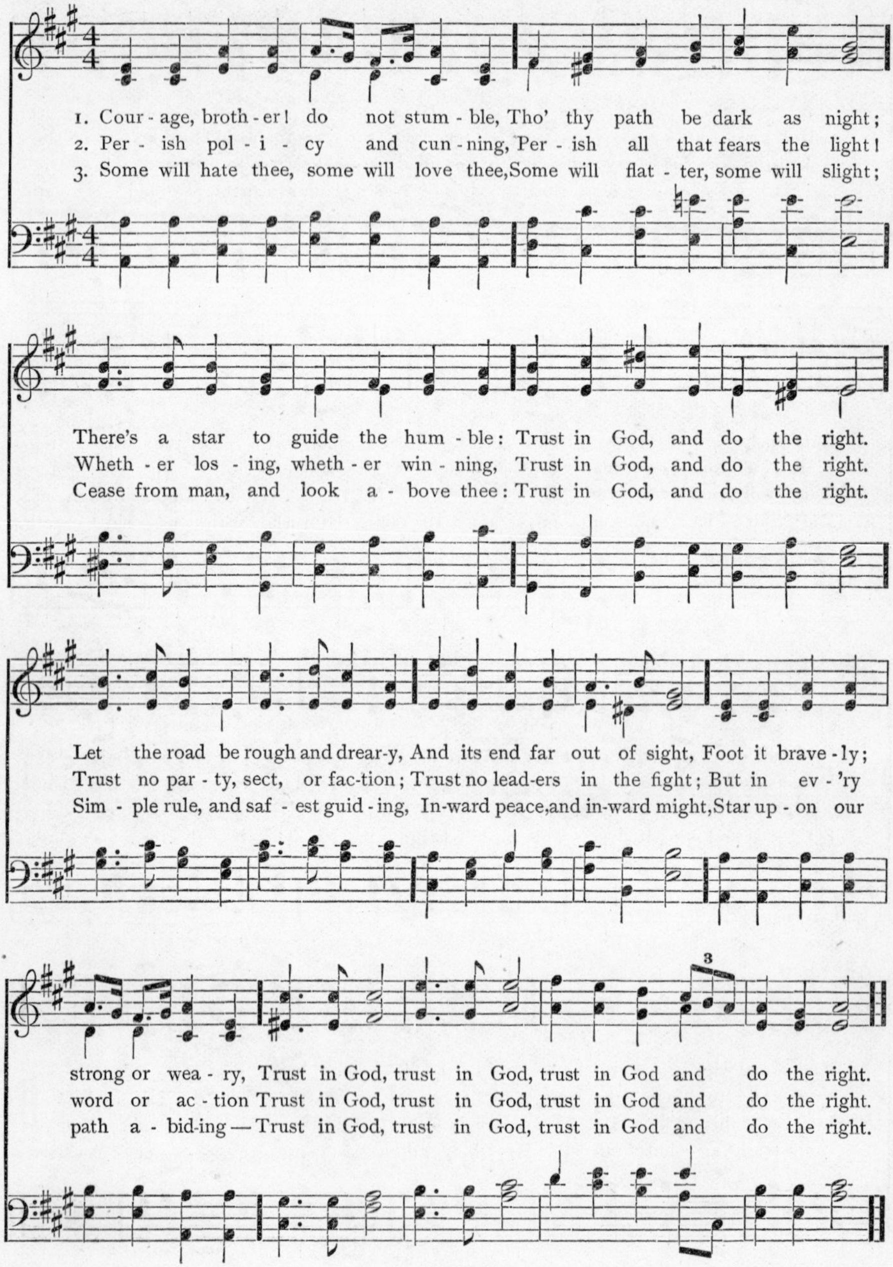
1. Cour - age, broth - er! do not stum - ble, Tho' thy path be dark as night;
2. Per - ish pol - i - cy and cun - ning, Per - ish all that fears the light!
3. Some will hate thee, some will love thee, Some will flat - ter, some will slight;
There's a star to guide the hum - ble: Trust in God, and do the right.
Wheth - er los - ing, wheth - er win - ning, Trust in God, and do the right.
Cease from man, and look a - bove thee: Trust in God, and do the right.
Let the road be rough and drear-y, And its end far out of sight, Foot it brave - ly;
Trust no par - ty, sect, or fac-tion; Trust no lead-ers in the fight; But in ev - 'ry
Sim - ple rule, and saf - est guid - ing, In-ward peace, and in-ward might, Star up - on our
strong or wea - ry, Trust in God, trust in God, trust in God and do the right.
word or ac - tion Trust in God, trust in God, trust in God and do the right.
path a - bid-ing — Trust in God, trust in God, trust in God and do the right.
3

Battle Hymn of the Republic

Julia Ward Howe, 1862

Wm. Steffe, 1855

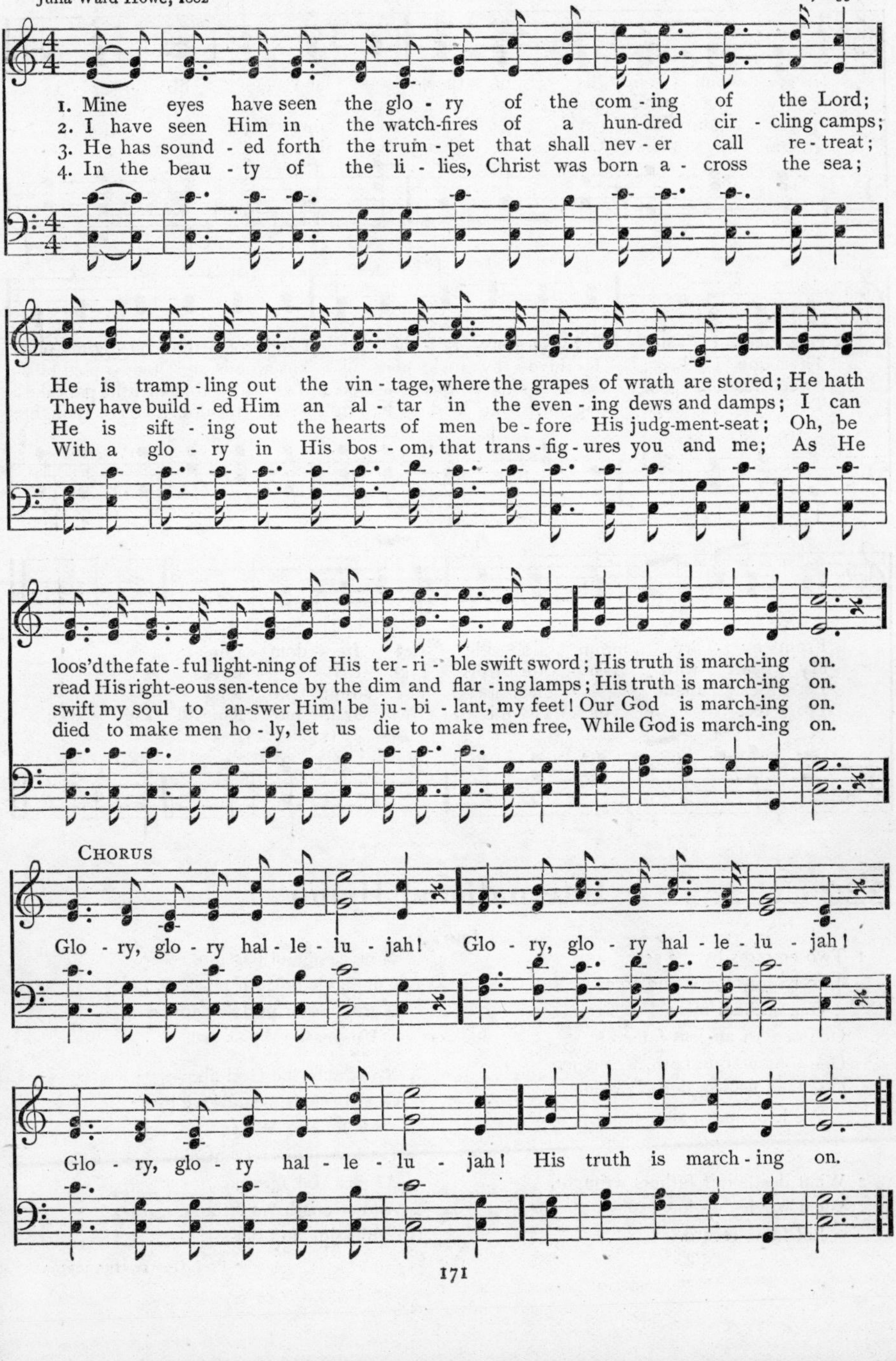
1. Mine eyes have seen the glo - ry of the com - ing of the Lord;
2. I have seen Him in the watch-fires of a hun-dred cir - cling camps;
3. He has sound - ed forth the trum - pet that shall nev - er call re - treat;
4. In the beau - ty of the li - lies, Christ was born a - cross the sea;
He is tramp - ling out the vin - tage, where the grapes of wrath are stored; He hath
They have build - ed Him an al - tar in the even - ing dews and damps; I can
He is sift - ing out the hearts of men be - fore His judg-ment-seat; Oh, be
With a glo - ry in His bos - om, that trans - fig - ures you and me; As He
loos'd the fate - ful light-ning of His ter - ri - ble swift sword; His truth is march-ing on.
read His right-eous sen-tence by the dim and flar - ing lamps; His truth is march-ing on.
swift my soul to an-swer Him! be ju - bi - lant, my feet! Our God is march-ing on.
died to make men ho - ly, let us die to make men free, While God is march-ing on.
CHORUS
Glo - ry, glo - ry hal - le - lu - jah! Glo - ry, glo - ry hal - le - lu - jah!
Glo - ry, glo - ry hal - le - lu - jah! His truth is march - ing on.

221 My Country, 'Tis of Thee

S. F. Smith, 1832 (*America* 6. 6. 4. 6. 6. 6. 4) Harmonia Anglicana, 1744

1. My coun - try, 'tis of thee, Sweet land of lib - er - ty,
2. My na - tive coun - try, thee, Land of the no - ble free,
3. Let mu - sic swell the breeze, And ring from all the trees
4. Our fa - thers' God, to Thee, Au - thor of lib - er - ty,
Of thee I sing; Land where my fa - thers died, Land of the pil - grims' pride,
Thy name I love; I love thy rocks and rills, Thy woods and tem - pled hills;
Sweet freedom's song; Let mor - tal tongues a-wake; Let all that breathe par-take;
To Thee we sing; Long may our land be bright With free-dom's ho - ly light;
From ev - 'ry moun - tain side Let free - dom ring.
My heart with rap - ture thrills Like that a - bove.
Let rocks their si - lence break, The sound pro - long.
Pro - tect us by Thy might, Great God, our King. A - MEN.

222 International Hymn

(*America*)

1 Two empires by the sea,
Two nations great and free,
One anthem raise.
One race of ancient fame,
One tongue, one faith, we claim,
One God whose glorious name
We love and praise.

2 What deeds our fathers wrought,
What battles we have fought,
Let fame record.
Now, vengeful passion, cease,
Come, victories of peace;
Nor hate nor pride's caprice
Unsheathe the sword.

3 Now, may the God above
Guard the dear lands we love;
Or East or West;
Let love more fervent glow,
As peaceful ages go,
And strength yet stronger grow,
Blessing and blest.

Prof. George Huntington

Priceless Treasure 223

Howard B. Grose, 1901 (*Castle Eden 6s. 5s*) R. W. Dixon

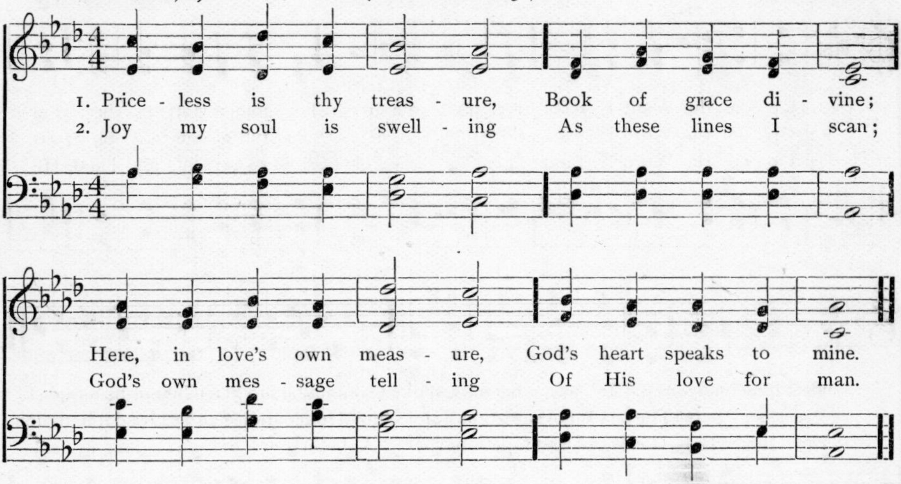
1. Price - less is thy treas - ure, Book of grace di - vine;
2. Joy my soul is swell - ing As these lines I scan;
Here, in love's own meas - ure, God's heart speaks to mine.
God's own mes - sage tell - ing Of His love for man.

Thy Word is Like a Garden, Lord 224

E. Hodder, 1868 (*Grigg C. M.*) Fr. Rippon's Coll., 1806

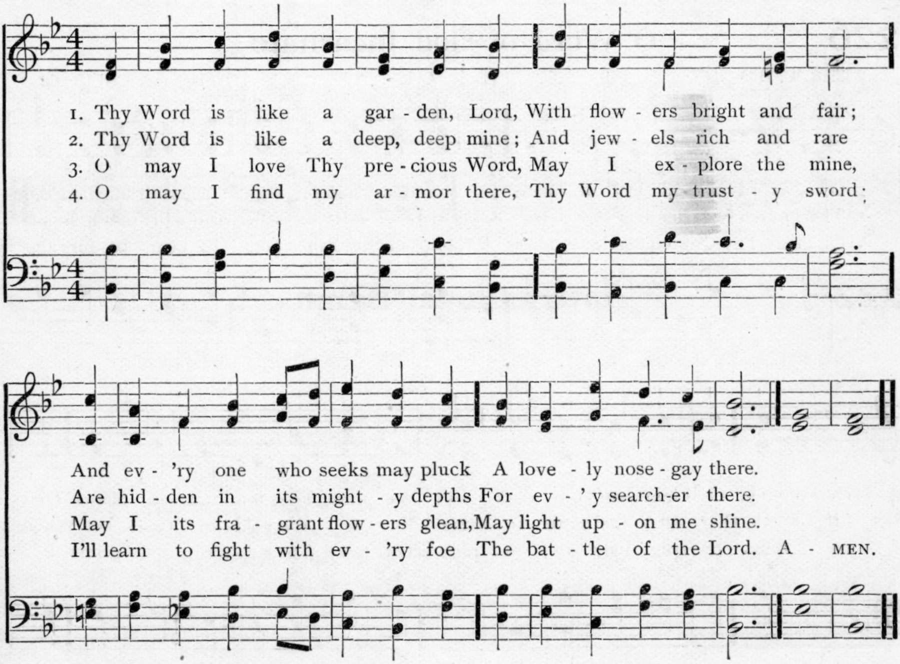
1. Thy Word is like a gar - den, Lord, With flow - ers bright and fair;
2. Thy Word is like a deep, deep mine; And jew - els rich and rare
3. O may I love Thy pre - cious Word, May I ex - plore the mine,
4. O may I find my ar - mor there, Thy Word my trust - y sword;
And ev - 'ry one who seeks may pluck A love - ly nose - gay there.
Are hid - den in its might - y depths For ev - 'y search-er there.
May I its fra - grant flow - ers glean, May light up - on me shine.
I'll learn to fight with ev - 'ry foe The bat - tle of the Lord. A - MEN.

225 The Sure Word

Frances R. Havergal — M. B. Willis, 1901

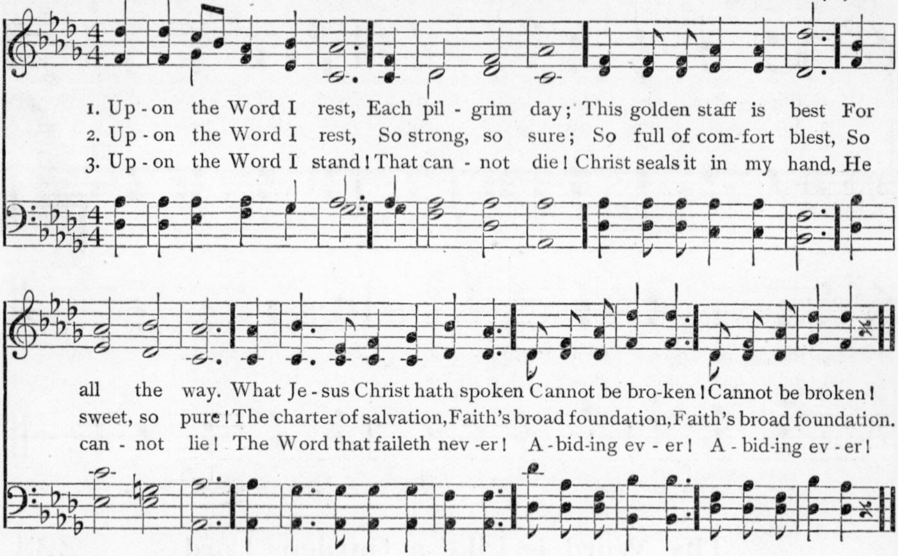
1. Up - on the Word I rest, Each pil - grim day; This golden staff is best For
2. Up - on the Word I rest, So strong, so sure; So full of com-fort blest, So
3. Up - on the Word I stand! That can - not die! Christ seals it in my hand, He
all the way. What Je - sus Christ hath spoken Cannot be bro-ken! Cannot be broken!
sweet, so pure! The charter of salvation, Faith's broad foundation, Faith's broad foundation.
can - not lie! The Word that faileth nev -er! A - bid-ing ev - er! A - bid-ing ev - er!

Copyright, 1901, by U. S. C. E.

226 O Word of God Incarnate

William W. How, 1867 — (*7s. 6s. D.*) — Benjamin Carl Unseld

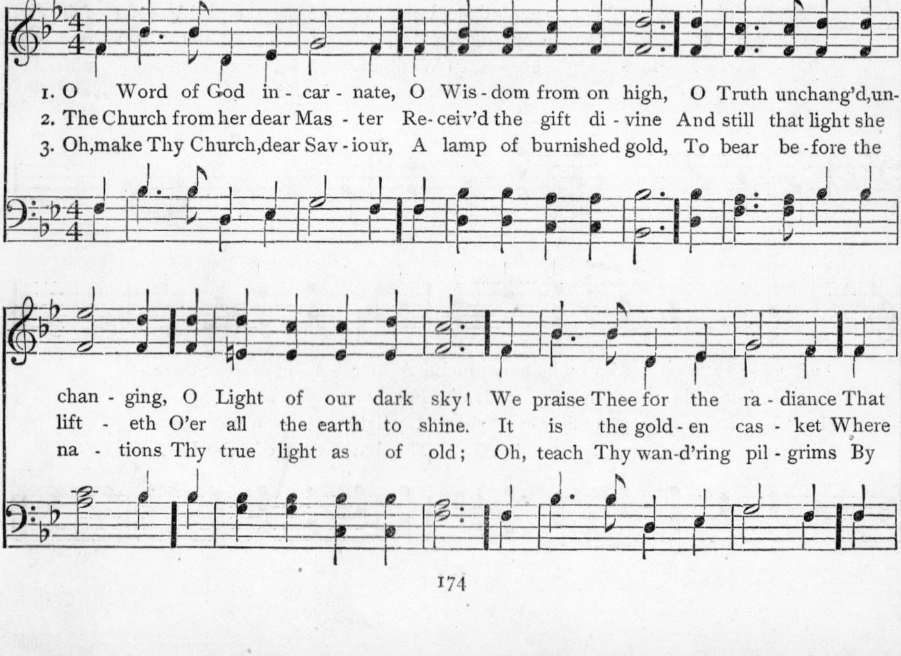
1. O Word of God in - car - nate, O Wis - dom from on high, O Truth unchang'd, un-
2. The Church from her dear Mas - ter Re - ceiv'd the gift di - vine And still that light she
3. Oh, make Thy Church, dear Sav - iour, A lamp of burnished gold, To bear be - fore the
chan - ging, O Light of our dark sky! We praise Thee for the ra - diance That
lift - eth O'er all the earth to shine. It is the gold - en cas - ket Where
na - tions Thy true light as of old; Oh, teach Thy wan-d'ring pil - grims By

O Word of God Incarnate

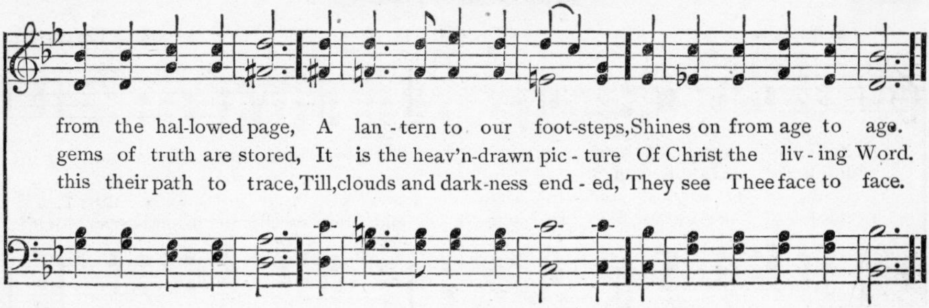
from the hal-lowed page, A lan-tern to our foot-steps, Shines on from age to age.
gems of truth are stored, It is the heav'n-drawn pic-ture Of Christ the liv-ing Word.
this their path to trace, Till, clouds and dark-ness end-ed, They see Thee face to face.

Thy Word, O Lord 227

Albert Midlane, 1834 (*Lux Beata* 10s. 4s) A. L. Peace

1. Thy Word, O Lord, Thy pre-cious Word a-lone, Can lead me on;
2. What-e'er my path, led by the Word, 'tis good, Oh, lead me on!
3. Led by aught else, I tread a de-vious way, Oh, lead me on!
By this, un-til the dark-some night be gone, Lead Thou me on! Thy Word is
Be my poor heart Thy blessed Word's a-bode, Lead Thou me on! Thy Ho-ly
Speak, Lord, and help me ev-er to o-bey, Lead Thou me on! My ev-'ry
light, Thy Word is life and power; By it, oh, guide me in each try-ing hour!
Spir-it gives the light to see, And leads me by Thy Word, close following Thee.
step shall then be well de-fined, And all I do ac-cord-ing to Thy mind.

228 Book of Grace

Thomas Mackellar (*Clyde* 8s. 4) Arr. by Emmelar

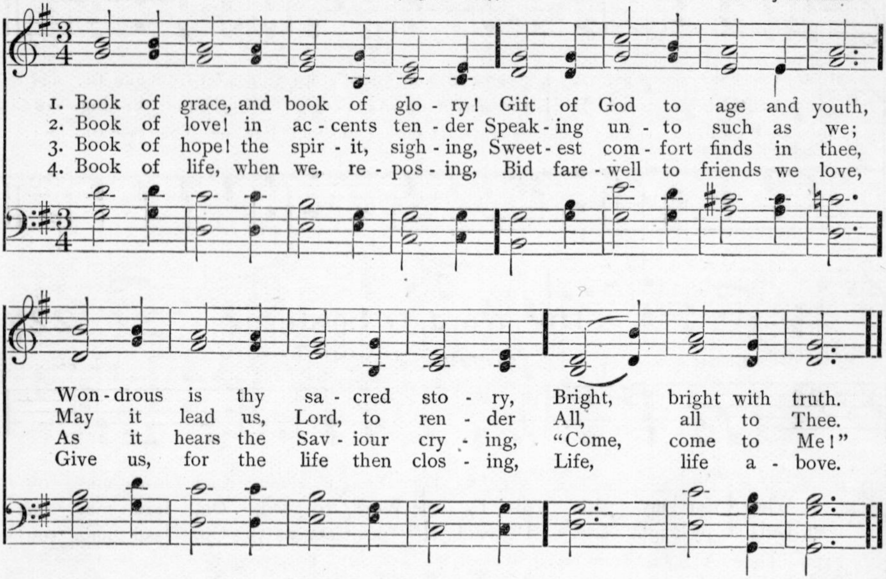
1. Book of grace, and book of glo - ry! Gift of God to age and youth,
2. Book of love! in ac - cents ten - der Speak - ing un - to such as we;
3. Book of hope! the spir - it, sigh - ing, Sweet - est com - fort finds in thee,
4. Book of life, when we, re - pos - ing, Bid fare - well to friends we love,
Won - drous is thy sa - cred sto - ry, Bright, bright with truth.
May it lead us, Lord, to ren - der All, all to Thee.
As it hears the Sav - iour cry - ing, "Come, come to Me!"
Give us, for the life then clos - ing, Life, life a - bove.

229 Upon the Gospel's Sacred Page

John Bowring (*Capello* L. M.) R. Kreutzer

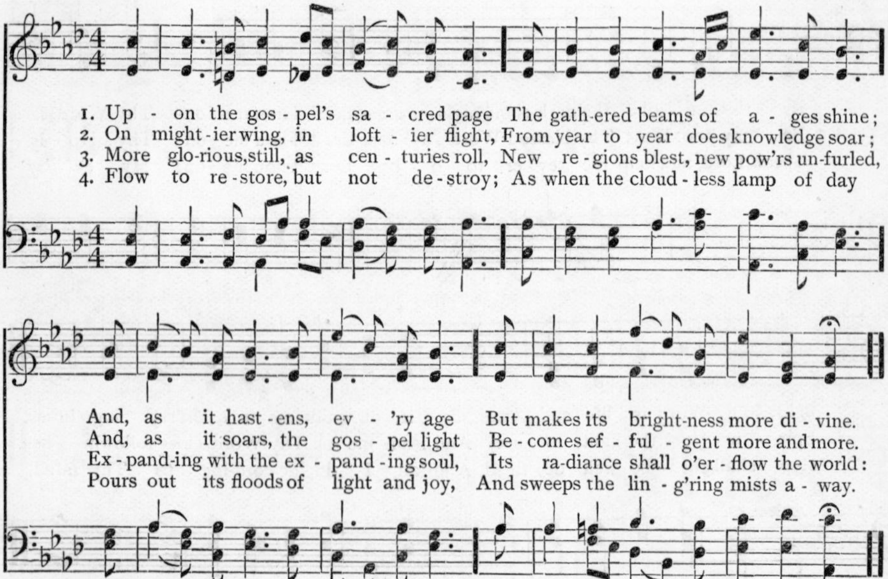
1. Up - on the gos - pel's sa - cred page The gath - ered beams of a - ges shine;
2. On might - ier wing, in loft - ier flight, From year to year does knowledge soar;
3. More glo - rious, still, as cen - turies roll, New re - gions blest, new pow'rs un - furled,
4. Flow to re - store, but not de - stroy; As when the cloud - less lamp of day
And, as it hast - ens, ev - 'ry age But makes its bright - ness more di - vine.
And, as it soars, the gos - pel light Be - comes ef - ful - gent more and more.
Ex - pand - ing with the ex - pand - ing soul, Its ra - diance shall o'er - flow the world:
Pours out its floods of light and joy, And sweeps the lin - g'ring mists a - way.

Light of the World, We Hail Thee

230

(20th Century Ecumenical Hymn of Missions)

J. S. B. Monsell, 1863 — R. Huntington Woodman, 1900

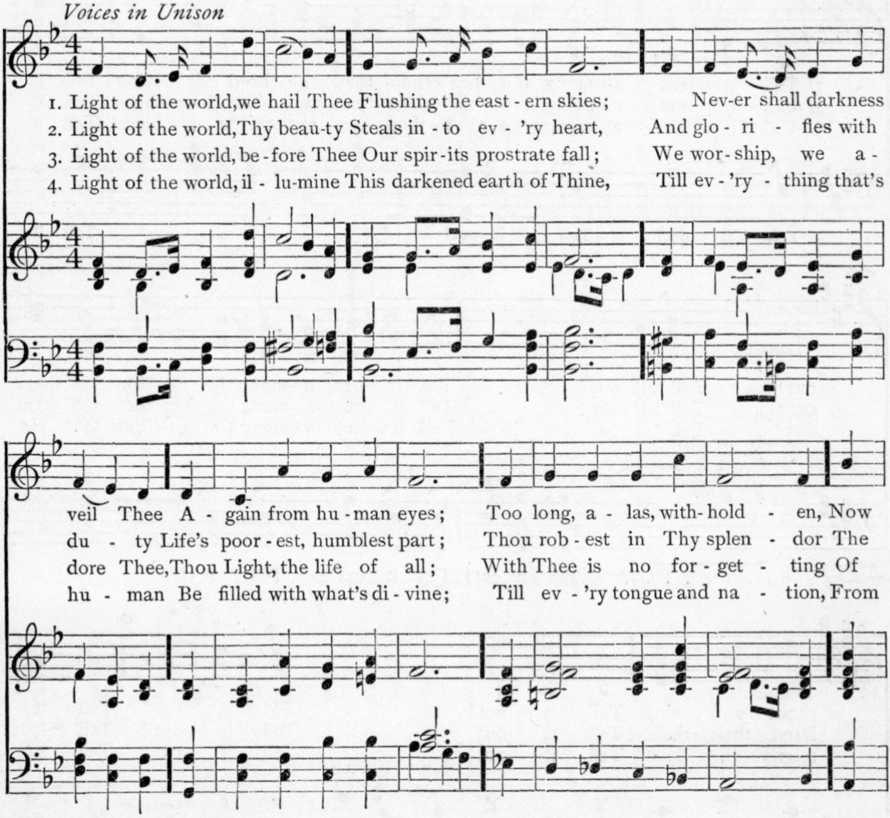
Voices in Unison
1. Light of the world, we hail Thee Flushing the east - ern skies; Nev-er shall darkness
2. Light of the world, Thy beau-ty Steals in - to ev - 'ry heart, And glo - ri - fies with
3. Light of the world, be - fore Thee Our spir - its prostrate fall; We wor - ship, we a -
4. Light of the world, il - lu-mine This darkened earth of Thine, Till ev - 'ry - thing that's
veil Thee A - gain from hu - man eyes; Too long, a - las, with - hold - en, Now
du - ty Life's poor - est, humblest part; Thou rob - est in Thy splen - dor The
dore Thee, Thou Light, the life of all; With Thee is no for - get - ting Of
hu - man Be filled with what's di - vine; Till ev - 'ry tongue and na - tion, From
spread from shore to shore, Thy light, so glad and gold - en, Shall set on earth no more.
sim - ple ways of men, And help - est them to ren - der Light back to Thee a - gain.
all Thine hand hath made; Thy ris - ing hath no set - ting, Thy sunshine hath no shade.
sin's do - min - ion free, Rise in the new cre - a - tion Which springs from Love and Thee.

Copyright, 1900, by S. M. Travis. Used by per.

231 Tell It Out

(*P. M.*)

F. R. H. — Frances R. Havergal

1. Tell it out a-mong the hea-then that the Lord is King! Tell it out! Tell it out!
2. Tell it out a-mong the na-tions that the Sav-iour reigns! Tell it out! Tell it out!
3. Tell it out a-mong the hea-then, Je-sus reigns a-bove! Tell it out! Tell it out!
Tell it out! Tell it out!
Tell it out! Tell it out!........
Tell it out! Tell it out! Tell it out!
Tell it out a-mong the na-tions, bid them shout and sing! Tell it out!
Tell it out a-mong the hea-then, bid them burst their chains! Tell it out!
Tell it out a-mong the na-tions that He reigns in love! Tell it out!
Tell it out!
Tell it out! Tell it out with ad-o-ra-tion that He shall increase, That the might-y King of
Tell it out! Tell it out a-mong the weep-ing ones that Je-sus lives! Tell it out a-mong the
Tell it out! Tell it out a-mong the high-ways and the lanes at home; Let it ring a-cross the
Tell........ it out! Tell it
out!..................... He shall in-crease,
out!..................... that Je-sus lives!
out!..................... the lanes at home;

Tell It Out

Glo - ry is the King of Peace. Tell it out with ju - bi - la - tion, tho' the
wea - ry ones what rest He gives; Tell it out a - mong the sin - ners that He
mountains and the o - cean foam! Like the sound of ma - ny wa - ters let our
waves may roar, That He sit - teth on the wa - ter- floods, our King for ev - er - more!
came to save, Tell it out a - mong the dy - ing that He triumphed o'er the grave.
glad shout be, Till it ech - o and re - ech - o from the is - lands of the sea!
CHORUS
Tell it out a - mong the hea - then that the Lord is King! Tell it
Tell it out! Tell it out! Tell it
out! Tell it out! Tell it out! a - mong the na - tions, bid them
Tell it out! . . . Tell it out!
out! . . . . Tell it out! Tell it out! Tell it out!
shout and sing! Tell it out! Tell it out!
Tell it out!
Tell . . . . it out!

232 Hail to the Lord's Anointed

James Montgomery, 1821 (*St. Anselm 7s. 6s. D.*) Sir Joseph Barnby, 1868

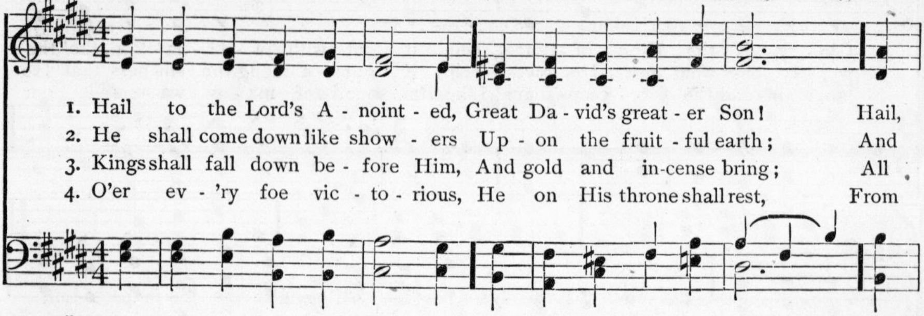
1. Hail to the Lord's A - noint - ed, Great Da - vid's great - er Son! Hail,
2. He shall come down like show - ers Up - on the fruit - ful earth; And
3. Kings shall fall down be - fore Him, And gold and in-cense bring; All
4. O'er ev - 'ry foe vic - to - rious, He on His throne shall rest, From

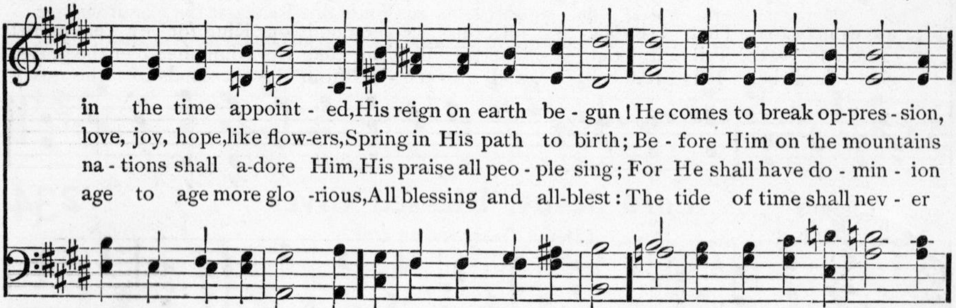
in the time appoint - ed, His reign on earth be - gun! He comes to break op-pres - sion,
love, joy, hope, like flow-ers, Spring in His path to birth; Be - fore Him on the mountains
na - tions shall a-dore Him, His praise all peo - ple sing; For He shall have do - min - ion
age to age more glo - rious, All blessing and all-blest: The tide of time shall nev - er

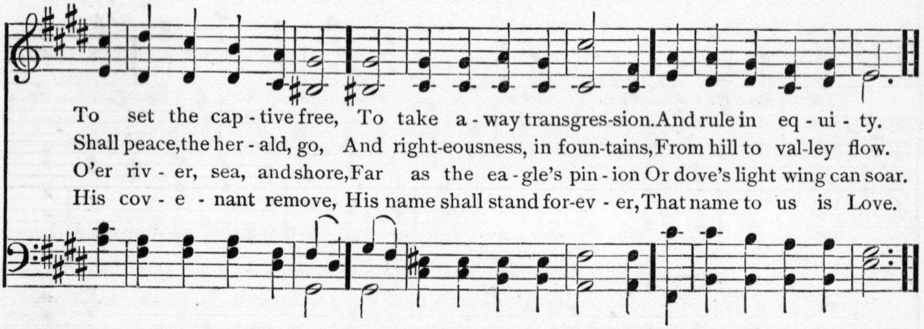
To set the cap - tive free, To take a - way transgres-sion, And rule in eq - ui - ty.
Shall peace, the her - ald, go, And right-eousness, in foun-tains, From hill to val-ley flow.
O'er riv - er, sea, and shore, Far as the ea - gle's pin - ion Or dove's light wing can soar.
His cov - e - nant remove, His name shall stand for-ev - er, That name to us is Love.

233 Our Country's Voice is Pleading

Mrs. M. F. Anderson, 1848 (*7. 6. 7. 6. D.*)

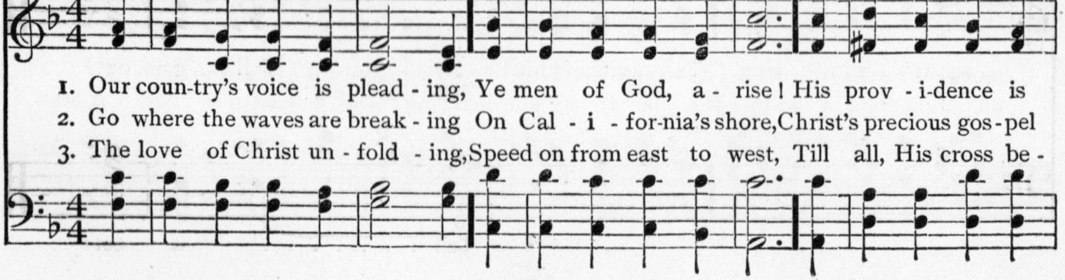
1. Our coun-try's voice is plead - ing, Ye men of God, a - rise! His prov - i-dence is
2. Go where the waves are break - ing On Cal - i - for-nia's shore, Christ's precious gos - pel
3. The love of Christ un - fold - ing, Speed on from east to west, Till all, His cross be -

Our Country's Voice is Pleading

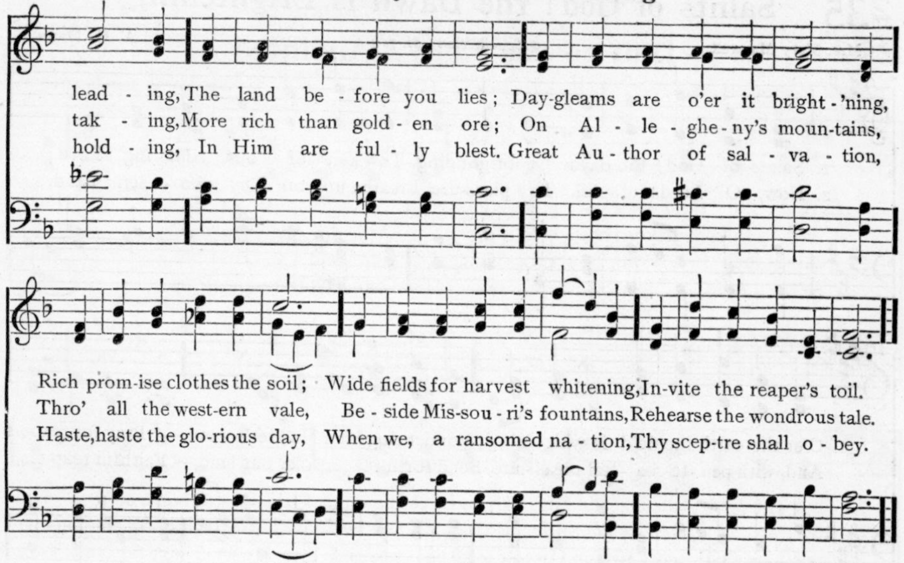
lead - ing, The land be - fore you lies; Day-gleams are o'er it bright - 'ning,
tak - ing, More rich than gold - en ore; On Al - le - ghe - ny's moun-tains,
hold - ing, In Him are ful - ly blest. Great Au - thor of sal - va - tion,
Rich prom-ise clothes the soil; Wide fields for harvest whitening, In-vite the reaper's toil.
Thro' all the west-ern vale, Be - side Mis-sou - ri's fountains, Rehearse the wondrous tale.
Haste, haste the glo-rious day, When we, a ransomed na - tion, Thy scep-tre shall o - bey.

Lord Jesus, Blessed Giver

234

Amos R. Wells

(*Union Square* 7s. 6s. 8l)

J. B. Dykes, 1872

1. Lord Je - sus, bless - ed Giv - er, We give of Thine to Thee; Thy gifts are like a
2. O give us of Thy spir - it That joys to give its all; Thy voice — O when we
riv - er, Full - flow - ing, wide, and free. So let our love, out - go - ing A -
hear it May we o - bey its call. That voice whose call is plead - ing From
mong the sons of men, Thy strength and joy be-stow-ing, Return Thy gifts a-gain.
na - tions far a - way — We hear it, we are heed-ing; Lord, help us to o - bey. A-MEN.

235 Saints of God! the Dawn is Brightening

Mrs. Mary Maxwell — (*Benediction* 8s. 7s) — A. H. Mann

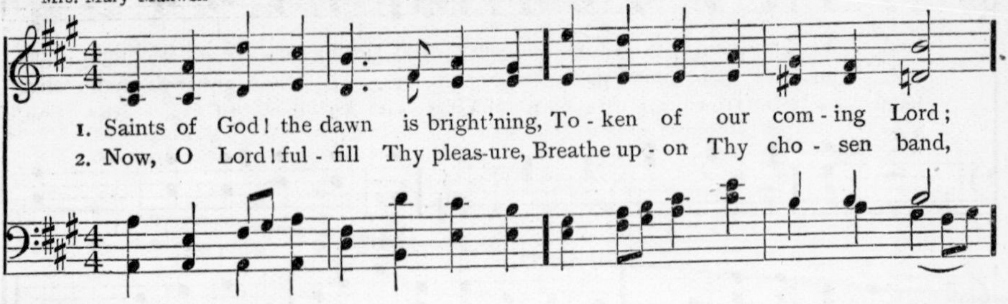
1. Saints of God! the dawn is bright'ning, To - ken of our com - ing Lord;
2. Now, O Lord! ful - fill Thy pleas-ure, Breathe up - on Thy cho - sen band,

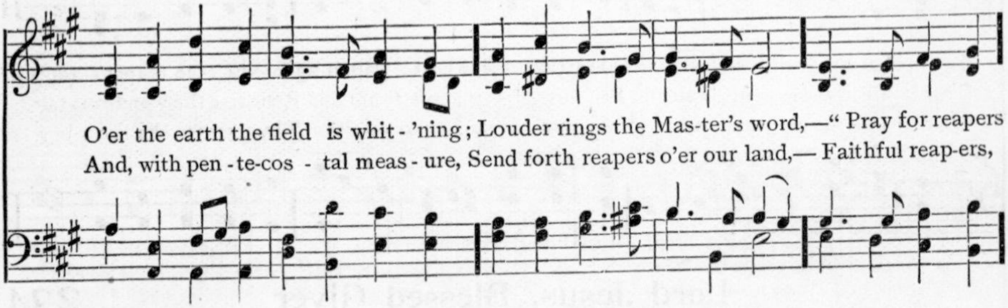
O'er the earth the field is whit - 'ning; Louder rings the Mas-ter's word,—" Pray for reapers
And, with pen - te-cos - tal meas - ure, Send forth reapers o'er our land,— Faithful reap-ers,

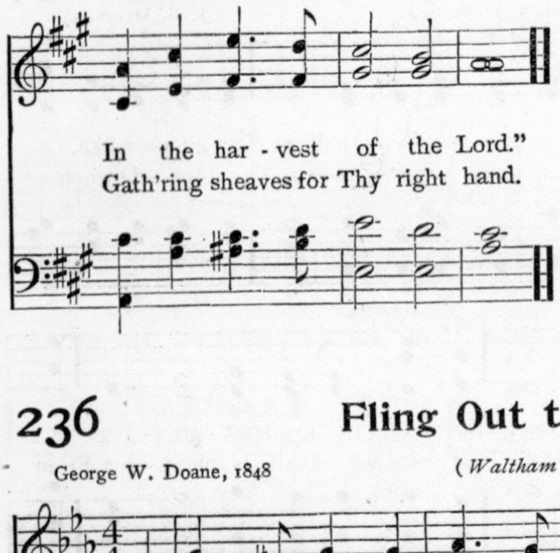
In the har - vest of the Lord."
Gath'ring sheaves for Thy right hand.

3 Broad the shadow of our nation,
Eager millions hither roam;
Lo! they wait for Thy salvation;
Come, Lord Jesus! quickly come!
By Thy Spirit,
Bring Thy ransomed people home.

4 Soon shall end the time of weeping,
Soon the reaping time will come,—
Heaven and earth together keeping
God's eternal harvest home:
Saints and angels!
Shout the world's great harvest home.

236 Fling Out the Banner

George W. Doane, 1848 — (*Waltham* L. M.) — J. B. Calkin, 1872

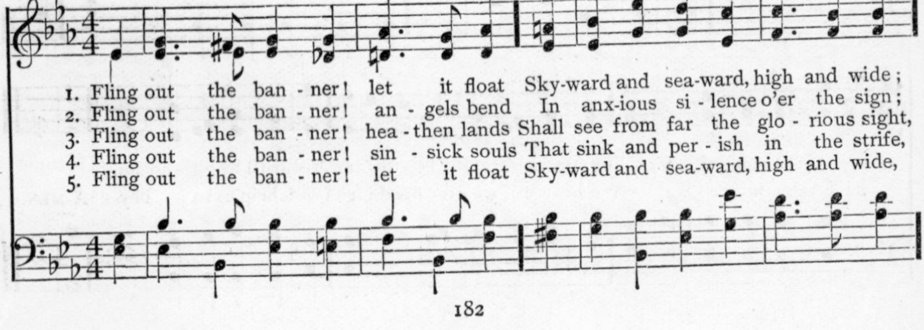
1. Fling out the ban - ner! let it float Sky-ward and sea-ward, high and wide;
2. Fling out the ban - ner! an - gels bend In anx-ious si - lence o'er the sign;
3. Fling out the ban - ner! hea - then lands Shall see from far the glo - rious sight,
4. Fling out the ban - ner! sin - sick souls That sink and per - ish in the strife,
5. Fling out the ban - ner! let it float Sky-ward and sea-ward, high and wide,

Fling Out the Banner

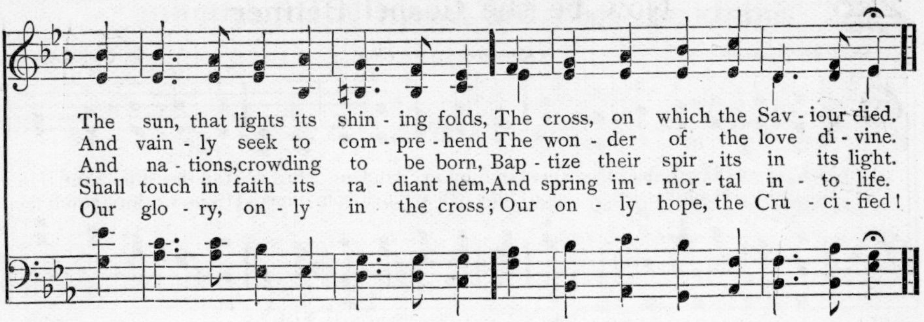
The sun, that lights its shin - ing folds, The cross, on which the Sav - iour died.
And vain - ly seek to com - pre - hend The won - der of the love di - vine.
And na - tions,crowding to be born, Bap - tize their spir - its in its light.
Shall touch in faith its ra - diant hem,And spring im - mor - tal in - to life.
Our glo - ry, on - ly in the cross; Our on - ly hope, the Cru - ci - fied!

The Morning Light is Breaking 237

S. F. Smith (7s. 6s. D.) George J. Webb

1. The morn - ing light is break - ing; The dark-ness dis - ap - pears; The sons of earth are
2. Rich dews of grace come o'er us In ma - ny a gen - tle show'r, And bright - er scenes be -
3. See hea - then na-tions bend-ing Be - fore the God we love, And thou-sand hearts as -
4. Blest riv - er of sal - va - tion! Pur - sue thine on-ward way; Flow thou to ev - 'ry
wak - ing To pen - i - ten - tial tears; Each breeze that sweeps the o - cean
fore us Are op - 'ning ev - 'ry hour; Each cry to heav - en go - ing,
cend - ing In grat - i - tude a - bove; While sin - ners, now con - fess - ing,
na - tion, Nor in thy rich - ness stay: Stay not till all the low - ly
Brings tid-ings from a - far,.. Of na - tions in com - mo - tion Pre-pared for Zi - on's war.
A - bun-dant an-swer brings, And heav'nly gales are blow-ing, With peace up-on their wings.
The gos - pel call o - bey, And seek the Saviour's blessing, A na - tion in a day.
Tri - umphant reach their home: Stay not till all the ho - ly Pro-claim "The Lord is come!"

238 Now be the Gospel Banner

Thos. Hastings, 1828 (*Excelsior* 7s. 6s. 12l.) E. C. Rowley

1. Now be the gos-pel ban - ner In ev -'ry land un - furl'd, And be the shout, "Ho -
2. What tho' th' em-battled le - gions Of earth and hell com - bine? His pow'r, throughout their
Unison
san - na!" Re - ech - oed thro' the world; Till ev -'ry isle and na - tion,
re - gions, Shall soon re - splen - dent shine. Ride on, O Lord, vic - to - rious,
Harmony
Till ev -'ry tribe and tongue, Re-ceive the great sal-va - tion, And join the happy throng.
Im - manuel, Prince of peace; Thy triumph shall be glorious, Thine empire still in - crease.
And join the happy throng.
Thine em - pire still increase.
Refrain
Now be the gos - pel ban - ner In ev -'ry land un - furl'd, And be the shout, "Ho -
What tho' th'em-battled le - gions Of earth and hell com-bine? His pow'r, throughout their

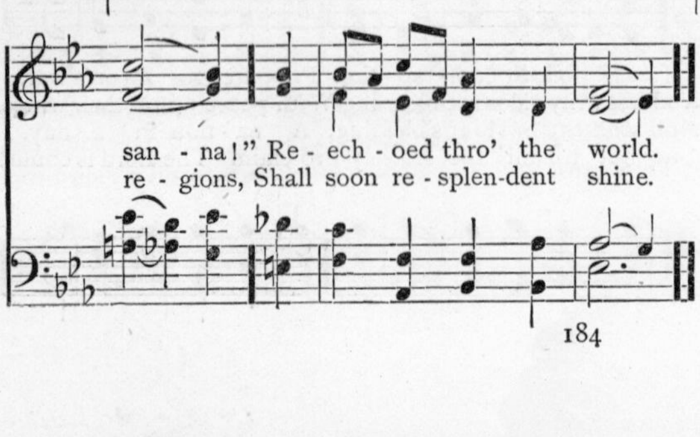
san - na!" Re - ech - oed thro' the world.
re - gions, Shall soon re - splen-dent shine.

3 Yes, Thou shalt reign forever,
O Jesus, King of kings:
Thy light, Thy love, Thy favor,
Each ransomed captive sings.
The isles for Thee are waiting,
The deserts learn Thy praise,
The hills and valleys, greeting,
The song responsive raise.
CHO. Yes, Thou shalt, etc.

Christians, Up! the Day is Breaking 239

E. S. Porter, 1846 (*Hemy* 8s. 7s. D.) H. F. Hemy

1. Chris-tians, up! the day is break-ing, Gird your read - y arm - or on; Slumb'ring hosts a -
2. Hark! un-num-bered voi-ces cry-ing, "Save us, or we droop and die!" Suc-cor bear the
3. See the blest mil-len-nial dawning! Bright the beams of Bethlehem's star; Eastern lands, be-
round are wak - ing, Rouse ye! in the Lord be strong! While ye sleep or i - dly lin - ger,
faint and dy - ing, On the wings of mer - cy fly: Lead them to the crys - tal foun-tain
hold the morn - ing; Lo! it glim-mers from a - far: O'er the moun-tain-top as-cend-ing,
Thou - sands sink, with none to save; Hasten! Time's un-err-ing finger Points to many an o-pen grave.
Gush - ing with the streams of life; Guide them to the shelt'ring mountain, For the gale with death is rife.
Soon the scattered light shall rise, Till, in radiant glory blending, Heav'n's high noon shall greet our eyes.

Heal Me, O My Saviour, Heal 240

Godfrey Thring W. H. Monk

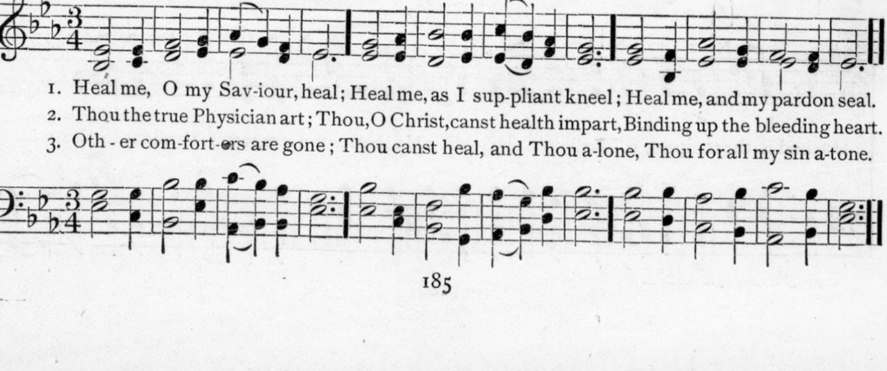
1. Heal me, O my Sav-iour, heal; Heal me, as I sup-pliant kneel; Heal me, and my pardon seal.
2. Thou the true Physician art; Thou, O Christ, canst health impart, Binding up the bleeding heart.
3. Oth - er com-fort-ers are gone; Thou canst heal, and Thou a-lone, Thou for all my sin a-tone.

241 When Winds are Raging

Harriet Beecher Stowe. Ref. by H. G. (*Oberland P. M.*) Arr. fr. Swiss Melody

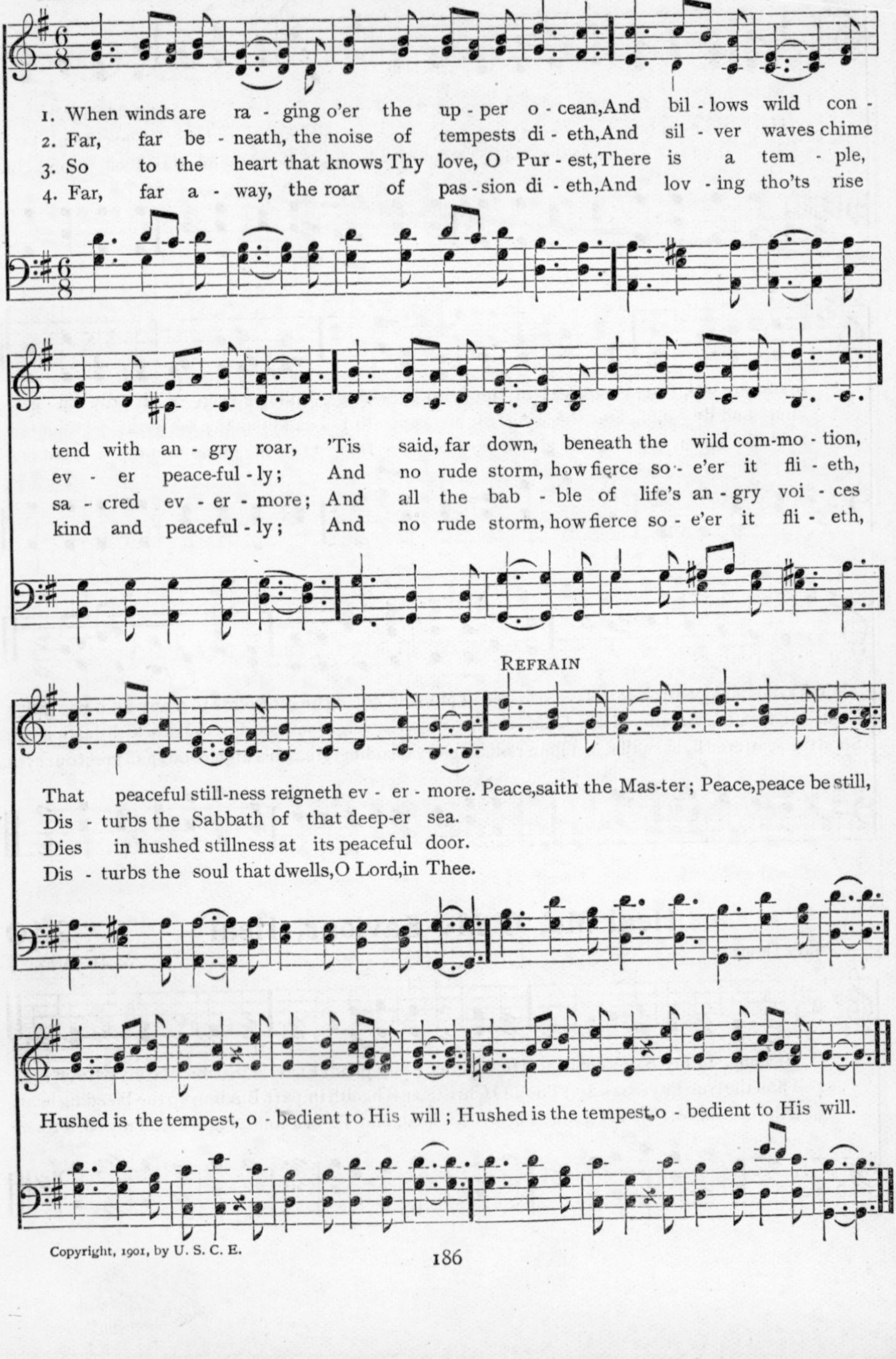
1. When winds are ra - ging o'er the up - per o - cean, And bil - lows wild con -
2. Far, far be - neath, the noise of tempests di - eth, And sil - ver waves chime
3. So to the heart that knows Thy love, O Pur - est, There is a tem - ple,
4. Far, far a - way, the roar of pas - sion di - eth, And lov - ing tho'ts rise
tend with an - gry roar, 'Tis said, far down, beneath the wild com-mo - tion,
ev - er peace-ful - ly; And no rude storm, how fierce so - e'er it fli - eth,
sa - cred ev - er - more; And all the bab - ble of life's an - gry voi - ces
kind and peaceful - ly; And no rude storm, how fierce so - e'er it fli - eth,
REFRAIN
That peaceful still-ness reigneth ev - er - more. Peace, saith the Mas-ter; Peace, peace be still,
Dis - turbs the Sabbath of that deep-er sea.
Dies in hushed stillness at its peaceful door.
Dis - turbs the soul that dwells, O Lord, in Thee.
Hushed is the tempest, o - bedient to His will; Hushed is the tempest, o - bedient to His will.

Copyright, 1901, by U. S. C. E.

I Have Heard of a Saviour's Love 242

Air by Wherahiko Rawei, Maori Evangelist

As sung by Rawei

1. I have heard of a Sav - iour's love, And a won - der - ful love it must be; But
2. I have heard how He suffered and bled, How He languished and died on the tree; But
3. I've been told of a heav-en on high, Which the children of Je - sus shall see; But
did He come down from a - bove Out of love and com-pas-sion for me?
oh, is it a - ny - where said That He languished and suf-fered for me?
is there a place in the sky Made rea - dy and furnished for me?
CHORUS
Yes, oh, yes, out of love and com-pas - sion for me, Yes, oh, yes, He
suffered and died on the tree. Yes, oh, yes, out of love and com-pas - sion for
pp
me, . . Yes, oh, yes, . . He suf - fered and died on the tree. .

243 The Sinner and the Song*

Will L. Thompson

SOLO
1. A sin - ner was wand'ring at e - ven - tide, The Temp - ter was watch - ing close by at his side, In his heart raged a bat - tle for right a - gainst wrong; But hark! from the church he hears the sweet song:—
2. He lin - gered and lis - tened to ev - 'ry sweet chord; He re-member'd the time he once lov'd the Lord. "Come on," says the Tempter, "come on with the throng;" But hark! from the church a - gain swells the song:
QUARTET OR CHORUS
To be sung very softly
D.C. for second verse.
Je - sus, lov - er of my soul, Let me to Thy bos - om fly.
While the bil - lows near me roll, While the tem - pest still is high.

* This piece may be made very effective by having the portion arranged for quartet or chorus sung by a choir in an adjoining room.

By permission of Will L. Thompson, East Liverpool, Ohio.

EVANGELISTIC

The Sinner and the Song

SOLO
3. Oh, Tempter, de - part, I have serv'd thee too long, I fly to the Saviour, He dwells in that
song. Oh, Lord, can it be that a sinner like me, May find a sure refuge by coming to Thee?
QUARTET OR CHORUS
To be sung very softly
Oth - er ref - uge have I none, Hangs my help- less soul on Thee.
SOLO
CHORUS
pp
I come, Lord, I come, Thou'lt forgive the dark past, And Oh, re-ceive my soul at last. .

244 For You and for Me

W. L. T. (*11. 7. 11. 7. with Refrain*) Will L. Thompson, 1880

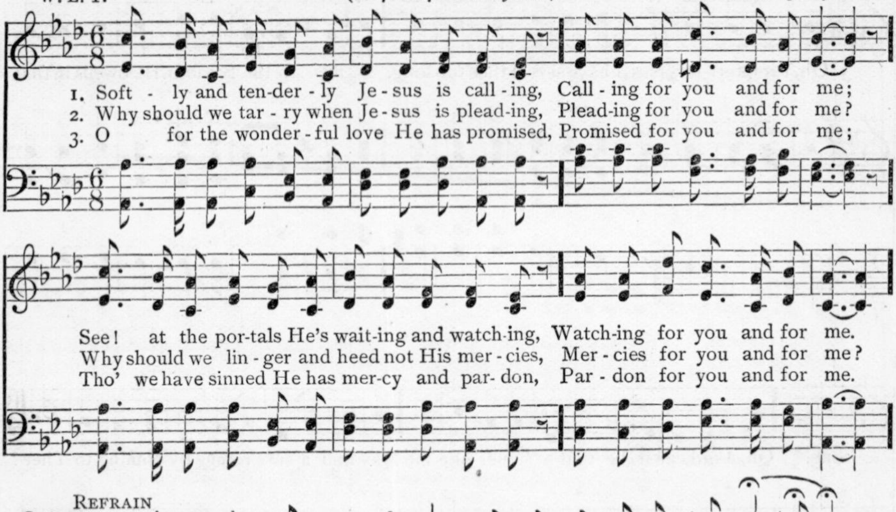
1. Soft - ly and ten-der - ly Je - sus is call - ing, Call - ing for you and for me;
2. Why should we tar - ry when Je - sus is plead-ing, Plead-ing for you and for me?
3. O for the wonder - ful love He has promised, Promised for you and for me;
See! at the por-tals He's wait-ing and watch-ing, Watch-ing for you and for me.
Why should we lin - ger and heed not His mer - cies, Mer - cies for you and for me?
Tho' we have sinned He has mer - cy and par - don, Par - don for you and for me.
REFRAIN
Come home, . Come home, . . Ye who are wea-ry, come home; .
Come home,
Come home,
Ear-nest - ly, ten-der-ly, Je - sus is call-ing, Call-ing, "O sin-ner, come home!" A - MEN.

Copyright by Will L. Thompson & Co. Used by per.

245 God from on High

C. Coffin, 1676 F. Spinney

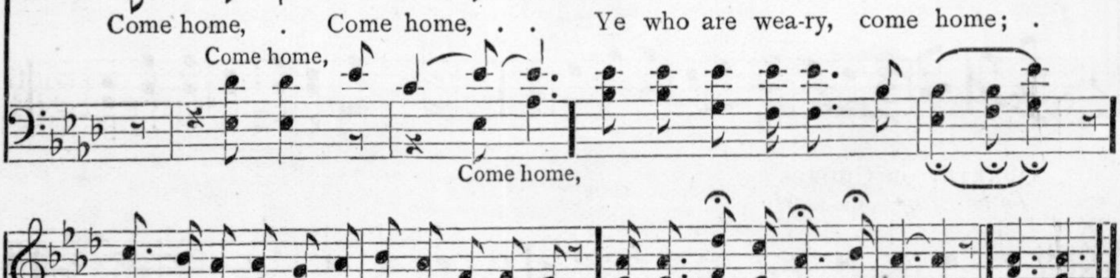
God from on high hath heard! Let sighs and sorrows cease; The skies unfold, and lo! Descends the gift of peace!

Oh, to be More Like Jesus

Not too fast

Words and music by Will L. Thompson

1. Oh, to be more like Je - sus, Oh, to have more of His love; . Deep in my heart,
2. Oh, to be more like Je - sus, Help-ing the fall-en to rise; . . Giv-ing a hand,
His love;
to rise;
Filling my soul, From the great heart above. Jesus came loving and cheering, Giv-ing the
Bidding to stand, Firm in the faith we prize. Cheering the broken heart-ed, Wip-ing a -
hun - gry food, . . Helping the poor and need - y, Je-sus was kind and good.
way their tears, . . Comforting ma-ny in sor - row, Banishing doubts and fears.
pp
the hun - gry food, Helping the need - y,
a - way their tears, Com-forting sor - row,
CHORUS
Oh, to be more like Je - sus, Guid-ing the sin-ner a - bove; Nev - er cease trying,

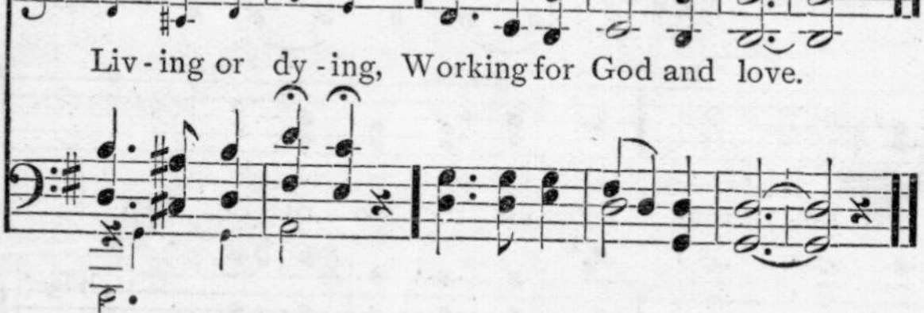
Liv - ing or dy - ing, Working for God and love.

3 Oh, to be more like Jesus,
Merciful, loving, and kind;
Leading the way,
Bright'ning the day,
Helping the lame and blind.
Jesus came saving the fallen,
Helping them sin o'ercome,
Rescuing perishing sinners,
Bringing the wayward home.

By permission of Will L. Thompson, East Liverpool, Ohio.

247 Tell Me the Story of Jesus

N. W. F.

Nellie Whipple Fawcett

1. Tell me the story of Jesus, Who left His throne on high, Who came to earth to suffer, Upon the cross to die.
2. Tell me the story of Jesus, The spotless Son of God, Who carried our griefs and sorrows; The wine-press of wrath He trod.
3. Tell me the story of Jesus, Who went about doing good, Who healed the sick and suff'ring, And led the people to God.
4. Tell me the story of Jesus, Redeemer, Saviour, King! O what a glorious Saviour! His praises I will sing.

Tell me the story of Jesus, The story of God's only Son, Who gave His life to redeem us; Behold then, the crucified One!
Tell me the story of Jesus, Of how He died for me, The sinless One for the guilty, He died to set me free.
Tell me the story of Jesus, Of the resurrection morn, When life and immortality To us thro' Him was born.
He ever lives in glory, When He hath gone to prepare A place for us in the mansions, "Many mansions" of Heaven, so fair.

CHORUS

Tell me the story of Jesus, Tell me the story of Jesus,

Copyright, 1893, by Nellie Whipple Fawcett. Used by per. 192

Tell Me the Story of Jesus

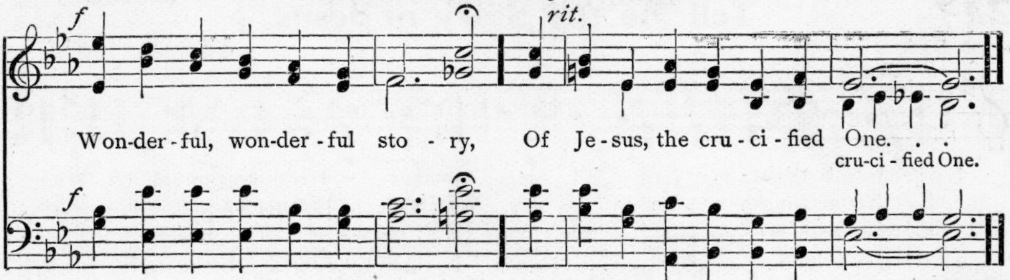
f
rit.
Won-der-ful, won-der-ful sto - ry, Of Je-sus, the cru-ci-fied One.
cru-ci-fied One.
f

Rescue the Perishing 248

Fanny J. Crosby
W. H. Doane

1. Res - cue the per - ish - ing, Care for the dy - ing, Snatch them in pit - y from
2. Tho' they are slight-ing Him, Still He is wait - ing, Wait - ing, the pen - i - tent
3. Down in the hu-man heart, Crush'd by the tempt - er, Feel - ings lie bur - ied that
4. Res - cue the per - ish - ing, Du - ty de - mands it; Strength for thy la - bor the
sin and the grave; Weep o'er the err - ing one, Lift up the fall - en,
child to re - ceive; Plead with them ear - nest - ly, Plead with them gen - tly:
grace can re - store: Touched by a lov - ing heart, Wak - ened by kind - ness,
Lord will pro - vide: Back to the nar - row way Pa - tient - ly win them
CHORUS
Tell them of Je - sus the might - y to save. Res - cue the per - ish - ing,
He will for - give if they on - ly be - lieve.
Chords that were bro - ken will vi - brate once more.
Tell the poor wan - d'rer a Sav - iour has died.
Care for the dy - ing; Je - sus is mer - ci - ful, Je - sus will save.

Copyright, by W. H. Doane. By per.

249 Looking This Way

J. W. V. | J. W. Van De Venter

DUET
1. O - ver the riv - er fa - ces I see, Fair as the morning, look-ing for me;
2. Fa - ther and moth-er, safe in the vale, Watch for the boatman, wait for the sail,
3. Broth-er and sis - ter, gone to that clime, Wait for the oth - ers, com -ing sometime;
4. Sweet lit - tle dar - ling, light of the home, Looking for someone, beck- on - ing come;
5. Je - sus the Sav-iour,bright morning star, Look - ing for lost ones, straying a - far;
Free from their sor- row, grief, and de- spair, Wait -ing and watching, pa-tient - ly there.
Bear - ing the loved ones o - ver the tide In - to the har - bor, near to their side.
Safe with the an - gels, whi - ter than snow, Watch-ing for dear ones wait -ing be - low.
Bright as a sun-beam,pure as the dew, Anx-ious - ly look - ing, moth- er, for you.
Hear the glad mes-sage; why will you roam? Je - sus is call - ing,"Sin - ner,come home."
CHORUS
Look- ing this way, yes, look - ing this way; Loved ones are wait- ing, look- ing this way;
Fair as the morning,bright as the day, Dear ones in glo - ry look- ing this way.

Copyright, 1895, by J. W. Van De Venter. Used by per.

Jesus is Tenderly Calling

Fanny J. Crosby

(*P. M.*)

Arthur Berridge
Arr. for this work

1. Je - sus is ten - der - ly call - ing thee home — Call - ing to - day,
2. Je - sus is call - ing the wea - ry to rest — Call - ing to - day,
3. Je - sus is wait - ing, O come to Him now — Wait - ing to - day,
4. Je - sus is plead - ing; O list to His voice — Hear Him to - day,

call - ing to - day! Why from the sun - shine of love wilt thou roam,
call - ing to - day! Bring Him thy bur - den, and thou shalt be blest,
wait - ing to - day! Come with thy sins, at His feet low - ly bow;
hear Him to - day! They who be - lieve on His name shall re - joice;

REFRAIN

far - ther and far - ther a - way? Call - ing to - day!
He will not turn thee a - way.
Come, and no long - er de - lay!
Quick - ly a - rise, and a - way!

Call - ing to -

call - ing to - day! Je - sus is call - ing, ...
day, to - day; is ten - der - ly

rall. . . . .

call - ing, Is ten - der - ly call - ing to - day.

Copyright, 1901, by U. S. C. E.

251 Have You Heard of Christ

J. E. Hall (8. 7. 8. 7 with Chorus) Edwyn Vincent

pp Gently
1. Have you heard of Christ the Sav - iour? How He suf - fered on the tree?
2. Have you heard how thou-sands wit - ness What His love and grace have done?
3. Have you heard that thro' death's val - ley Je - sus' hand you sure will need;
rit.
How His blood hath paid our par - don; How He died for you and me?
How from sin they have been res - cued By the pow'r of God's dear Son?
Thro' the black- ness of its sha - dow All the way thy steps to lead?
CHORUS Faster
f
Joy - ous - ly I'll tell the sto - ry! How His blood hath set me free;
rall.
How the Lord, the King of glo - ry Hath re-deemed and ran-somed me.

252 O Jesus, Thou art Standing

W. W. How, 1867 (St. Hilda 7s. 6s. 8l.) J. H. Knecht, 1799, and E. Husband, 1871

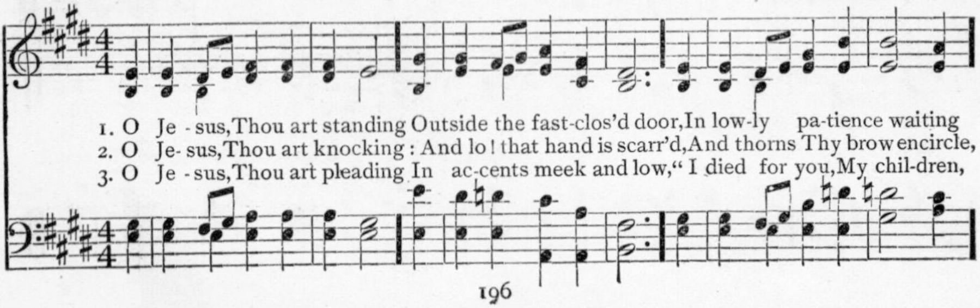
1. O Je - sus, Thou art standing Outside the fast-clos'd door, In low-ly pa-tience waiting
2. O Je- sus, Thou art knocking: And lo! that hand is scarr'd, And thorns Thy brow encircle,
3. O Je - sus, Thou art pleading In ac-cents meek and low, "I died for you, My chil-dren,

O Jesus, Thou art Standing

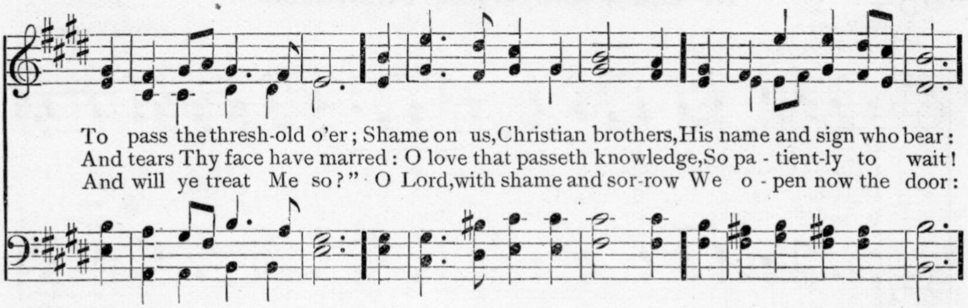
To pass the thresh-old o'er; Shame on us, Christian brothers, His name and sign who bear:
And tears Thy face have marred: O love that passeth knowledge, So pa - tient-ly to wait!
And will ye treat Me so?" O Lord, with shame and sor-row We o - pen now the door:

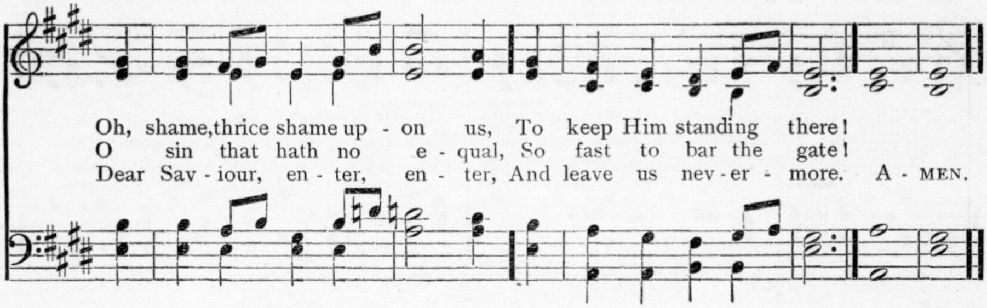
Oh, shame, thrice shame up - on us, To keep Him standing there!
O sin that hath no e - qual, So fast to bar the gate!
Dear Sav - iour, en - ter, en - ter, And leave us nev - er - more. A - MEN.

Behold, a Stranger at the Door 253

Joseph Grigg, 1765 — Henry K. Oliver

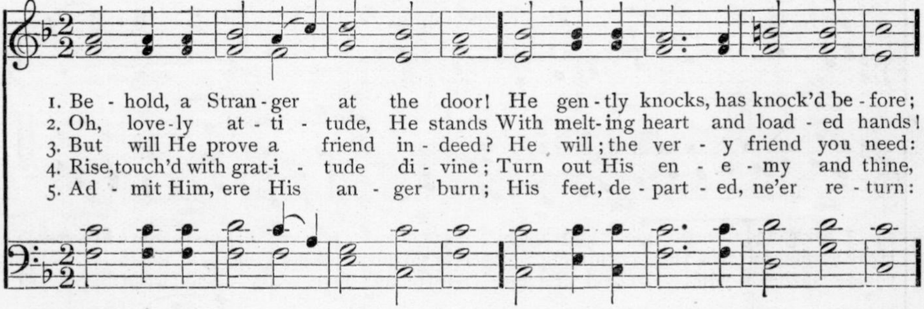
1. Be - hold, a Stran - ger at the door! He gen - tly knocks, has knock'd be - fore;
2. Oh, love-ly at - ti - tude, He stands With melt-ing heart and load - ed hands!
3. But will He prove a friend in - deed? He will; the ver - y friend you need:
4. Rise, touch'd with grat-i - tude di - vine; Turn out His en - e - my and thine,
5. Ad - mit Him, ere His an - ger burn; His feet, de - part - ed, ne'er re - turn:

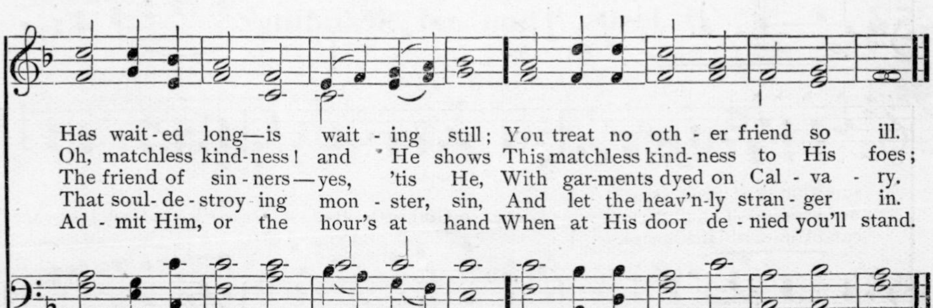
Has wait-ed long—is wait - ing still; You treat no oth - er friend so ill.
Oh, matchless kind-ness! and He shows This matchless kind-ness to His foes;
The friend of sin - ners—yes, 'tis He, With gar-ments dyed on Cal - va - ry.
That soul-de-stroy ing mon - ster, sin, And let the heav'n-ly stran - ger in.
Ad - mit Him, or the hour's at hand When at His door de - nied you'll stand.

254 In the Field with Their Flocks

F. W. Farrar

J. Farmer

Moderato SOLO OR UNISON
1. In the field with their flocks a - bid - ing, They lay on the dew - y ground; And
2. "To you in the Cit-y of Da - vid, A Sav-iour is born to - day!" And
3. And the shep-herds came to the man - ger, And gaz'd on the Ho - ly Child; And
glim - m'ring un - der the star - light, The sheep lay white a-round, When the
sud-den a host of the heav'n-ly ones Flash'd forth to join the lay! O
calm-ly o'er that rude cra - dle The Vir - gin Moth - er smil'd; And the
light of the Lord stream'd o'er them, And lo! from the heav - en a - bove, An
nev- er hath sweet - er mes-sage Thrill'd home to the souls of men, And the
sky, in the star - lit si - lence, Seem'd full of the an - gel lay; "To
rit.
CHORUS IN UNISON p a tempo
an - gel leaned from the glory And sang his song of love:— He sang, that first sweet Christmas, The
Heav'ns themselves had never heard A gladder choir, till then, For they sang that Christmas Carol, That
you in the Cit-y of Da-vid A Saviour is born today;" O they sang—and I ween that never The
f
song that shall never cease,
nev-er on earth shall cease,
car-ol on earth shall cease,
"Glory to God in the highest, On earth good-will and peace."

Hark! the Herald Angels Sing

Charles Wesley, 1739 (*Herald Angels 7s. D.*) Felix Mendelssohn, 1846

1. Hark! the her - ald an - gels sing "Glo - ry to the new-born King; Peace on
2. Christ, by high - est heaven a - dored; Christ, the ev - er - last - ing Lord; Late in
3. Hail! the heaven-born Prince of Peace! Hail the Sun of Right-eous-ness! Light and
earth, and mer - cy mild, God and sin - ners rec - on-ciled!" Joy-ful, all ye na-tions, rise,
time be-hold Him come, Off-spring of the Virgin's womb: Vailed in flesh the Godhead see;
life to all He brings, Ris'n with heal-ing in His wings: Mild He lays His glo-ry by,
Join the tri-umph of the skies; With th' an-gel - ic host pro - claim, "Christ is
Hail th' in - car - nate De - i - ty, Pleased as man with men to dwell; Je - sus,
Born that man no more may die; Born to raise the sons of earth, Born to
born in Beth - le - hem!" With th' angel-ic host pro - claim, "Christ is born in Beth-le-hem!"
our Im-man - u - el! Pleased as man with men to dwell; Je - sus, our Im-man - u - el!
give them sec-ond birth. Born to raise the sons of earth, Born to give them sec-ond birth.

256 Holy Night! Peaceful Night

Joseph Mohr, 1818 — J. Barnby, 1868

Moderato

1. Ho - ly night! peaceful night! Thro' the darkness beams a light; Ho-ly night! peaceful night!
2. Si - lent night! ho -liest night! Darkness flies and all is light! Shepherds hear the angels sing,
3. Si - lent night! ho -liest night! Guiding star, O lend thy light! See the eastern wise men bring
4. Si - lent night! ho -liest night! Wondrous star, O lend thy light! With the angels let us sing

CHORUS

Thro' the darkness beams a light, Thro' the darkness beams a light. Yonder, where they sweet
"Hal - le - lu - jah! hail the King! Je - sus Christ is here, is here!"
Gifts and hom - age to our King! Je - sus Christ is here, is here!
Hal - le - lu - jah to our King! Je - sus Christ is here, is here!

rall.

vig- ils keep O'er the Babe, who in silent sleep, Rests in heav'nly peace, Rests in heav'nly peace.

257 Angels, from the Realms of Glory

J. Montgomery, 1819 — (*Wildersmouth* 8s. 7s) — E. J. Hopkins, 1879

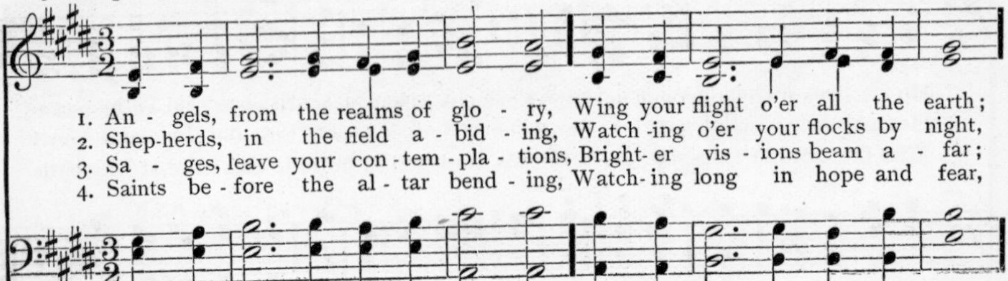

1. An - gels, from the realms of glo - ry, Wing your flight o'er all the earth;
2. Shep-herds, in the field a - bid - ing, Watch -ing o'er your flocks by night,
3. Sa - ges, leave your con - tem - pla - tions, Bright- er vis - ions beam a - far;
4. Saints be - fore the al - tar bend - ing, Watch- ing long in hope and fear,

Angels, from the Realms of Glory

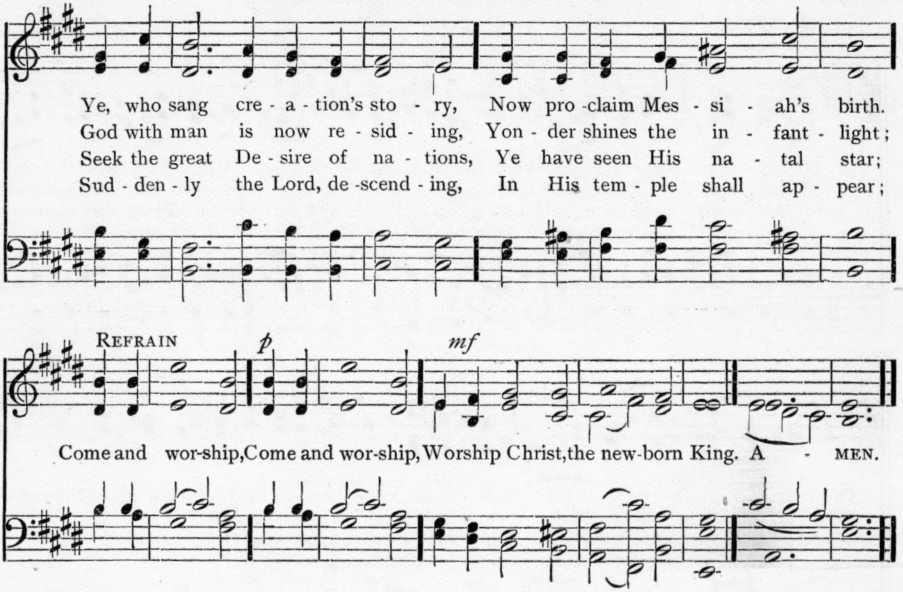
Ye, who sang cre - a - tion's sto - ry, Now pro - claim Mes - si - ah's birth.
God with man is now re - sid - ing, Yon - der shines the in - fant - light;
Seek the great De - sire of na - tions, Ye have seen His na - tal star;
Sud - den - ly the Lord, de - scend - ing, In His tem - ple shall ap - pear;
REFRAIN
p
mf
Come and wor-ship, Come and wor-ship, Worship Christ, the new-born King. A - MEN.

Silent Night, Holy Night

258

(*Christmas Carol*)

Michael Haydn

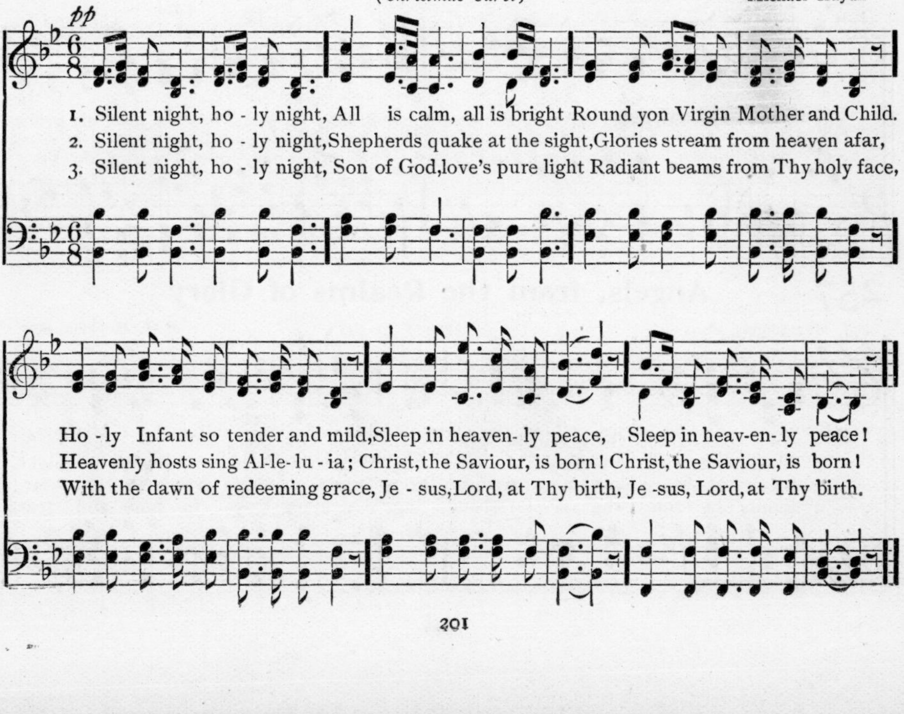
pp
1. Silent night, ho - ly night, All is calm, all is bright Round yon Virgin Mother and Child.
2. Silent night, ho - ly night, Shepherds quake at the sight, Glories stream from heaven afar,
3. Silent night, ho - ly night, Son of God, love's pure light Radiant beams from Thy holy face,
Ho - ly Infant so tender and mild, Sleep in heaven - ly peace, Sleep in heav-en - ly peace!
Heavenly hosts sing Al - le - lu - ia; Christ, the Saviour, is born! Christ, the Saviour, is born!
With the dawn of redeeming grace, Je - sus, Lord, at Thy birth, Je - sus, Lord, at Thy birth.

259 Glory to God! Peace on the Earth

Charles S. Robinson (*Glory to God* P. M.) Arr. from Wagner

1. "Glo - ry to God! peace on the earth! Goodwill to men!" sang the an-gels a-bove;
2. Praise ye the Lord! lift to His name High hal - le - lu - jahs from each happy voice;
3. O Christ of God! ris - en and crown'd! Come with Thy presence, Thy Spirit impart!

Glo - ry to God! peace on the earth! Good-will to men! — sound the chorus of love!
Strike the loud chord! praise ye the Lord! Let ev - 'ry soul in His glo - ry re - joice!
Come with Thy love! come with Thy power! Breathe on our souls, and enrich ev - 'ry heart!

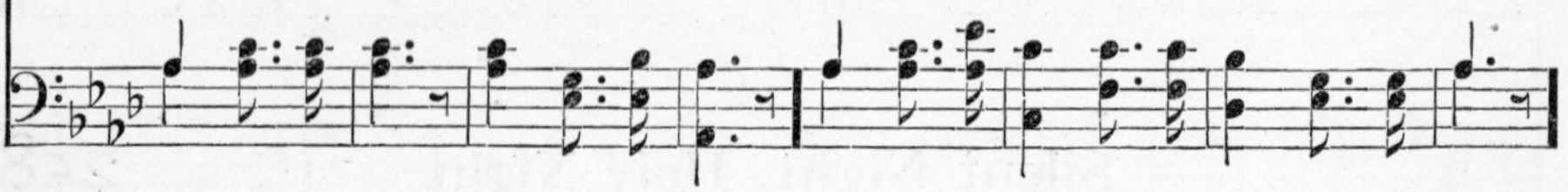

Bright dawns the morning, when heav'n is so near; Sweet be our an-them, for Je - sus is here,
Oh, for a strain such as an - gels re-peat, When the redeem'd cast their crowns at His feet;
Sad were Thy suf - fer-ings, shameful Thy cross, Sharing our punishment, bearing our loss;

Come, let us sing, sing of His grace, Grate - ful thanksgiving shall ut - ter His praise.
"Wor-thy the Lamb! once He was slain, Now on His throne He is reign - ing a - gain!"
Now, Lord of all, Thee we a - dore! Bring we our souls to be Thine ev - er - more!

The Story of the Cross

Edward Monro, Abbr.

A. Redhead

UNISON
HARMONY
In His own raiment clad, With His blood dyed; Wom-en walk sorrow-ing By His side.
Fol-low to Cal - va - ry, Tread where He trod, He who for-ev - er was Son of God.
UNISON
HARMONY
On the cross lift-ed up, Thy face we scan, Bear - ing that cross for us, Son of man.
Thorns form Thy di - a-dem, Rough wood Thy throne, For us Thy blood is shed, Us a - lone.
UNISON
HARMONY
O I will fol-low Thee, Star of my soul, Thro' the deep shades of life To the goal.
UNISON
HARMONY
Yes, let Thy cross be borne Each day by me, Mind not how heavy if But with Thee.

261 Welcome, Happy Morning

6th Century, Fortunatus; Tr. J. Ellerton (*11s with Refrain*) J. B. Calkin

1. "Wel-come, hap - py morn - ing!" age to age shall say; Hell to - day is
2. Earth her joy con - fess - es, cloth-ing her for spring, All good gifts re -
3. Mak - er and Re - deem - er, Life and Health of all, Thou from heav'n be-
4. Loose the souls long pris - oned, bound with Sa - tan's chains; All that now is
vanquished, Heav'n is won to - day. Lo! the Dead is liv - ing, God for - ev - er-
turned with her re - turn-ing King: Bloom in ev - 'ry meadow, leaves on ev - 'ry
hold - ing hu - man na - ture's fall; Of the Fa-ther's Godhead true and on - ly
fall - en raise to life a - gain; Show Thy face in brightness, bid the na-tions
more! Him, their true Cre - a - tor, all His works a - dore!
bough, Speak His sor - rows end - ed, hail His tri - umph now.
Son, Man - hood to de - liv - er, man-hood didst put on.
see, Bring a - gain our day-light: day re - turns with Thee!
ff
8vas.
ff Refrain in Unison
"Wel-come, hap - py morn - ing!" age to age shall say; Hell to-day is
Inst.

Welcome, Happy Morning

vanquished, Heav'n is won to - day! Lo! the Dead is liv - ing,
God for ev - er - more! Him, their true Cre - a - tor, all His works a - dore!
rall.
rall.

Christ, the Lord, is Risen Today 262

Charles Wesley (*Christ is Risen*) Charles S. Brown

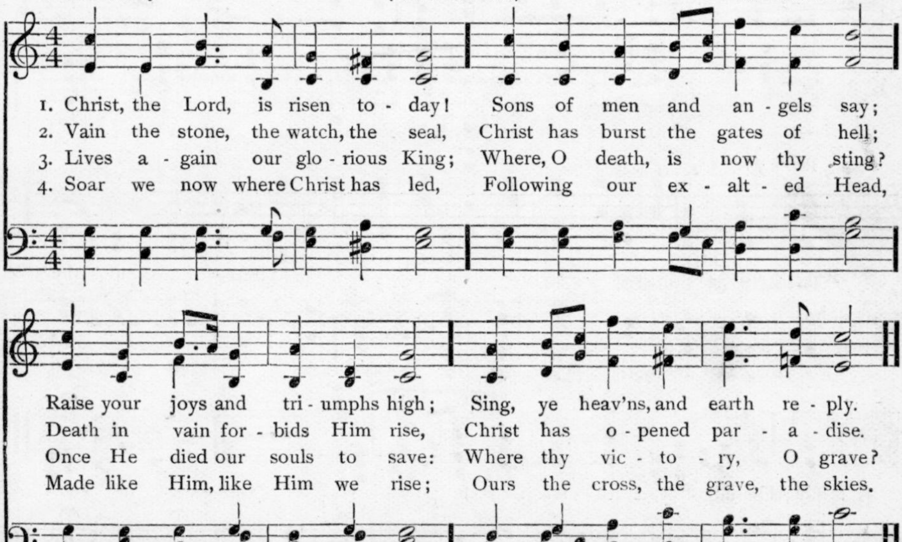
1. Christ, the Lord, is risen to - day! Sons of men and an - gels say;
2. Vain the stone, the watch, the seal, Christ has burst the gates of hell;
3. Lives a - gain our glo - rious King; Where, O death, is now thy sting?
4. Soar we now where Christ has led, Following our ex - alt - ed Head,
Raise your joys and tri - umphs high; Sing, ye heav'ns, and earth re - ply.
Death in vain for - bids Him rise, Christ has o - pened par - a - dise.
Once He died our souls to save: Where thy vic - to - ry, O grave?
Made like Him, like Him we rise; Ours the cross, the grave, the skies.

Copyright, 1901, by U. S. C. E.

263 He Did Not Die in Vain

Mrs. Frank A. Breck

Grant Colfax Tullar
Refrain har. for this work

(DUET FOR MEZZO SOP. AND TENOR, OR UNISON CHORUS)

1. My bless-ed Lord was cru-ci-fied— And day was dark—and grief was wide—
2. He brings His great sal-va-tion nigh, And on His love bids us re-ly;
3. O, wondrous news of life and love! That Je-sus lives and reigns a-bove!
For hope was crushed, and all seemed vain, Un-til that Sav-iour rose a-gain.
He bought our peace thro' grief and pain; But oh! He did not die in vain!
He made the path to glo-ry plain; Ah, no! He did not die in vain.
REFRAIN
Ring out the bless-ed news a-gain! Oh! bear a-loft the
cres.
strain; The might-y Lord is risen in pow'r— He did not die in vain!

Copyright, 1901, by Tullar-Meredith Co.

Lift Your Glad Voices

264

Henry Ware, 1817 (*Filby P. M.*) W. C. Filby

1. Lift your glad voi - ces in tri-umph on high, For Je - sus hath ris - en, and
2. Glo - ry to God, in full an-thems of joy; The be - ing He gave us death
man shall not die; . Vain were the ter - rors that gath - ered a - round Him,
can - not de - stroy: . Sad were the life we may part with to - mor - row,
And short the do - min - ion of death and the grave; He burst from the fet - ters of
If tears were our birth-right, and death were our end; But Je - sus hath cheer'd the dark
dark-ness that bound Him, Re-splen - dent in glo - ry, to live and to save; Loud was the
val - ley of sor - row, And bade us, im - mor - tal, to heav - en as - cend: Lift then your
cho - rus of an - gels on high, The Sav-iour hath ris - en, and man shall not die.
voi - ces in tri-umph on high, For Je - sus hath ris - en, and man shall not die.

265 We Plough the Fields

Tr. Jane M. Campbell (*Dresden P. M.*) J. A. P. Schulz

1. We plough the fields, and scat - ter The good seed on the land, But it is fed and
2. We thank Thee then, O Fa - ther, For all things bright and good, The seed-time and the
watered By God's almighty hand; He sends the snow in win - ter, The warmth to swell the grain,
harvest, Our life, our health, our food. No gifts have we to of - fer For all Thy love im - parts,
The breez-es, and the sun-shine, And soft, re - fresh-ing rain.
But that which Thou de-sir - est, Our hum-ble, thankful hearts.
REFRAIN
All good gifts a - round us
Are sent from heav'n a - bove, Then thank the Lord, O thank the Lord, For all . . His love.

266 God Hath Given Us Harvest

J. Alford Davies (*Shepherd 6. 5. 8l.*) G. A. Macfarren

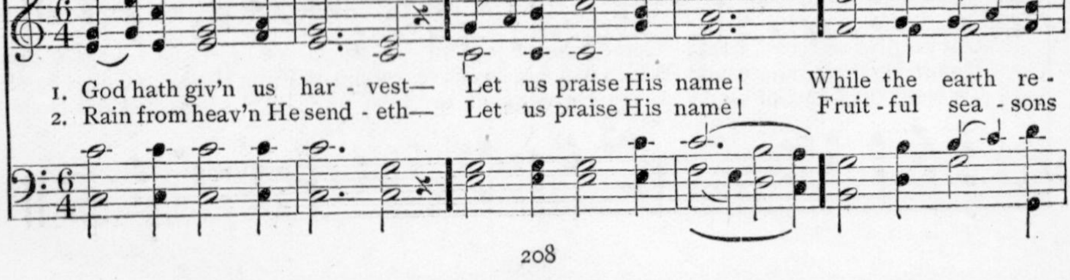
1. God hath giv'n us har - vest— Let us praise His name! While the earth re -
2. Rain from heav'n He send - eth— Let us praise His name! Fruit - ful sea - sons

God Hath Given Us Harvest

main - eth He is still the same! Year by year His prom - ise
show us He is still the same! Hearts with food and glad - ness
Faith-ful - ly en - dures; Seed-time, sun-shine, har - vest, He for man en-sures.
He has filled once more; Kind-ness is His wit - ness, As in days of yore.

Come, Christian Youths and Maidens 267

Anon. (7s. 6s. 8l.) S. Salvatori

1. Come, Christian youths and maid - ens, Come, broth-ers, old and young, Up -
2. Come, sing with us the prais - es Of God's pre - serv - ing care, Who
3. Come, sing with us the prais - es Of God's re - deem - ing love, That
lift your hearts and voi-ces, Be praise on ev - 'ry tongue. In God's own house we gath-er,
safe from harm has kept us Throughout an-oth - er year; And crowned our lives with mercies
song which nev-er ceas - es A - round the throne a-bove; The voice of ma - ny an - gels,
Our year-ly feast to hold; Come, join our joy - ful an - them, Ye broth-ers, young and old.
Unnumber'd as the sand, Which day by day have reach'd us From His all-gra-cious hand.
"Worthy the Lamb of God; For He was slain to save us By His most precious blood."

268 A New Year's Message

Anon. May Whittle Moody

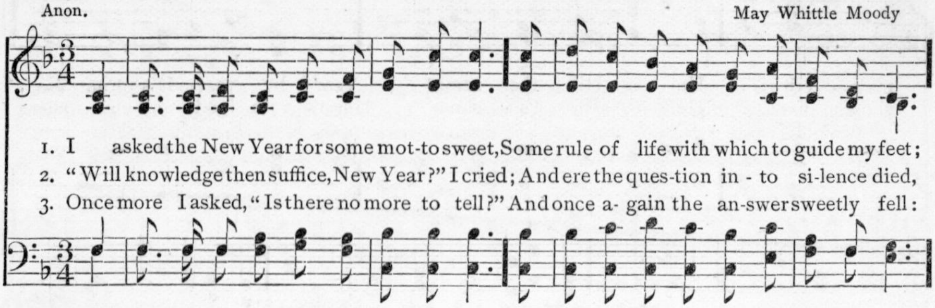
1. I asked the New Year for some mot-to sweet, Some rule of life with which to guide my feet;
2. "Will knowledge then suffice, New Year?" I cried; And ere the ques-tion in - to si-lence died,
3. Once more I asked, "Is there no more to tell?" And once a- gain the an-swer sweetly fell:

p rit.
I asked and paused; he answered soft and low, "God's will, God's will to know, God's will to know."
The answer came, "Nay, but re-mem-ber, too, God's will, God's will to do, God's will to do."
"Yes, this one thing, all oth-er things above, God's will, God's will to love, God's will to love."

Copyright, 1898, by May Whittle Moody

269 From Glory unto Glory

Frances R. Havergal (*Berthold* 13. 13. 13. 14) B. Tours

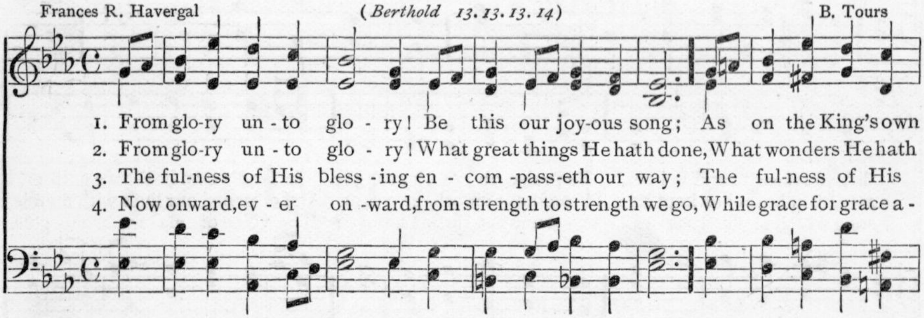
1. From glo-ry un - to glo - ry! Be this our joy-ous song; As on the King's own
2. From glo-ry un - to glo - ry! What great things He hath done, What wonders He hath
3. The ful-ness of His bless - ing en - com -pass-eth our way; The ful-ness of His
4. Now onward, ev - er on -ward, from strength to strength we go, While grace for grace a -

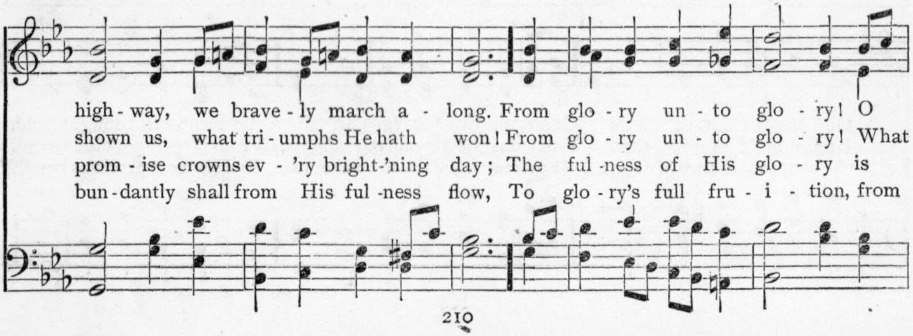
high - way, we brave - ly march a - long. From glo - ry un - to glo - ry! O
shown us, what tri - umphs He hath won! From glo - ry un - to glo - ry! What
prom - ise crowns ev - 'ry bright-'ning day; The ful - ness of His glo - ry is
bun - dantly shall from His ful -ness flow, To glo - ry's full fru - i - tion, from

From Glory unto Glory

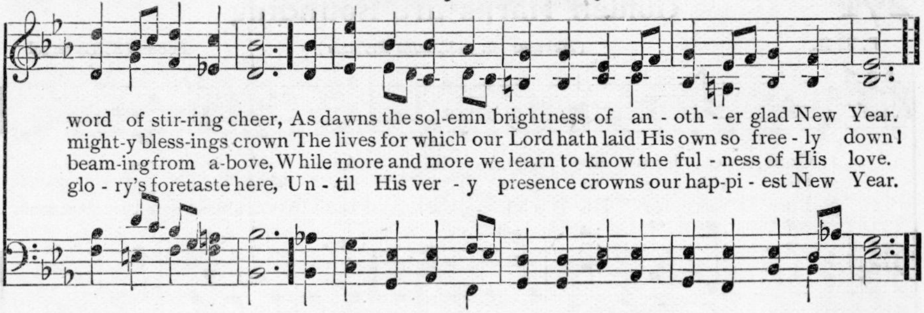
word of stir-ring cheer, As dawns the sol-emn brightness of an - oth - er glad New Year.
might-y bless-ings crown The lives for which our Lord hath laid His own so free - ly down!
beam-ing from a-bove, While more and more we learn to know the ful - ness of His love.
glo - ry's foretaste here, Un - til His ver - y presence crowns our hap-pi - est New Year.

Standing at the Portal 270

Frances R. Havergal, 1873 (*Deva 6s. 5s. 12l.*) E. J. Hopkins

1. Stand-ing at the por-tal Of the op'n-ing year, Words of com-fort meet us,
2. "I, the Lord, am with thee, Be thou not a-fraid! I will keep and strengthen,
3. He will nev-er fail us, He will not for-sake; His e-ter-nal cov-'nant
Hush-ing ev-'ry fear; Spo-ken thro' the si-lence By our Fa-ther's voice,
Be thou not dis-mayed! Yea, I will up-hold thee With My own right hand,
He will nev-er break! Rest-ing on His prom-ise, What have we to fear?
CHORUS
Ten-der, strong, and faith-ful, Mak-ing us re-joice. Onward then, and fear not,
Thou art called and cho-sen In My sight to stand."
God is all-suf-fi-cient For the com-ing year.
Chil-dren of the day! For His word shall nev-er, Nev-er pass a-way.

271 Golden Harps are Sounding

F. R. H. (*Hermas* 6. 5. 8l. *with Refrain*) Frances R. Havergal

1. Gold - en harps are sound - ing, An - gel voi - ces ring,
2. He who came to save us, He who bled and died,
3. Pray - ing for His chil - dren, In that bless - ed place,
Pearl - y gates are o - pened— O - pened for the King; Christ, the King of
Now is crown'd with glo - ry At His Fa - ther's side. Nev - er more to
Call - ing them to glo - ry, Send - ing them His grace; His bright home pre -
Glo - ry, Je - sus, King of Love, Is gone up in tri - umph
suf - fer, Nev - er more to die, Je - sus, King of Glo - ry,
par - ing, Faith - ful ones, for you; Je - sus ev - er liv - eth,
Refrain
To His throne a - bove. All His work is end - ed,
Has gone up on high.
Ev - er lov - eth too.
Joy - ful - ly we sing, Je - sus hath as - cend - ed, Glo - ry to our King!

God Will Understand

Anon.

Charles S. Brown

With life and expression
1. They brought their flow'rs to the al - tar, Blos-soms of white and red;
2. She crept up close to the al - tar, And there, 'neath a li - ly's crown,
3. Sweet child - ish faith! Oh, teach us Our lit - tle best to give,
Lilies and pan-sies and ro - ses The sweetest of per - fumes shed;
With tender and rev - er - ent fin - gers She laid her of-fer - ing down;
Though the works of oth - ers are great - er Than the hum - ble life we live;
But none of the rich and might - y, Who lav - ished their gifts that day
And said to a cu - rious ques - tion, As she o - pened her ti - ny hand,
And to of - fer our grate - ful ser - vice, For - ev - er with lov - ing hand,
Took heed of a child a - mong them, Who tim - id - ly pressed her way.
"It is on - ly a lit - tle dai - sy— But God will un - der - stand."
And rest in the blest as - sur - ance That God will un - der - stand.

Copyright, 1901, by U. S. C. E.

273 O! the Flowers of Summer

J. Barker (6. 5. 8l. and Refrain) A. Watson

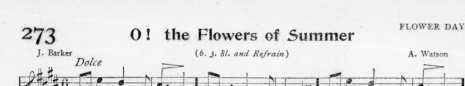

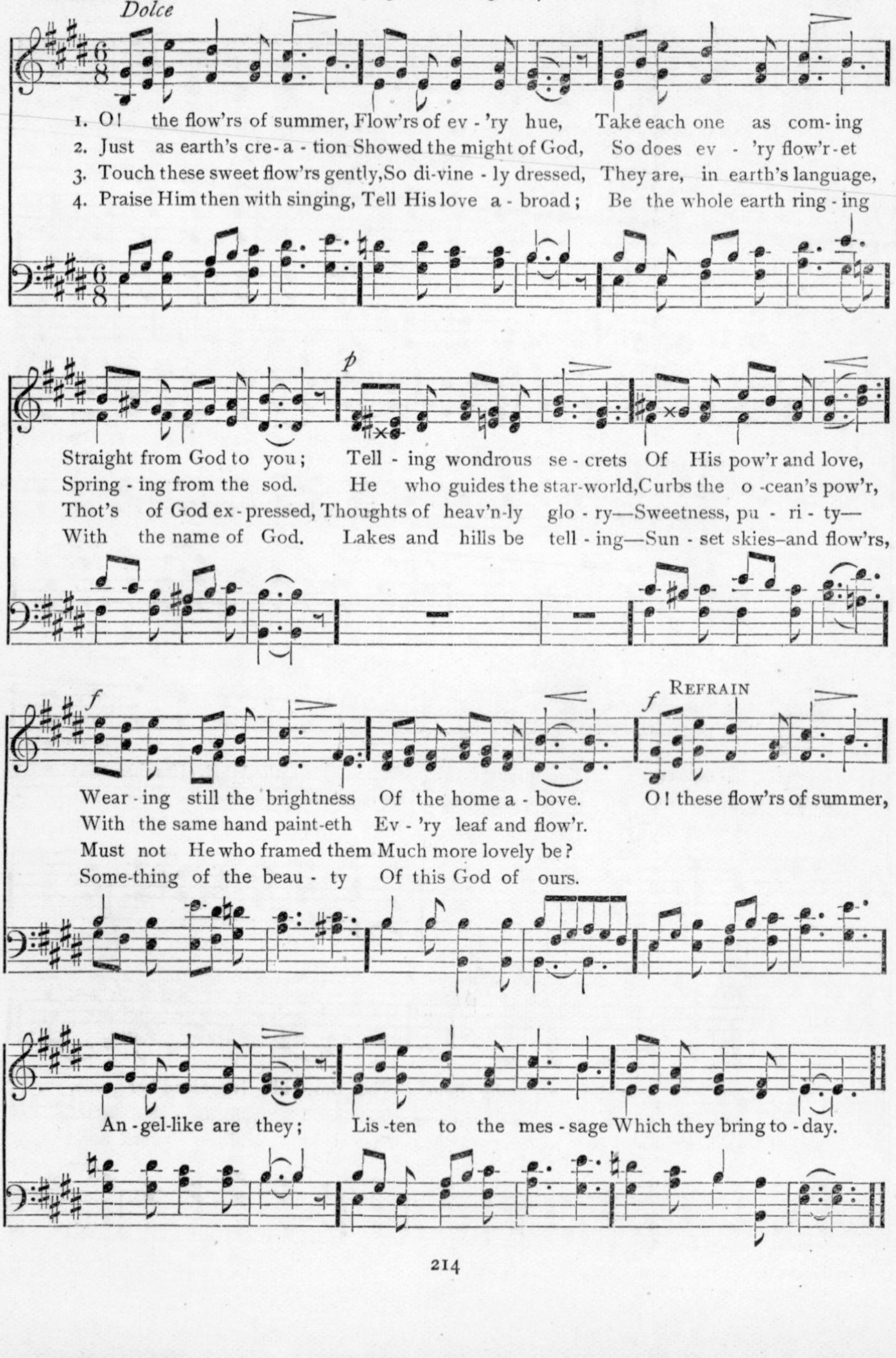
Dolce
1. O! the flow'rs of summer, Flow'rs of ev - 'ry hue, Take each one as com-ing
2. Just as earth's cre-a - tion Showed the might of God, So does ev - 'ry flow'r-et
3. Touch these sweet flow'rs gently, So di-vine - ly dressed, They are, in earth's language,
4. Praise Him then with singing, Tell His love a - broad; Be the whole earth ring - ing
p
Straight from God to you; Tell - ing wondrous se - crets Of His pow'r and love,
Spring - ing from the sod. He who guides the star-world, Curbs the o -cean's pow'r,
Thot's of God ex - pressed, Thoughts of heav'n-ly glo - ry—Sweetness, pu - ri - ty—
With the name of God. Lakes and hills be tell - ing—Sun - set skies–and flow'rs,
f
Wear - ing still the brightness Of the home a - bove.
With the same hand paint-eth Ev - 'ry leaf and flow'r.
Must not He who framed them Much more lovely be?
Some-thing of the beau - ty Of this God of ours.
Refrain
f
O! these flow'rs of summer,
An - gel-like are they; Lis - ten to the mes - sage Which they bring to - day.

I Must Tell Jesus

274

E. A. H. Elisha A. Hoffman

1. I must tell Je - sus all of my tri - als; I can - not bear these bur-dens a - lone; In my dis-tress He kind-ly will help me; He ev - er loves and cares for His own.
2. I must tell Je - sus all of my trou - bles; He is a kind, com - pas-sion-ate Friend; If I but ask Him, He will de - liv - er, Make of my trou - bles quick - ly an end.
3. Tempted and tried I need a great Sav - iour, One who can help my bur-dens to bear; I must tell Je - sus, I must tell Je - sus; He all my cares and sor - rows will share.
4. O how the world to e - vil al - lures me! O how my heart is tempted to sin! I must tell Je - sus, And He will help me O - ver the world the vic - t'ry to win.
CHORUS
I must tell Je - sus! I must tell Je - sus! I can - not bear my bur - dens a - lone; I must tell Je - sus! I must tell Je - sus! Je - sus can help me, Je - sus a - lone.
rit.

Copyright, 1893, by The Hoffman Music Co. Used by per.

Could I Tell It

Ina Duley Ogdon P. P. Bilhorn

1. If I could on - ly tell Him as I know Him, My Re-deem-er who has
2. If I could on - ly tell you how He loves you, And if we could thro' the
3. If I could tell how sweet will be His wel - come, In that home whose wondrous
4. But I can nev - er tell Him as I know Him; Human tongue can nev-er
bright - ened all my way; If I could tell how pre - cious is His pres - ence,
lone - ly gar - den go, If I could tell His dy - ing pain and par - don,
beau - ty ne'er was told; And tell you how He waits and longs to save you,
tell of love di - vine; I on - ly can en - treat you to ac - cept Him;
CHORUS
I am sure that you would make Him yours today. Could I tell it, could I
You would worship at His wounded feet I know.
You would seek Him, and abide within His fold.
Come and know the joy and peace for-ev-er mine. Could I tell it, yes, I would, Could I
tell it, How the sun-shine of His pres-ence lights my way, I would tell it,
tell it as I should, I would tell you, yes, I would,
I would tell it, And I'm sure that you would make Him yours to-day.
I would tell you if I could,

Words and music copyright, 1901, by P. P. Bilhorn. By per. of author, from "Century Songs"

276

Welcome Hymn

(*For Conventions*)

W. W. B. — W. W. Barker, 1900

Spirited ff
1. Wel - come ! thrice wel - come ! Ye loy - al host of God, Wel-come ! thrice
2. Wel - come ! thrice wel - come ! Be - liev - ers in the Lord ; Wel-come ! thrice
3. Wel - come ! thrice wel - come ! Be stead-fast in the fight, Wel-come ! thrice
p
wel - come ! From near and from a - broad. Though chang - ing years pass
wel - come ! Up - hold - ers of His word. We meet our Sav - iour's
wel - come ! Till faith is lost in sight, And when our vic - to -
ff
swift - ly by Our cause is still the same, And thus we glad - ly
name to praise, To learn what He re - quires ; And by His Spir - it's
ries are won We'll join the bless - ed throng ; Then God will wel - come
Chorus ff
greet you in Our Mas-ter's con-qu'ring Name. Wel-come ! thrice wel-come ! To
help re - solve To fol - low His de - sires.
us and we Will hear heav'ns wel-come song.
rall.
homes and hearts and love ; Welcome ! thrice welcome ! And blessings from a - bove.

Copyright, 1901, by U. S. C. E.

277 If the Saviour Journey with Me

D. B. Purinton

W. H. Doane

Gently DUET WITH CHORUS

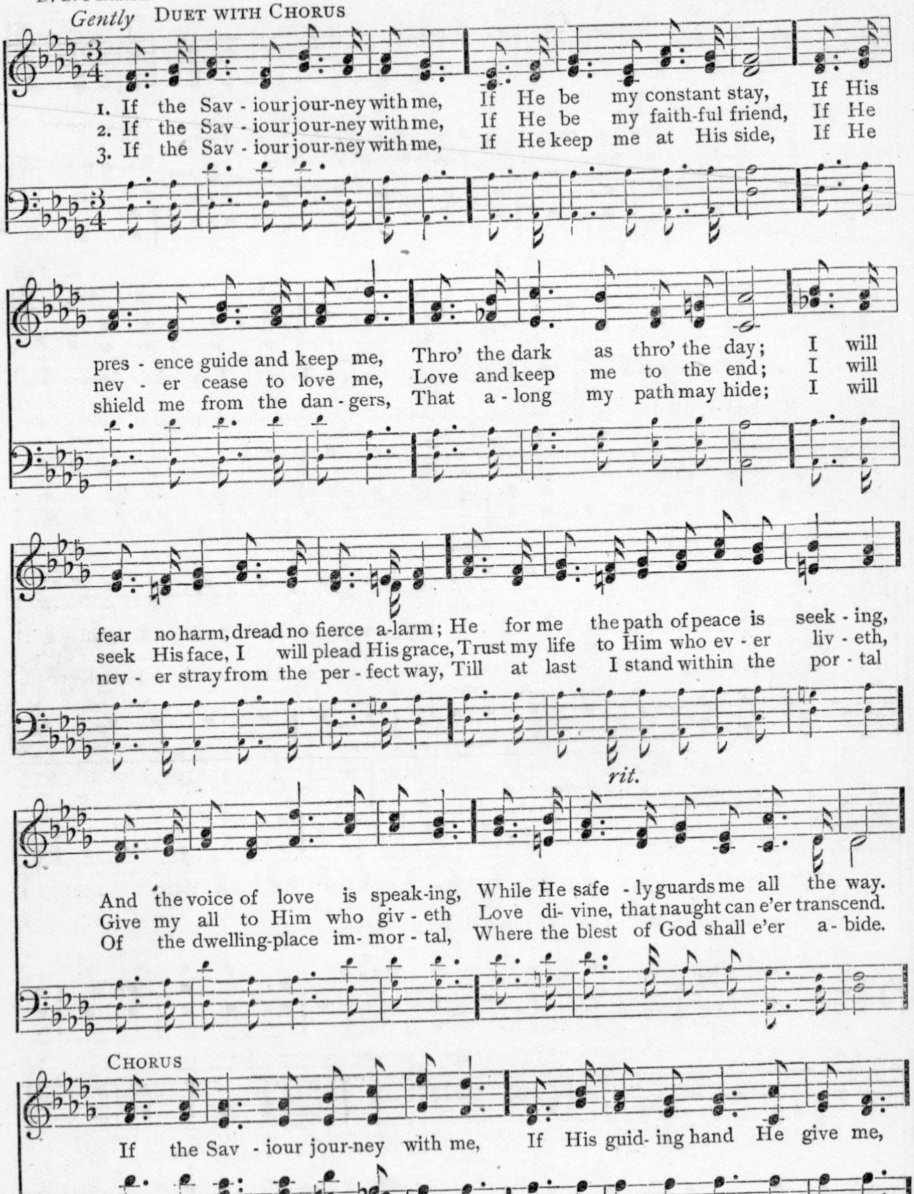
1. If the Sav - iour jour-ney with me, If He be my constant stay, If His pres - ence guide and keep me, Thro' the dark as thro' the day; I will fear no harm, dread no fierce a-larm; He for me the path of peace is seek - ing, And the voice of love is speak-ing, While He safe - ly guards me all the way.
2. If the Sav - iour jour-ney with me, If He be my faith-ful friend, If He nev - er cease to love me, Love and keep me to the end; I will seek His face, I will plead His grace, Trust my life to Him who ev - er liv - eth, Give my all to Him who giv - eth Love di - vine, that naught can e'er transcend.
3. If the Sav - iour jour-ney with me, If He keep me at His side, If He shield me from the dan - gers, That a - long my path may hide; I will nev - er stray from the per - fect way, Till at last I stand within the por - tal Of the dwelling-place im - mor - tal, Where the blest of God shall e'er a - bide.
rit.
CHORUS
If the Sav - iour jour-ney with me, If His guid - ing hand He give me,

Copyright, 1898, by W. H. Doane

If the Saviour Journey with Me

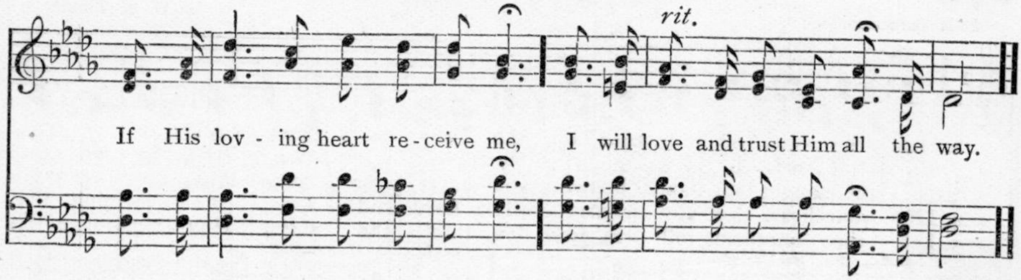
rit.
If His lov - ing heart re - ceive me, I will love and trust Him all the way.

At the Cross 278

Isaac Watts

R. E. Hudson

1. A - las! and did my Saviour bleed, And did my Sovereign die? Would He devote that sa - cred head For such a worm as I?
2. Was it for crimes that I have done, He groaned upon the tree? A - maz - ing pit - y, grace un - known, And love be - yond de - gree!
3. But drops of grief can ne'er re-pay The debt of love I owe; Here, Lord, I give my - self a - way, 'Tis all that I can do!
CHORUS
At the cross, at the cross, where I first saw the light, And the bur - den of my heart rolled a - way,
rolled a-way,
It was there by faith I re-ceived my sight, And now I am hap-py all the day.

Copyright, 1885, by R. E. Hudson

279 Bring Ye All the Tithes

(*Mal. 3: 10*)

Helen E. Rasmussen — H. L. Gilmour

1. Hear the words of scrip-ture from the a - ges past, "Bring ye all the
2. Do you seek to know the Ho - ly Spir - it's power? "Bring ye all the
3. Is there aught that stands be-tween you and your Lord? "Bring ye all the
4. Lift your heart this mo - ment: claim Him Lord and King, As ye bring the
5. Let the an-thems roll in gran-deur thro' the skies, Hav - ing brought the
tithes in - to the store-house," Make a con - se - cra - tion that will ev - er last,
tithes in - to the store-house." Live in sweet commun - ion with Him hour by hour,
tithes in - to the store-house." Bring them on con - di - tions prom-ised in His word,
tithes in - to the store-house. Trust the bless - ed prom - ise, and your praise shall ring,
tithes in - to the store-house; Joy - ous hal - le - lu - jahs from our hearts a - rise
Trust - ing for the prom-ised bless - ing.
While He gives the prom-ised bless - ing.
And He'll pour you out a bless - ing.
From the heart He is pos - sess - ing.
For we have the prom-ised bless - ing.
CHORUS
"Bring ye all the tithes in - to the store - house, And prove me now saith the Lord of hosts; And I will pour you out a bless - ing, There shall not be room e - nough to re - ceive it."

Copyright, 1899, by H. L. Gilmour. Used by per.

The Hope of the Coming of the Lord

Major D. W. Whittle

May Whittle Moody

1. A lamp in the night, a song in time of sor - row; A great glad hope which faith can ev - er bor - row To gild the pass-ing day with the glo - ry of the mor-row,
2. A star in the sky, a bea - con bright to guide us; An an - chor sure to hold when storms betide us; A ref - uge for the soul, where in qui - et we may hide us,
3. A call of command, like trum-pet clear - ly sound - ing, To make us bold when e - vil is sur-round-ing; To stir the slug-gish heart, and to keep in good a-bound-ing,
4. A word from the One to all our hearts the dear - est, A part - ing word to make Him aye the near - est; Of all His precious words, the sweet-est, bright-est, clear-est,
Is the hope of the com-ing of the Lord.
CHORUS
Bless-ed hope, . . . bless-ed hope, . .
blessed hope, blessed hope,
Bless - ed hope of the com - ing of the Lord;
How the ach - ing heart it cheers,
How it glis - tens thro' our tears,
Bless-ed hope of the com - ing of the Lord.

Copyright, 1896, by May Whittle Moody

281 Will There be Any Stars

E. E. Hewitt — Jno. R. Sweney

1. I am think - ing to - day of that beau - ti - ful land I shall reach when the
2. In the strength of the Lord let me la - bor and pray, Let me watch as a
3. Oh, what joy will it be when His face I be - hold, Liv - ing gems at His
sun go - eth down; When thro' wonder - ful grace by my Sav - iour I stand, Will there
win - ner of souls; That bright stars may be mine in the glo - ri - ous day, When His
feet to lay down; It would sweet-en my bliss in the cit - y of gold, Should there
CHORUS
be a - ny stars in my crown? Will there be a - ny stars, a - ny stars in my crown,
praise like the sea - bil - low rolls.
be a - ny stars in my crown.
When at eve - ning the sun go - eth down? . . When I wake with the blest
go - eth down?
In the man - sions of rest, Will there be a - ny stars in my crown? . .
a - ny stars in my crown?

Copyright, 1897, by Jno. R. Sweney. Used by per.

The Heavenly Summer-land

Alice Jean Cleator

J. Lincoln Hall

1. Be - yond the win-ter's storm and blight, Be - yond the sum-mer's shin - ing strand,
2. No lin - g'ring shad-ow of the night Shall dim the glo - ry of that shore;
3. No part - ing word, no tears nor pain, Shall pass those por - tals fair and bright,
There waits a land of joy and light— O bright and fade-less sum-mer - land!
There all is joy and song and light And rest and peace for - ev - er - more!
There part - ed friends shall meet a - gain, With - in that land of love and light!
CHORUS
O summer-land, . . . that gleams a - far, ... Beyond the light . . .
O summerland, that gleams a-far, be-yond the light
of sun or star, ... O sum-mer - land, ... O sum-mer -
of sun or star, O sum-mer-land,
land, . . . We long for thee, ... dear sum-mer - land.
O sum-mer-land, we long for thee, dear sum-mer-land.

Copyright, 1899, by Hall-Mack Co. Used by per.

283 The Length of Life

Amos R. Wells — Percy S. Foster

1. Are your sor - rows hard to bear? Life is short! Do you drag the chain of care? Life is short! Soon will come the glad re - lease In - to joy and rest and peace; Soon the wea - ry thread be spun, And the fi - nal la - bor done.
2. Are you faint with hope de - layed? Life is long! Tar - ries that for which you prayed? Life is long! What de - lights may not a - bide,— What am - bi - tions sat - is - fied, What pos - ses - sions may not be, In God's great e - ter - ni - ty?
rall.
Refrain
Keep your cour - age, hold the fort! Life is short! Keep your cour - age, hold the fort! Life is short!
Lift the heart, be glad and strong! Life is long! Lift the heart, be glad and strong! Life is long!
3
3

Copyright, 1901, by Percy S. Foster.

"In His Steps"

284

F. E. O.

French E. Oliver

1. "In His steps" how sweet to fol - low; "In His steps," in joy or sor - row;
2. "In His steps," my sin con - fess - ing; "In His steps," His love pos - sess - ing;
3. "In His steps," my - self de - ny - ing; "In His steps," on Him re - ly - ing;
4. "In His steps," the spir - it giv - ing; "In His steps," more grace re - ceiv - ing,
"In His steps," to - day, to - mor - row, Fol - low Je - sus all the way.
"In His steps" I find a bless - ing, Fol-low-ing Je - sus day by day.
"In His steps," for grace I'm sigh - ing, E'er to fol - low on - ly Him.
"In His steps," with Christ I'm liv - ing, Pre - cious Sav - iour, Thou art mine.
CHORUS
For here - un - to were you call - ed, Christ hath suf-fered for you,
Thus leav - ing you an ex - am - ple To fol - low in His steps.

Words and music copyright, 1898, by French E. Oliver

285 Nor Silver nor Gold

James M. Gray D. B. Towner

1. Nor sil - ver nor gold hath ob-tained my re-demp-tion, No val - ue on
2. Nor sil - ver nor gold hath ob-tained my re-demp-tion, The guilt on my
3. Nor sil - ver nor gold hath ob-tained my re-demp-tion, The ho - ly com-
4. Nor sil - ver nor gold hath ob-tained my re-demp-tion, The way in - to
earth could have saved my poor soul; The blood of the cross is my
con - science too heav - y had grown; The blood of the cross is my
mand - ment for - bade me draw near; The blood of the cross is my
heav - en could not thus be bought; The blood of the cross is my
on - ly foun - da - tion, The death of my Sav - iour now mak - eth me whole.
on - ly foun - da - tion, The death of my Sav - iour could on - ly a - tone.
on - ly foun - da - tion, The death of my Sav - iour re - mov - eth my fear.
on - ly foun - da - tion, The death of my Sav - iour re - demption hath wrought.
CHORUS
I am re - deemed, ... but not with sil - ver,
I am re - deemed, I am re - deemed, but not with sil - ver,
I am bought, . . . but not with gold,
I am bought, I am bought, but not with gold,
Bought with a

Copyright, 1900, by D. B. Towner

Nor Silver Nor Gold

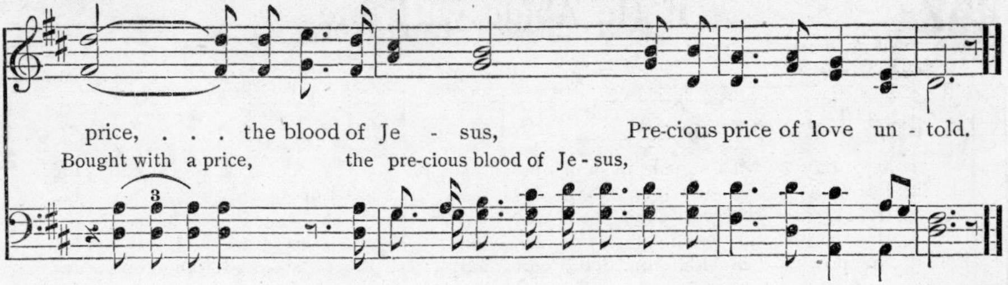
price, . . . the blood of Je - sus, Pre-cious price of love un - told.
Bought with a price, the pre-cious blood of Je - sus,
3

I Love to Tell the Story

286

Kate Hankey

W. G. Fischer

1. I love to tell the sto - ry Of un-seen things above, Of Je - sus and His glo - ry,
2. I love to tell the sto - ry, 'Tis pleasant to re - peat What seems,each time I tell it,
3. I love to tell the sto - ry, For those who know it best Seem hungering and thirsting
Of Je - sus and His love. I love to tell the sto - ry, Be - cause I know 'tis true;
More won-der - ful - ly sweet. I love to tell the sto - ry, For some have nev-er heard
To hear it like the rest. And when,in scenes of glory, I sing the new,new song,
CHORUS
It sat - is-fies my longings As noth - ing else can do. I love to tell the sto - ry,
The mes-sage of sal - va-tion, From God's own holy word.
'Twill be the old,old sto - ry, That I have loved so long.
'Twill be my theme in glory, To tell the old, old sto - ry, Of Je - sus and His love.

Used by per.

287 If He Abide with Me

Mrs. Frank A. Breck — Grant Colfax Tullar

DUET
1. My days with sun-shine shall be fraught, My sor - row, joy shall be,
2. No e - vil ev - er shall be - fall, No bur - dens heav - y be,
3. If shad - ows make my path - way dim, I shall not need to see;
4. My storms are calm at His be - hest, Who spoke to Gal - i - lee,
5. No pow'rs of life or death can harm, All griefs and dan - gers flee,
And thorn - y ways shall seem as naught, If Christ a - bide with me.
For Christ will glad - ly take them all If He a - bide with me.
But sweet - ly trust my way with Him Who will a - bide with me.
And fears shall nev - er rob my rest, If Christ a - bide with me.
If I but trust in Christ's strong arm, When He a - bides with me.
CHORUS
I shall be safe - - ly kept from sin, ... My life be
I shall be safe - ly, safe - ly kept from sin,
glad . . . . . and free; . . . . For I shall have . . . sweet peace with-
Each mo - ment glad and free, yes, glad and free; For I shall have sweet
in, ... If Christ a - bide . . . . . with me. . . . . .
peace, sweet peace with-in, If Christ a - bide with me, a - bide with me.
rit.

Copyright, 1899, by Tullar-Meredith Co, Used by per.

288 Crossing the Bar

Alfred Tennyson — Frank Leslie Stone, 1901

Earnestly

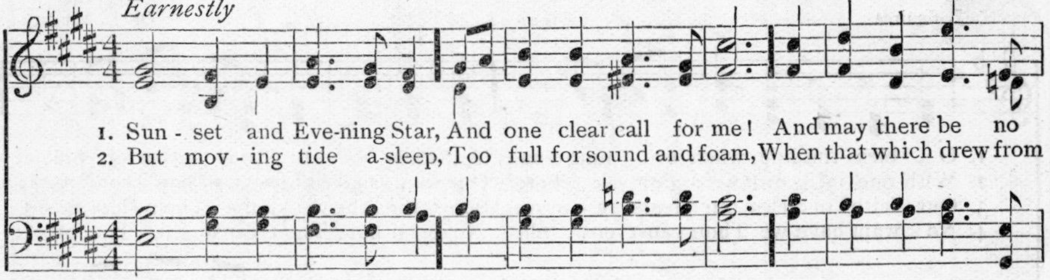
Earnestly
1. Sun - set and Eve-ning Star, And one clear call for me! And may there be no
2. But mov - ing tide a-sleep, Too full for sound and foam, When that which drew from

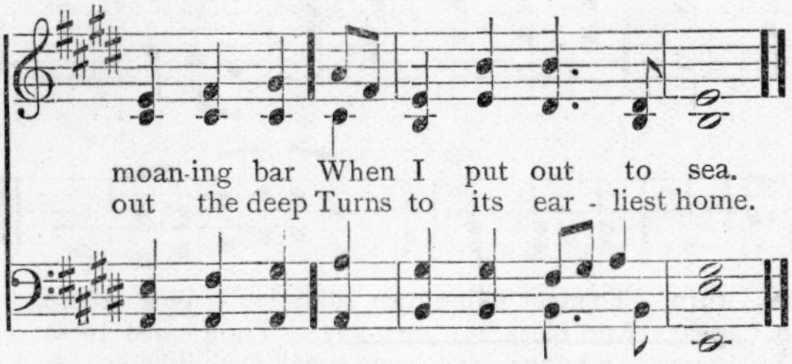
moan-ing bar When I put out to sea.
out the deep Turns to its ear - liest home.

3 Twilight and Evening Bell,
And after that the dark!
And may there be no sad farewell,
When I at last embark.

4 For tho' from Time and Place,
The flood may bear me far,
I hope to see my Pilot's face,
When I have crossed the bar.

Copyright, 1901, by U. S. C. E.

289 Sleep On, Beloved

Sarah Doudney — (*Doudney* 10. 10. 10. 4) — Carey Bonner

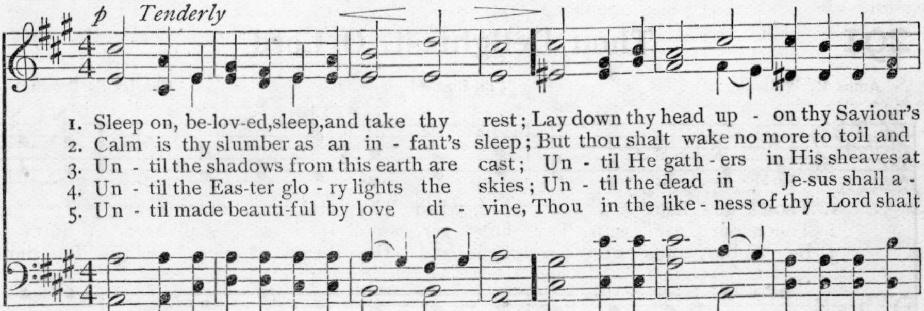
p Tenderly
1. Sleep on, be-lov-ed, sleep, and take thy rest; Lay down thy head up - on thy Saviour's
2. Calm is thy slumber as an in - fant's sleep; But thou shalt wake no more to toil and
3. Un - til the shadows from this earth are cast; Un - til He gath - ers in His sheaves at
4. Un - til the Eas-ter glo - ry lights the skies; Un - til the dead in Je-sus shall a -
5. Un - til made beauti-ful by love di - vine, Thou in the like - ness of thy Lord shalt

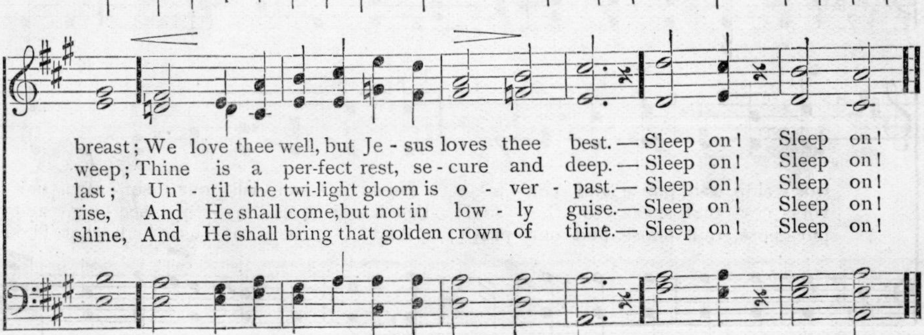
breast; We love thee well, but Je - sus loves thee best. — Sleep on! Sleep on!
weep; Thine is a per-fect rest, se - cure and deep. — Sleep on! Sleep on!
last; Un - til the twi-light gloom is o - ver - past.— Sleep on! Sleep on!
rise, And He shall come, but not in low - ly guise.— Sleep on! Sleep on!
shine, And He shall bring that golden crown of thine.— Sleep on! Sleep on!

Used by per.

290 O Bless the Hour

N. J. Squires (*Ernan L. M.*) Dr. L. Mason

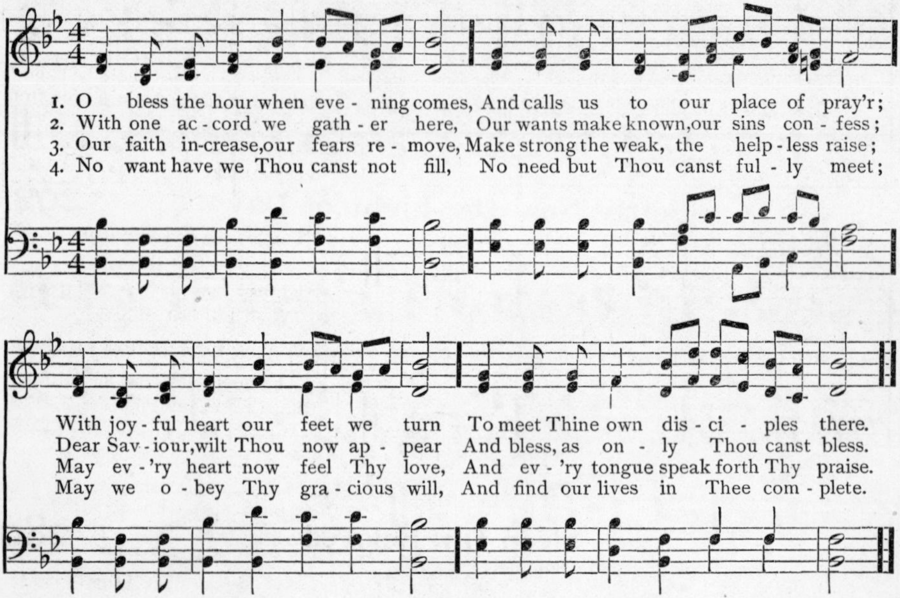
1. O bless the hour when eve - ning comes, And calls us to our place of pray'r;
2. With one ac - cord we gath - er here, Our wants make known, our sins con - fess;
3. Our faith in-crease, our fears re - move, Make strong the weak, the help - less raise;
4. No want have we Thou canst not fill, No need but Thou canst ful - ly meet;
With joy - ful heart our feet we turn To meet Thine own dis - ci - ples there.
Dear Sav - iour, wilt Thou now ap - pear And bless, as on - ly Thou canst bless.
May ev - 'ry heart now feel Thy love, And ev - 'ry tongue speak forth Thy praise.
May we o - bey Thy gra - cious will, And find our lives in Thee com - plete.

291 Thou Delightest, O Lord

Amos R. Wells (*12.8.12.8*) Charles S. Brown

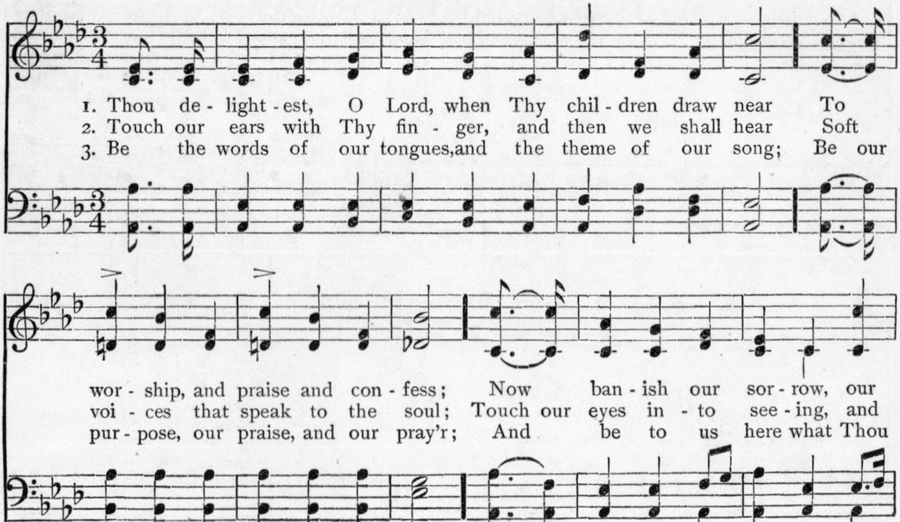
1. Thou de - light - est, O Lord, when Thy chil - dren draw near To
2. Touch our ears with Thy fin - ger, and then we shall hear Soft
3. Be the words of our tongues, and the theme of our song; Be our
wor - ship, and praise and con - fess; Now ban - ish our sor - row, our
voi - ces that speak to the soul; Touch our eyes in - to see - ing, and
pur - pose, our praise, and our pray'r; And be to us here what Thou

Copyright, 1901, by U. S. C. E,

Thou Delightest, O Lord

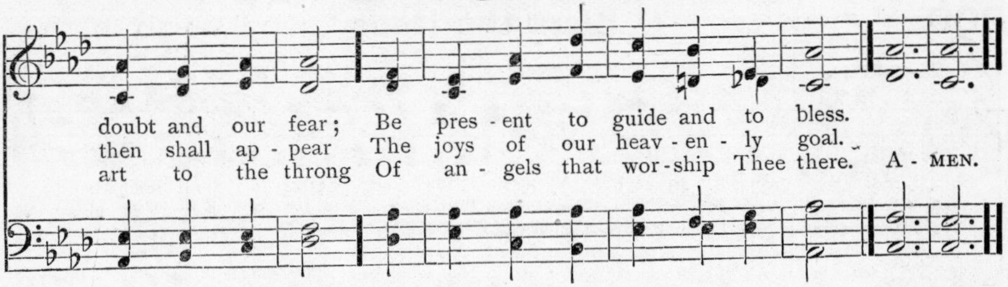
doubt and our fear; Be pres - ent to guide and to bless.
then shall ap - pear The joys of our heav - en - ly goal.
art to the throng Of an - gels that wor - ship Thee there. A - MEN.

Softly Now the Light of Day 292

G. W. Doane, 1827 (*Seymour 7s*) Arr. fr. C. M. Von Weber, 1826

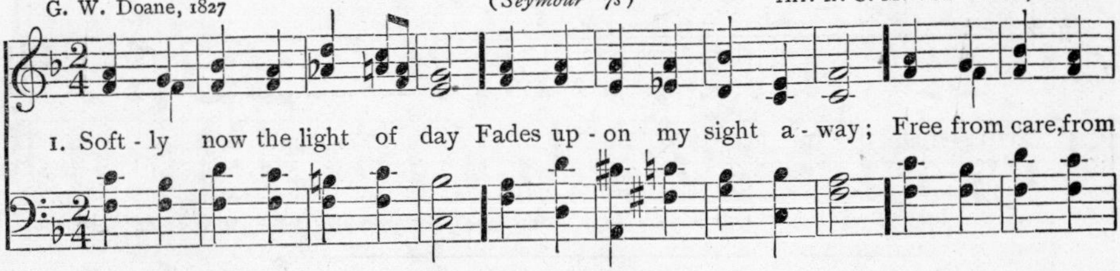
1. Soft - ly now the light of day Fades up - on my sight a - way; Free from care, from

la - bor free, Lord, I would commune with Thee.

2 Thou, whose all-pervading eye
Naught escapes, without, within,
Pardon each infirmity,
Open fault, and secret sin.

3 Soon, for me, the light of day
Shall forever pass away;
Then, from sin and sorrow free,
Take me, Lord, to dwell with Thee.

My God, is Any Hour So Sweet 293

Charlotte Elliott, 1834 (*Almsgiving 8s.4*) J. B. Dykes

1. My God, is a - ny hour so sweet, From blush of morn to eve - ning star, As that which
2. No words can tell what sweet re - lief Here for my ev - 'ry want I find; What strength for

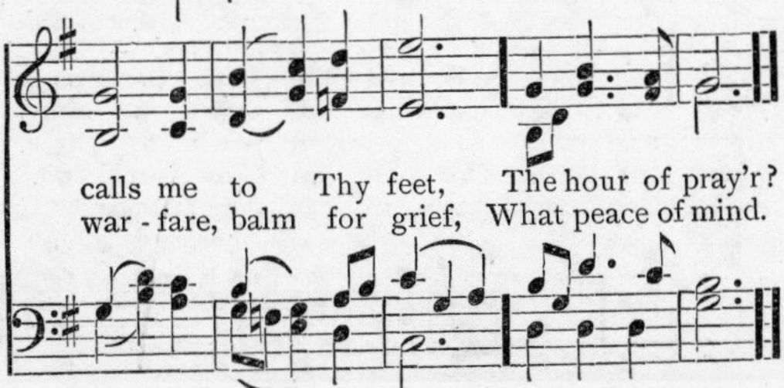
calls me to Thy feet, The hour of pray'r?
war - fare, balm for grief, What peace of mind.

3 Hushed is each doubt, gone every fear;
My spirit seems in heaven to stay;
And e'en the penitential tear
Is wiped away.

4 Lord, till I reach that blissful shore,
No privilege so dear shall be
As thus my inmost soul to pour
In prayer to Thee.

294 "Certainly I Will be with Thee"

Frances R. Havergal (8s. 7s) Arr. for this work by Laurence R. Grose

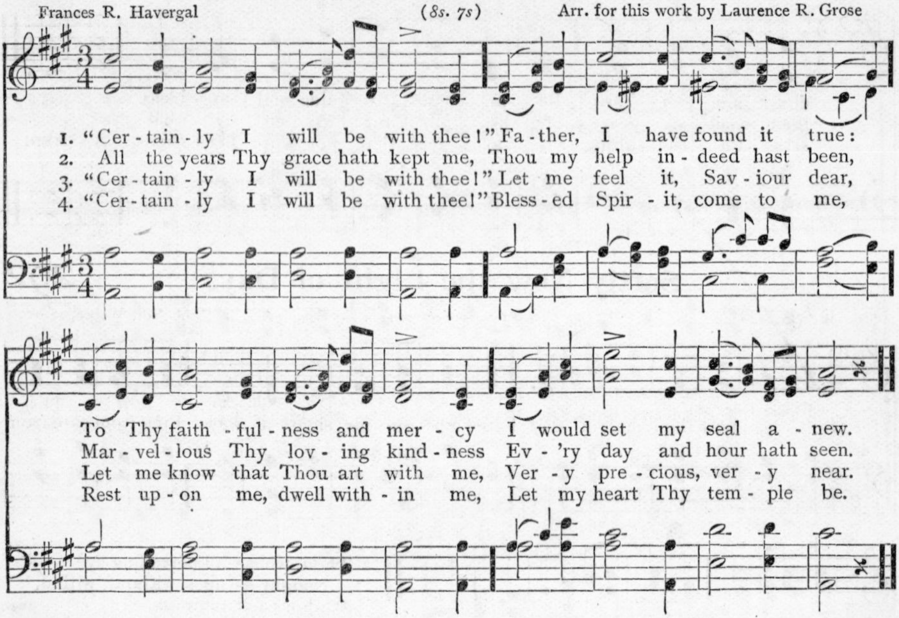
1. "Cer - tain - ly I will be with thee!" Fa - ther, I have found it true:
2. All the years Thy grace hath kept me, Thou my help in - deed hast been,
3. "Cer - tain - ly I will be with thee!" Let me feel it, Sav - iour dear,
4. "Cer - tain - ly I will be with thee!" Bless - ed Spir - it, come to me,
To Thy faith - ful - ness and mer - cy I would set my seal a - new.
Mar - vel - lous Thy lov - ing kind - ness Ev - 'ry day and hour hath seen.
Let me know that Thou art with me, Ver - y pre - cious, ver - y near.
Rest up - on me, dwell with - in me, Let my heart Thy tem - ple be.

295 *Saviour, Like a Shepherd Lead Us*

Dorothy Ann Thrupp, 1838 William Gillespie

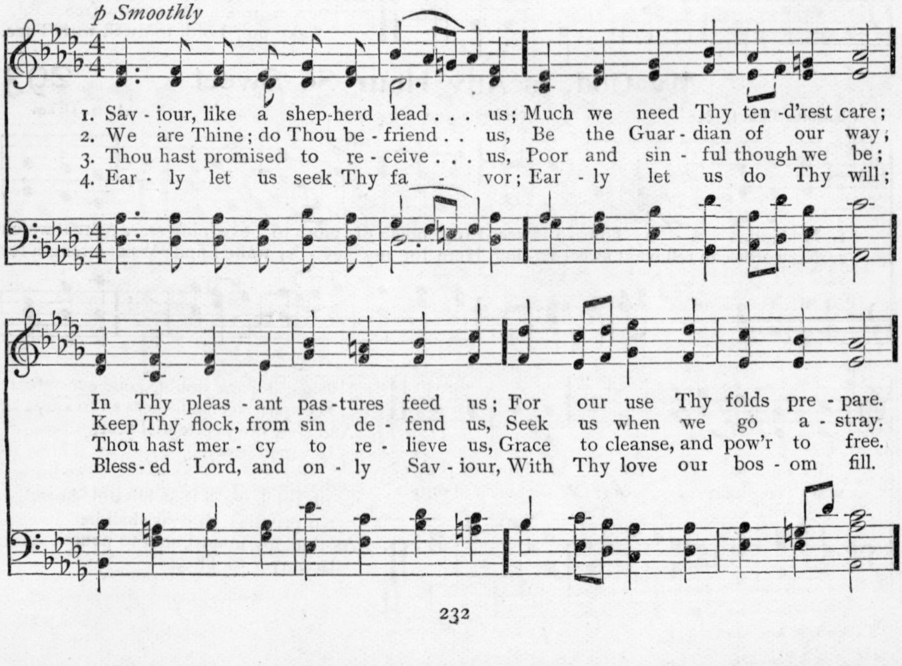
p Smoothly
1. Sav - iour, like a shep-herd lead . . . us; Much we need Thy ten-d'rest care;
2. We are Thine; do Thou be - friend . . us, Be the Guar - dian of our way;
3. Thou hast promised to re - ceive . . . us, Poor and sin - ful though we be;
4. Ear - ly let us seek Thy fa - vor; Ear - ly let us do Thy will;
In Thy pleas - ant pas - tures feed us; For our use Thy folds pre - pare.
Keep Thy flock, from sin de - fend us, Seek us when we go a - stray.
Thou hast mer - cy to re - lieve us, Grace to cleanse, and pow'r to free.
Bless - ed Lord, and on - ly Sav - iour, With Thy love our bos - om fill.

Saviour, Like a Shepherd Lead Us

p CHORUS
Bless - ed Je - sus, Bless - ed Je - sus, Thou hast bought us, Thine we are;
Bless - ed Je - sus, Bless - ed Je - sus, Hear, O hear us, when we pray;
Bless - ed Je - sus, Bless - ed Je - sus, We will ear - ly turn to Thee;
Bless - ed Je - sus, Bless - ed Je - sus, Thou hast loved us, love us still;
cres.
Bless - ed Je - sus, Bless-ed Je - sus, . Thou hast bought us, Thine we are.
Bless - ed Je - sus, Bless-ed Je - sus, . Hear, O hear us, when we pray.
Bless - ed Je - sus, Bless-ed Je - sus, . We will ear - ly turn to Thee.
Bless - ed Je - sus, Bless-ed Je - sus, . Thou hast loved us, love us still.

Evening Prayer 296

Samuel Longfellow

(*L. M.*)

Arr. from von Weber by F. L. Stone

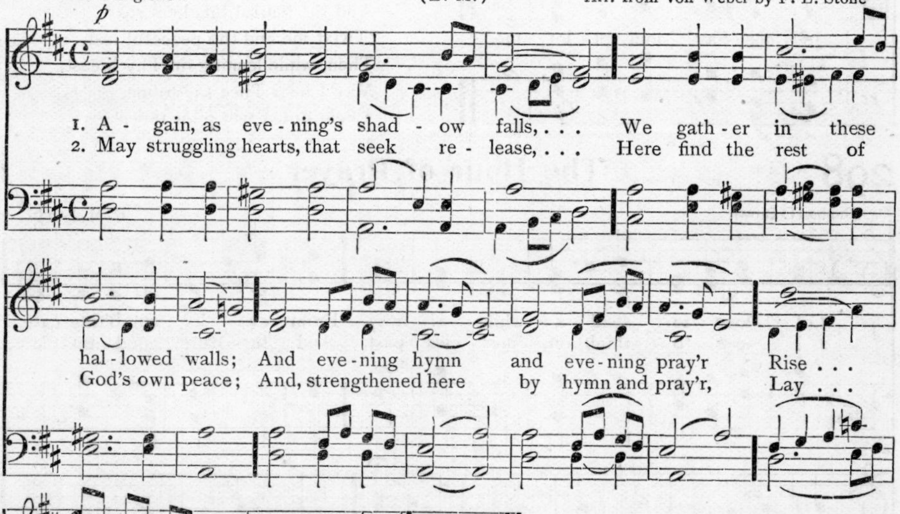
p
1. A - gain, as eve - ning's shad - ow falls, . . . We gath - er in these
2. May struggling hearts, that seek re - lease, . . . Here find the rest of
hal - lowed walls; And eve - ning hymn and eve - ning pray'r Rise . . .
God's own peace; And, strengthened here by hymn and pray'r, Lay . . .

ming - ling on the ho - ly air.
down the bur - den and the care. A - MEN.

3 O God our Light, to Thee we bow;
Within all shadows standest Thou;
Give deeper calm than night can bring,
Give sweeter songs than life can sing.

4 Life's tumult we must meet again,
We cannot at the shrine remain;
But in the spirit's secret cell,
May hymn and prayer forever dwell.
AMEN.

Copyright, 1901, by U. S. C. E.

297 Jesus, Saviour, Pilot Me

Edward Hopper, 1871 (*Pilot 7s. 6l.*) J. E. Gould

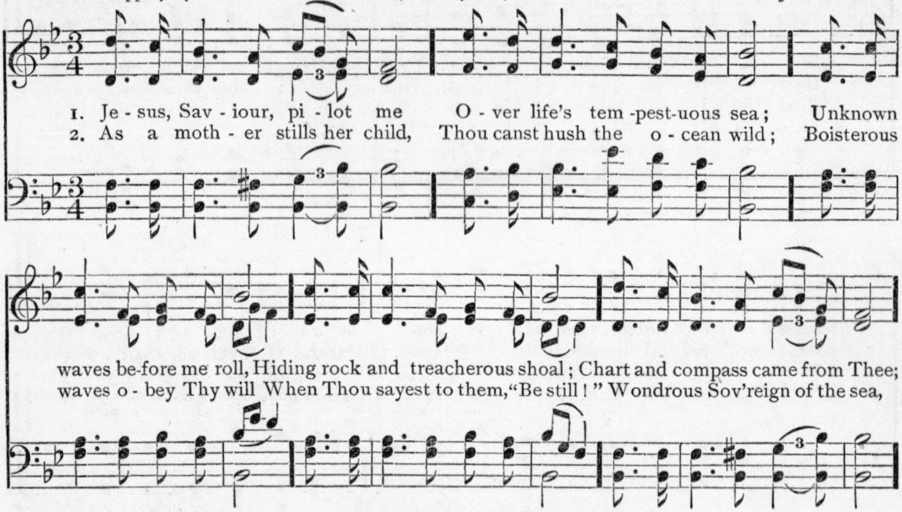
1. Je - sus, Sav - iour, pi - lot me O - ver life's tem - pest-uous sea; Unknown
2. As a moth - er stills her child, Thou canst hush the o - cean wild; Boisterous
waves be-fore me roll, Hiding rock and treacherous shoal; Chart and compass came from Thee;
waves o - bey Thy will When Thou sayest to them, "Be still!" Wondrous Sov'reign of the sea,

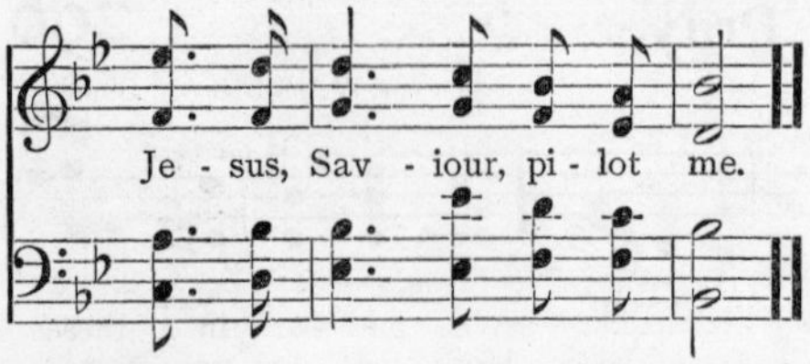
Je - sus, Sav - iour, pi - lot me.

3 When at last I near the shore,
And the fearful breakers roar
'Twixt me and the peaceful rest,
Then, while leaning on Thy breast,
May I hear Thee say to me,
"Fear not, I will pilot thee."

298 The Hour of Prayer

Phœbe H. Brown F. M. Lamb

1. I love to steal a - while a - way From ev - 'ry cumb'ring care,
2. I love to think on mer - cies past, And fu - ture good im - plore,
And spend the hours of set - ting day In hum - ble, grate - ful pray'r.
And all my cares and sor - rows cast On Him whom I a - dore.

Used by per.

The Hour of Prayer

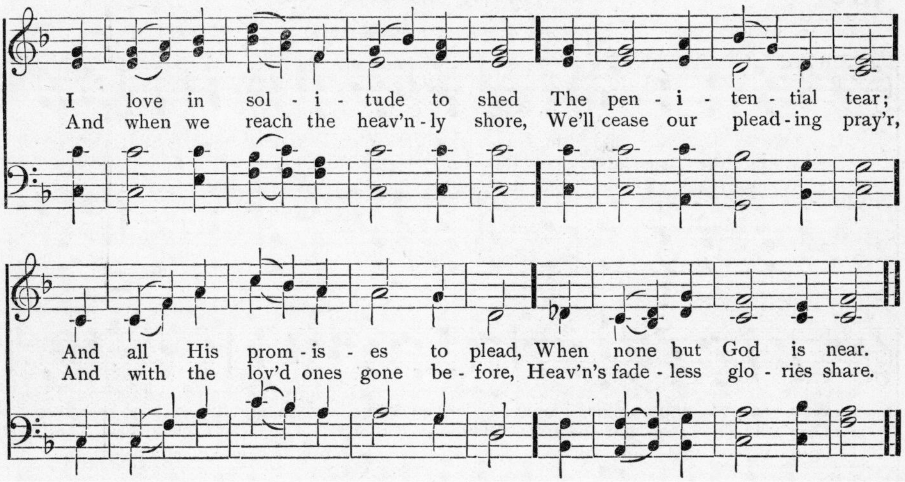
I love in sol - i - tude to shed The pen - i - ten - tial tear;
And when we reach the heav'n - ly shore, We'll cease our plead - ing pray'r,
And all His prom - is - es to plead, When none but God is near.
And with the lov'd ones gone be - fore, Heav'n's fade - less glo - ries share.

Jesus, My All

299

Fanny J. Crosby

Anon.

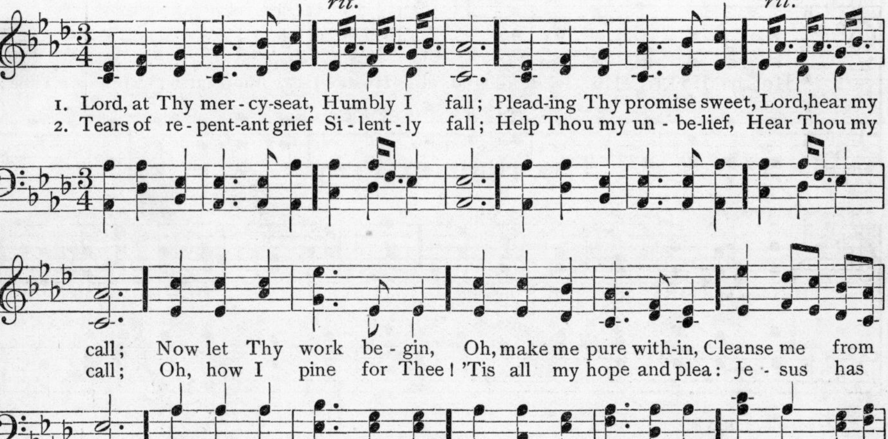
rit.
rit.
1. Lord, at Thy mer - cy-seat, Humbly I fall; Plead-ing Thy promise sweet, Lord, hear my call; Now let Thy work be - gin, Oh, make me pure with-in, Cleanse me from
2. Tears of re - pent-ant grief Si - lent - ly fall; Help Thou my un - be-lief, Hear Thou my call; Oh, how I pine for Thee! 'Tis all my hope and plea: Je - sus has

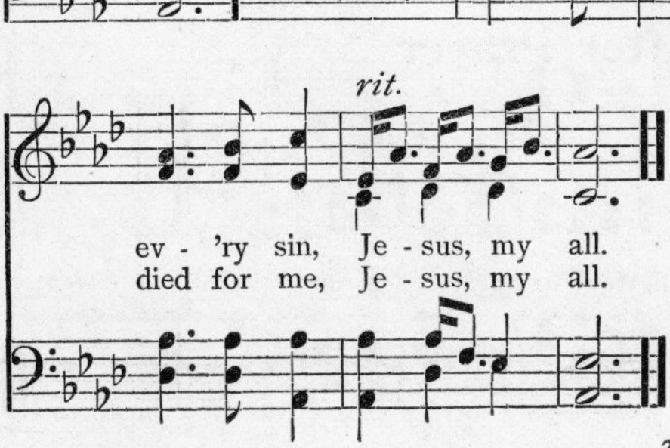
rit.
ev - 'ry sin, Je - sus, my all.
died for me, Je - sus, my all.

3 Still at Thy mercy-seat,
Saviour, I fall;
Trusting Thy promise sweet,
Heard is my call;
Faith wings my soul to Thee;
This all my song shall be:
Jesus has died for me,
Jesus, my all.

300 Day is Dying in the West

Mary Ann Lathbury, 1877 (*Evening Praise 7s. 4 with Refrain*) William F. Sherwin, 1877

1. Day is dy - ing in the west; Heav'n is touch - ing earth with rest;
2. While the deep - 'ning shad - ows fall, Heart of Love, en - fold - ing all,
3. When for ev - er from our sight Pass the stars, the day, the night,
Wait and wor-ship while the night Sets her ev - 'ning lamps a-light Thro' all the sky.
Thro' the glo - ry and the grace Of the stars that veil Thy face, Our hearts as - cend.
Lord of an - gels, on our eyes Let e - ter - nal morning rise, And shad-ows end.
pp REFRAIN
Ho - ly, Ho - ly, Ho - ly, Lord God of Hosts! Heav'n and earth are full of Thee;
f
Heaven and earth are prais - ing Thee, O Lord Most High!
ff
A - MEN.

Copyright by J. H. Vincent

301 Response After Prayer

(*Castle Eden 6s. 5s.*) R. W. Dixon

Hear us, Heav'nly Father; While on Thee we call, May Thy benediction On our spirits fall. A - MEN.

Whatever He Would Like 302

E. M. Fergusson (*Pledge Hymn*) Charles S. Brown

1. Com-ing in the name of Je - sus, Grace we seek with one ac-cord, Not to do the
2. Dai - ly seek-ing strength and guiding, Faithful to the church we love, In the life of
3. In our hap-py meet - ing hour We would al - ways claim a share, Own - ing Je - sus'

things that please us, But the things that please our Lord. Foll'wing Him is our en-deav - or,
trust a - bid - ing, Till we share the life a-bove; We will leave the Sav - iour nev - er,
love and pow - er, In a word, a song, a pray'r. Be our help, dear Lord, for - ev - er;

To our promise keeping true; Striving still to do what-ev-er He would like to have us do.
We would pledge ourselves anew; We will strive to do whatever He would like to have us do.
Nerve our courage, bring us thro', Till we love to do whatever Thou wouldst like to have us do.

Copyright, 1899, by U. S. C. E.

The Lord's Prayer 303

Gregorian

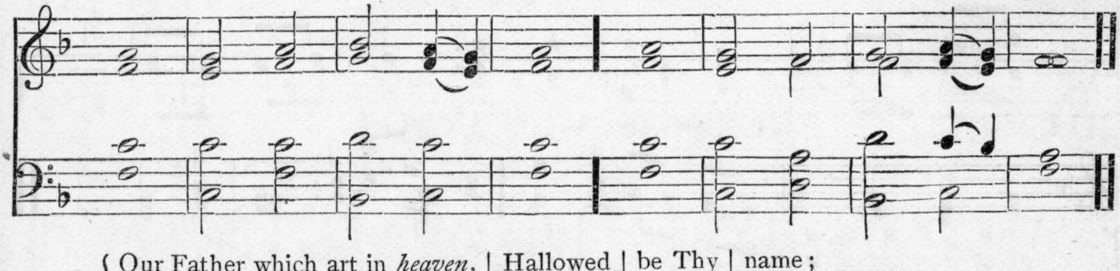

1. { Our Father which art in *heaven*, | Hallowed | be Thy | name;
   Thy kingdom come; Thy will be *done* on | earth · as it | is in | heaven;
2. { Give *us* this | day our | dai-ly | bread;
   And forgive us our *debts*, as | we for- | give our | debtors;
3. { And lead us not into temp*ta*tion, but de- | liv-er | us from | evil;
   For Thine is the kingdom, and the power, and the *glo*ry, for- | ev-er. | A- — | MEN.

304 Praise Ye the Lord

(*P. M.*)

J. E. H. J. E. Hall

f With spirit

1. Praise ye the Lord, lift up the voice with sing - ing, Tell to the world the
2. Praise ye the Lord, with ho - ly ad - o - ra - tion; Wor - thy is He of
3. Praise ye the Lord, and wor - ship Him with glad - ness, Thanks to His name for
glo - ry of His name; Join in the song while joy - ful notes are ring - ing
all our love and praise; Look un - to Him, the Rock of our Sal - va - tion;
all His won-drous love; Praise ye the Lord, let prais - es ban - ish sad - ness
Far o'er the earth, O spread a - broad His fame.
His gra - cious hand hath led us all our days.
Now and for - ev - er, till we meet a - bove.
Refrain
Yes, we'll tell the won - drous sto - ry, We will laud His ho - ly name;
And will give our best en - deav - or Still to spread a-broad His fame.

Jesus is Precious

305

Grant Colfax Tullar — I. H. Meredith

p
1. Peace like a riv - er is flood - ing my soul, Since Christ, my Sav - iour,
2. Joy is a-bounding—my heart gai - ly sings, Cleave I the heavens—
3. Oh, pre-cious Je - sus, how love - ly Thou art! Come and a - bid - ing
mak - eth me whole; Sweet peace a - bid - ing my por - tion shall be—
mount up on wings; Christ hath ex - alt - ed—my soul He set free—
rule in my heart; Break ev - 'ry fet - ter—Thy face let me see,
Je - sus, my Sav - iour, is pre - cious to me.
Je - sus, my Sav - iour, is pre - cious to me.
Then Thou shalt ev - er be pre - cious to me.
CHORUS
Pre - cious to me, ... Pre - - - cious is He; . . . .
Pre-cious to me, He is pre - cious to me, Je - sus, my Sav - iour, how pre - cious is He;
Je - sus shall ev - er . . . be pre - cious to me. . . .
Je - sus, my Sav - iour, ev - er shall be so pre-cious to me, so pre-cious to me.

Copyright, 1899, by Tullar-Meredith Co. Used by per.

306 Saviour, Breathe an Evening Blessing

J. Edmeston, 1820

Arr. fr. L. O. Emerson
by Laurence R. Grose

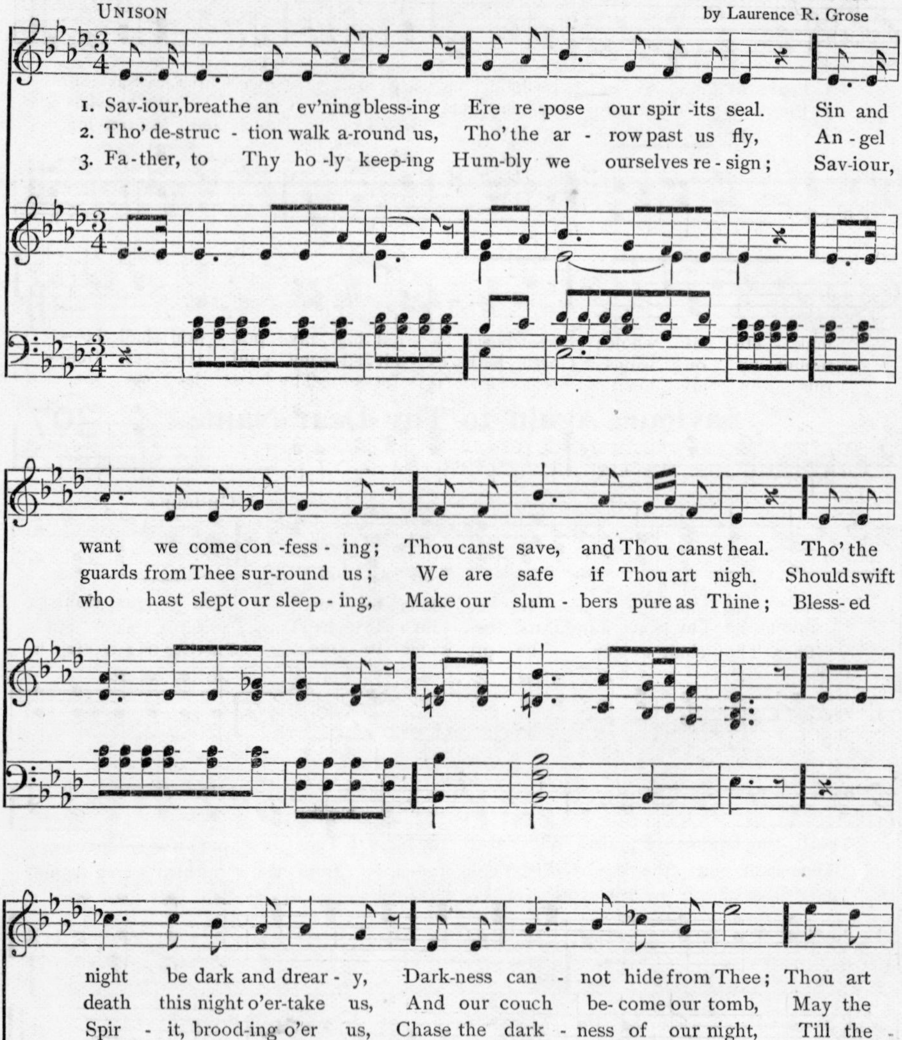
UNISON
1. Sav-iour, breathe an ev'ning bless-ing Ere re-pose our spir-its seal. Sin and
2. Tho' de-struc-tion walk a-round us, Tho' the ar-row past us fly, An-gel
3. Fa-ther, to Thy ho-ly keep-ing Hum-bly we ourselves re-sign; Sav-iour,
want we come con-fess-ing; Thou canst save, and Thou canst heal. Tho' the
guards from Thee sur-round us; We are safe if Thou art nigh. Should swift
who hast slept our sleep-ing, Make our slum-bers pure as Thine; Bless-ed
night be dark and drear-y, Dark-ness can-not hide from Thee; Thou art
death this night o'er-take us, And our couch be-come our tomb, May the
Spir-it, brood-ing o'er us, Chase the dark-ness of our night, Till the-

Copyright owned by O. Ditson & Co. By per.

Saviour, Breathe an Evening Blessing

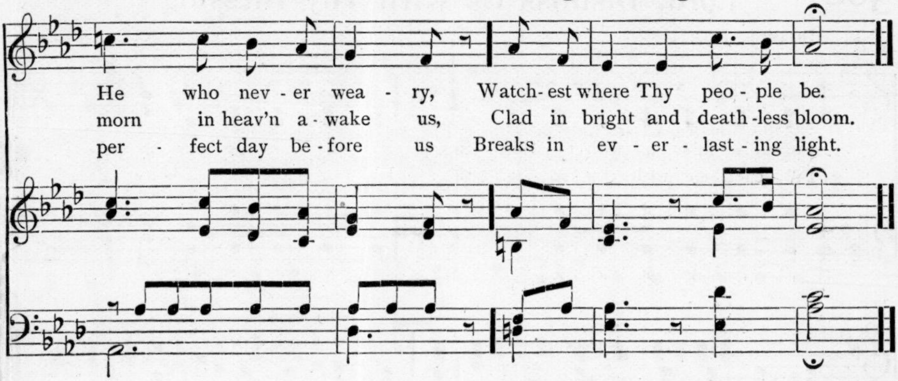
He who never wea - ry, Watch-est where Thy peo - ple be.
morn in heav'n a - wake us, Clad in bright and death-less bloom.
per - fect day be - fore us Breaks in ev - er - last - ing light.

Saviour, Again to Thy Dear Name 307

John Ellerton, 1866 (*Benediction* 10s) E. J. Hopkins, 1867

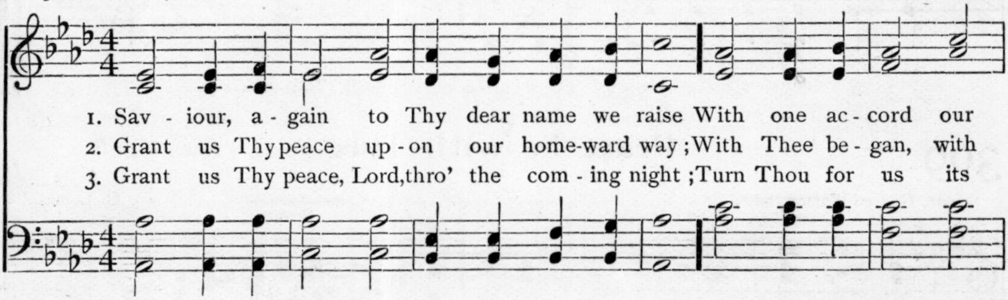
1. Sav - iour, a - gain to Thy dear name we raise With one ac - cord our
2. Grant us Thy peace up - on our home-ward way; With Thee be - gan, with
3. Grant us Thy peace, Lord, thro' the com - ing night; Turn Thou for us its

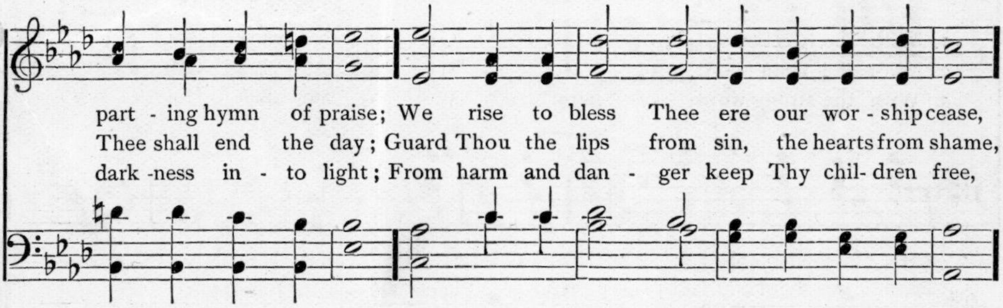
part - ing hymn of praise; We rise to bless Thee ere our wor - ship cease,
Thee shall end the day; Guard Thou the lips from sin, the hearts from shame,
dark - ness in - to light; From harm and dan - ger keep Thy chil - dren free,

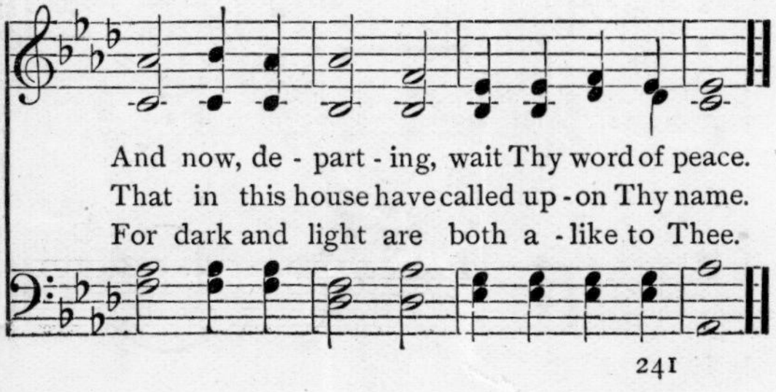
And now, de - part - ing, wait Thy word of peace.
That in this house have called up - on Thy name.
For dark and light are both a - like to Thee.

4 Grant us Thy peace throughout our earthly life,
Our balm in sorrow, and our stay in strife;
Then, when Thy voice shall bid our conflict cease,
Call us, O Lord, to Thine eternal peace.

308 Lord, Dismiss Us with Thy Blessing

Robert Hawkes, D.D. *(8s. 7s)* C. C. Converse

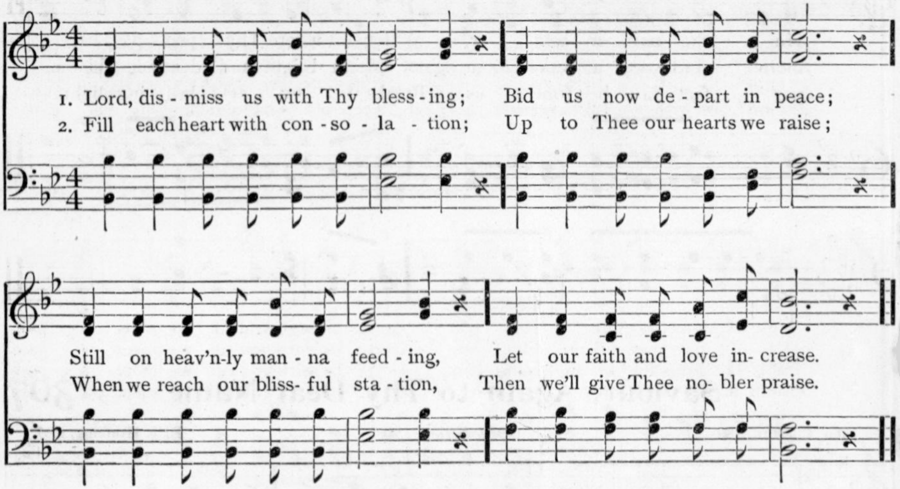
1. Lord, dis - miss us with Thy bless - ing; Bid us now de - part in peace;
2. Fill each heart with con - so - la - tion; Up to Thee our hearts we raise;
Still on heav'n-ly man - na feed - ing, Let our faith and love in - crease.
When we reach our bliss - ful sta - tion, Then we'll give Thee no - bler praise.

309 Peace be with Thee

From George Watson, ad. *(Verbum Pacis P. M.)* G. Lomas

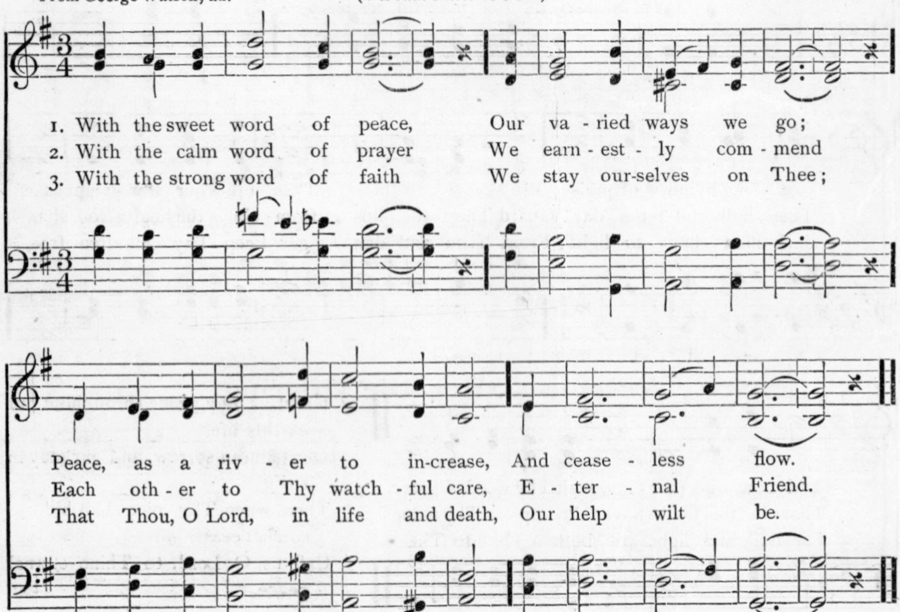
1. With the sweet word of peace, Our va - ried ways we go;
2. With the calm word of prayer We earn - est - ly com - mend
3. With the strong word of faith We stay our-selves on Thee;
Peace, as a riv - er to in-crease, And cease - less flow.
Each oth - er to Thy watch - ful care, E - ter - nal Friend.
That Thou, O Lord, in life and death, Our help wilt be.

God be with You 310

J. E. Rankin (*P. M.*) W. G. Tomer

1. God be with you till we meet a-gain, By His counsels guide, up-hold you,
2. God be with you till we meet a-gain, 'Neath His wings pro-tect-ing hide you;
3. God be with you till we meet a-gain; When life's per-ils thick con-found you;
4. God be with you till we meet a-gain; Keep love's ban-ner float-ing o'er you;
With His sheep se-cure-ly fold you, God be with you till we meet a-gain.
Dai-ly man-na still pro-vide you, God be with you till we meet a-gain.
Put His arms un-fail-ing round you, God be with you till we meet a-gain.
Smite death's threat'ning wave before you; God be with you till we meet a-gain.
CHORUS
Till we meet, . . . till we meet, Till we meet at Je-sus'
Till we meet, till we meet, till we meet,
feet; Till we meet, . . till we meet, God be with you till we meet a-gain.
till we meet; Till we meet, till we meet, till we meet,

Copyright by J. E. Rankin. Used by per.

Response after the Offering 311

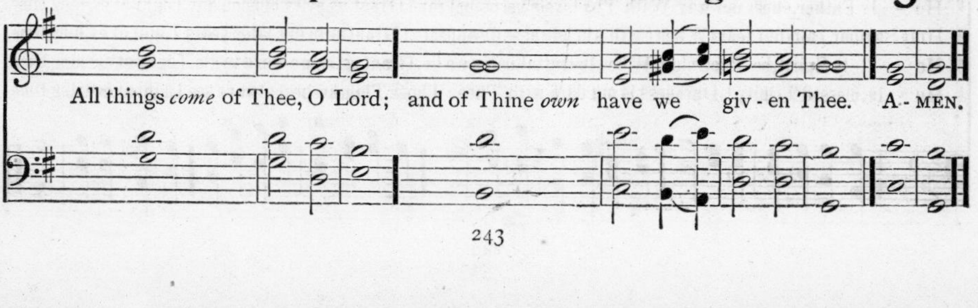
All things come of Thee, O Lord; and of Thine own have we giv-en Thee. A-MEN.

312 Thine are All the Gifts

J. G. Whittier, 1878 (*St. Piran* 7s. 5s) E. J. Hopkins

1. Thine are all the gifts, O God, Thine the broken bread; Let the naked feet be shod, And the starving fed.
2. Let Thy children, by Thy grace, Give as they abound, Till the poor have breathing-space, And the lost are found
3. Wis - er than the miser's hoards Is the giver's choice; Sweeter than the song of birds Is the thankful voice.
4. Wel-come smiles on fa-ces sad As the flow'rs of spring; Let the tender hearts be glad With the joy they bring.

313 Father, Hear Thy Children's Call

T. B. Pollock, 1872 (*Landon* 7s. 6) F. A. J. Hervey

1. Father, hear Thy children's call: Humbly at Thy feet we fall, Prodigals, confessing all, We beseech Thee, hear us.
2. Love that caused us first to be, Love that bled upon the tree, Love that draws us lovingly, We beseech Thee, hear us.
3. By the gracious saving call Spoken tenderly to all Who have shared man's guilt and fall, We beseech Thee, hear us.
4. We Thy call have disobey'd, Have neglected and delayed, Into paths of sin have strayed: We beseech Thee, hear us.
5. Lead us daily nearer Thee, Till at last Thy face we see, Crown'd with Thine own purity: We beseech Thee, hear us.

314 Holy Father, Cheer Our Way

R. H. Robinson, 1869 (*Walsall* 7. 7. 7. 5) C. C. Scholefield

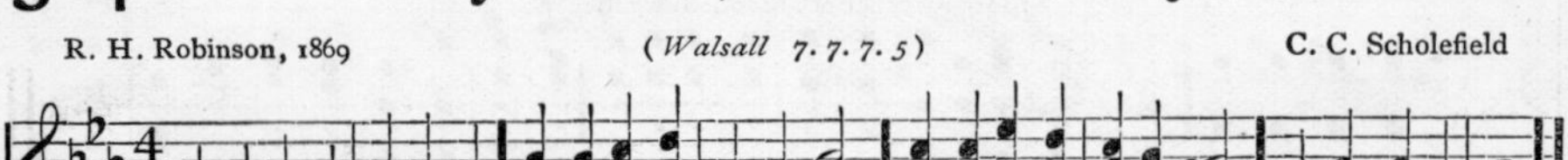

1. Ho - ly Father, cheer our way With Thy love's perpetual ray; Grant us ev'ry closing day Light at ev'ning time.
2. Holy Saviour, calm our fears When earth's brightness disappears; Grant us in our later years Light at ev'ning time.
3. Ho - ly Spirit, be Thou nigh, When in mortal pains we lie, Grant us, as we come to die, Light at evening time.
4. Ho - ly, blessed Trinity! Darkness is not dark with Thee: Those Thou keepest always see Light at evening time.

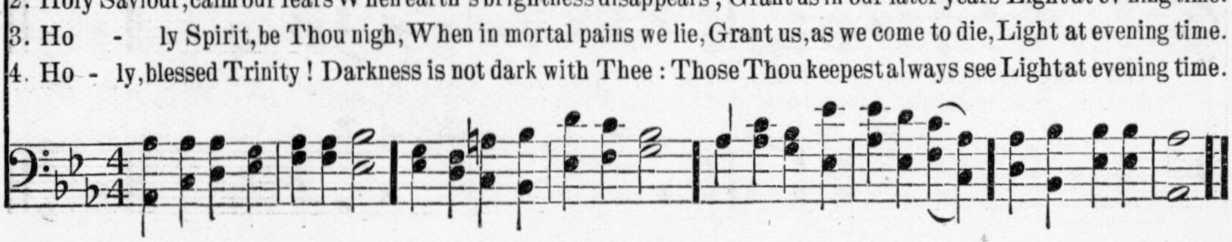

315

The Lord Watch

Genesis xxxi: 49 — (*The Mizpah Benediction*) — F. L. Stone, 1901

p With expression
The Lord watch be - tween me and thee, The Lord watch be - tween
me and thee, When we are ab - sent one from an - oth - er. A - MEN.

Copyright, 1901, by U. S. C. E.

316

The Lord Bless Us and Keep Us

Numbers vi: 24-26 — (*Benediction*) — Anon.

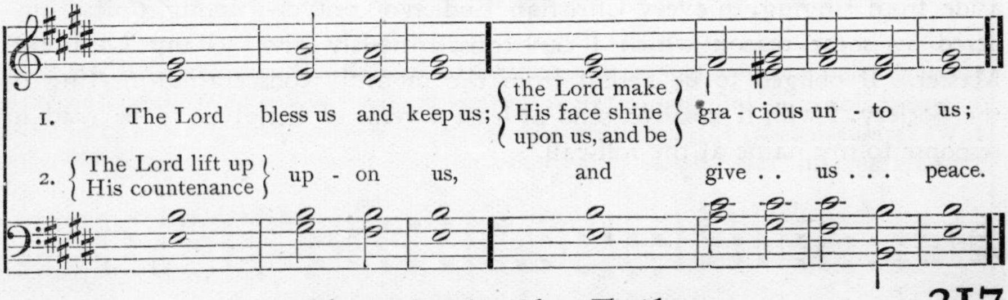
1. The Lord bless us and keep us; { the Lord make / His face shine / upon us, and be } gra - cious un - to us;
2. { The Lord lift up / His countenance } up - on us, and give . . us . . . peace.

317

Glory be to the Father

(*Gloria Patri Irr.*) — Greatorex Coll.

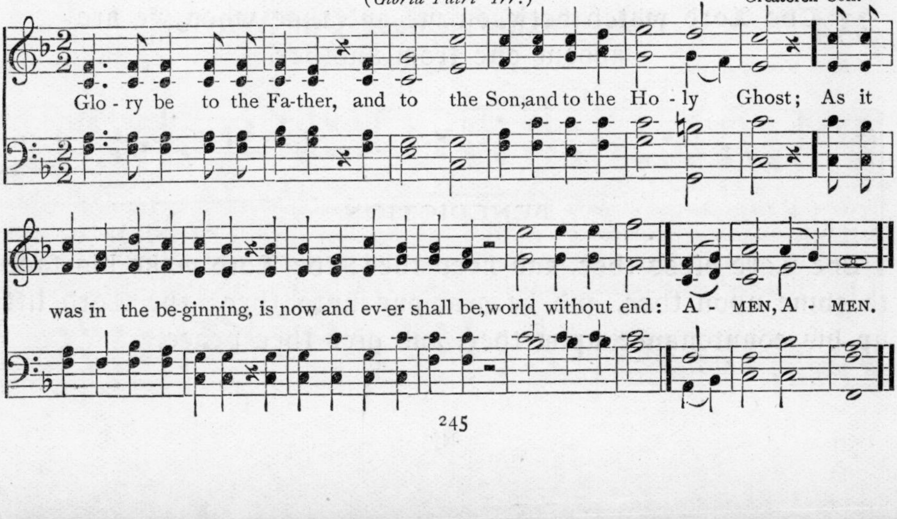
Glo - ry be to the Fa-ther, and to the Son, and to the Ho - ly Ghost; As it
was in the be-ginning, is now and ev-er shall be, world without end: A - MEN, A - MEN.

MOTTO

"For Christ and the Church"

✠

ACTIVE MEMBER'S PLEDGE

TRUSTING IN THE LORD JESUS CHRIST for strength, I promise Him that I will strive to do whatever He would like to have me do; that I will make it the rule of my life to pray and to read the Bible every day, and to support my own church in every way, especially by attending all her regular Sunday and mid-week services, unless prevented by some reason which I can conscientiously give to my Saviour; and that, just so far as I know how, throughout my whole life, I will endeavor to lead a Christian life. As an active member I promise to be true to all my duties; to be present at and to take some part, aside from singing, in every Christian Endeavor prayer-meeting, unless hindered by some reason which I can conscientiously give to my Lord and Master. If obliged to be absent from the monthly consecration-meeting of the Society, I will, if possible, send at least a verse of Scripture to be read in response to my name at the roll-call.

✠

MIZPAH

The Lord watch between me and thee when we are absent one from another.

✠

BENEDICTION

The Lord bless thee, and keep thee: the Lord make his face to shine upon thee, and be gracious unto thee: the Lord lift up his countenance upon thee, and give thee peace.

Responsive Readings

[THE ROMAN TYPE IS TO BE READ BY THE LEADER; THE FULL-FACE TYPE BY THE PEOPLE; AND THE SMALL-CAP TYPE IN UNISON]

Selection 1

(A SCRIPTURAL CONFESSION)

Behold the Lamb of God which taketh away the sin of the world.

All we like sheep have gone astray; we have turned every one to his own way, and the Lord hath laid on Him the iniquity of us all.

Let the wicked forsake his way and the unrighteous man his thoughts, and let him return unto the Lord, and He will have mercy upon him; and to our God, for He will abundantly pardon.

O GOD, I ACKNOWLEDGE MY TRANSGRESSIONS, AND MY SIN IS EVER BEFORE ME. WASH ME THOROUGHLY FROM MINE INIQUITY, AND CLEANSE ME FROM MY SIN. CAST ME NOT AWAY FROM THY PRESENCE, AND TAKE NOT THY HOLY SPIRIT FROM ME. CREATE IN ME A CLEAN HEART, O GOD, AND RENEW A RIGHT SPIRIT WITHIN ME.

God was in Christ reconciling the world unto Himself, not imputing their trespasses unto them, and hath committed unto us the word of reconciliation.

There is, therefore, now no condemnation to them which are in Christ Jesus, who walk not after the flesh, but after the spirit.

Let us therefore come boldly unto the throne of grace, that we may obtain mercy, and find grace to help us in time of need.

Jesus said, After this manner pray ye:

[REPEAT THE LORD'S PRAYER IN UNISON.]

Selection 2

(AN OPENING RESPONSE)

Surely the Lord is in this place.

This is none other than the house of God; and this is the gate of heaven.

Serve the Lord with gladness:

Come before His presence with singing.

Enter into His gates with thanksgiving,

And into His courts with praise.

Give thanks unto Him, and bless His name.

For the Lord is good; His mercy endureth forever.

O sing unto the Lord a new song:

For great is the Lord, and greatly to be praised:

Honor and majesty are before Him.

Strength and beauty are in His sanctuary.

GIVE UNTO THE LORD THE GLORY DUE UNTO HIS NAME:

O WORSHIP THE LORD IN THE BEAUTY OF HOLINESS.

Selection 3

(From PSALMS 122, 125)

I was glad when they said unto me,
Let us go unto the house of the Lord.

Pray for the peace of Jerusalem.

They shall prosper that love thee.

Peace be within thy walls,
And prosperity within thy palaces.

For my brethren and companions' sakes,
I will now say, Peace be within thee.

For the sake of the house of the Lord our God I will seek thy good.

They that trust in the Lord are as mount Zion, which cannot be moved, but abideth for ever.

As the mountains are round about Jerusalem,
So the Lord is round about his people,
From this time forth and for evermore.

Selection 4

(PSALM 23)

The Lord is my shepherd; I shall not want.

He maketh me to lie down in green pastures: He leadeth me beside the still waters.

He restoreth my soul:

He leadeth me in the paths of righteousness for His name's sake.

Yea, though I walk through the valley of the shadow of death, I will fear no evil:

For Thou art with me; Thy rod and Thy staff, they comfort me.

Thou preparest a table before me in the presence of mine enemies:

Thou anointest my head with oil; my cup runneth over.

Surely goodness and mercy shall follow me all the days of my life;

And I will dwell in the house of the Lord for ever.

[This psalm is adapted for reading in unison.]

Selection 5

(From JOHN 10. In Unison)

Then said Jesus unto them,
Verily, verily, I say unto you, I am the door of the sheep.
I am the door: by Me if any man enter in, he shall be saved.
The thief cometh not, but to steal, and to kill, and to destroy:
I am come that they might have life, and that they might have it more abundantly.
I am the good shepherd: The good shepherd giveth his life for the sheep.
I am the good shepherd, and know My sheep, and am known of Mine.
As the Father knoweth Me, even so know I the Father:
And I lay down My life for the sheep.
And other sheep I have, which are not of this fold: them also I must bring, and they shall hear My voice; and there shall be one fold, and one shepherd.

Selection 6

(PSALM 1)

Blessed is the man that walketh not in the counsel of the ungodly,

Nor standeth in the way of sinners,
Nor sitteth in the seat of the scornful.

But his delight is in the law of the Lord;

And in His law doth he meditate day and night.

And he shall be like a tree planted by the rivers of water,

That bringeth forth its fruit in its season,

Whose leaf also doth not wither;

And whatsoever he doeth shall prosper.

The wicked are not so; but are like the chaff which the wind driveth away.

Therefore the wicked shall not stand in the judgment, nor sinners in the congregation of the righteous.

For the Lord knoweth the way of the righteous:

But the way of the ungodly shall perish.

Selection 7

(From PSALM 19)

The heavens declare the glory of God;

And the firmament showeth his handiwork.

Day unto day uttereth speech,

And night unto night showeth knowledge.

There is no speech nor language where their voice is not heard.

Their line is gone out through all the earth, and their words to the end of the world.

The law of the Lord is perfect, restoring the soul:

The testimony of the Lord is sure, making wise the simple.

The precepts of the Lord are right, rejoicing the heart:

The commandment of the Lord is pure, enlightening the eyes.

The fear of the Lord is clean, enduring for ever:

The judgments of the Lord are true, and righteous altogether.

More to be desired are they than gold, yea, than much fine gold:

Sweeter also than honey and the honeycomb.

Moreover by them is thy servant warned:

In keeping of them there is great reward.

Who can discern his errors?

Cleanse thou me from secret faults.

Keep back thy servant also from presumptuous sins;

Let them not have dominion over me: then shall I be upright, and I shall be clear from great transgression.

LET THE WORDS OF MY MOUTH AND THE MEDITATION OF MY HEART BE ACCEPTABLE IN THY SIGHT, O LORD, MY STRENGTH, AND MY REDEEMER.

Selection 8

(MATTHEW 5: 1-12)

And seeing the multitudes, He went up into a mountain: and when He was set, His disciples came unto Him: and He opened His mouth, and taught them, saying,

Blessed are the poor in spirit:

For theirs is the kingdom of heaven.

Blessed are they that mourn:

For they shall be comforted.

Blessed are the meek:

For they shall inherit the earth.

Blessed are they which do hunger and thirst after righteousness:

For they shall be filled.

Blessed are the merciful:

For they shall obtain mercy.

Blessed are the pure in heart:

For they shall see God.

Blessed are the peacemakers:

For they shall be called the children of God.

Blessed are they which are persecuted for righteousness' sake:

For theirs is the kingdom of heaven.

Blessed are ye, when men shall revile you, and persecute you, and shall say all manner of evil against you falsely, for My sake.

REJOICE, AND BE EXCEEDING GLAD: FOR GREAT IS YOUR REWARD IN HEAVEN: FOR SO PERSECUTED THEY THE PROPHETS WHICH WERE BEFORE YOU.

Selection 9

(PSALM 121)

I will lift up mine eyes unto the hills, from whence cometh my help.

My help cometh from the Lord,
Who made heaven and earth.

He will not suffer thy foot to be moved:
He that keepeth thee will not slumber.

Behold, he that keepeth Israel
Shall neither slumber nor sleep.

The Lord is thy keeper:
The Lord is thy shade upon thy right hand.

The sun shall not smite thee by day,
Nor the moon by night.

The Lord shall keep thee from all evil;
He shall keep thy soul.

The Lord shall keep thy going out and thy coming in,
From this time forth and for evermore.

Selection 10

(From PSALM 27)

The Lord is my light and my salvation; whom shall I fear?

The Lord is the strength of my life; of whom shall I be afraid?

One thing have I asked of the Lord, that will I seek after;

That I may dwell in the house of the Lord all the days of my life,
To behold the beauty of the Lord, and to inquire in His temple.

For in the day of trouble He shall hide me in His pavilion:

In the secret of His tabernacle shall He hide me;
He shall set me up upon a rock.

And I will offer in His tabernacle sacrifices of joy;

I will sing, yea, I will sing praises unto the Lord.

Hear, O Lord, when I cry with my voice:

Have mercy also upon me, and answer me.

WHEN THOU SAIDST, SEEK YE MY FACE;
MY HEART SAID UNTO THEE,
THY FACE, LORD, WILL I SEEK.

Selection 11

(From PSALM 51)

Have mercy upon me, O God, according to Thy loving kindness:

According to the multitude of Thy tender mercies blot out my transgressions.

Hide Thy face from my sins,

And blot out all mine iniquities.

Create in me a clean heart, O God;

And renew a right spirit within me.

Cast me not away from Thy presence;

And take not Thy holy spirit from me.

Restore unto me the joy of Thy salvation:

And uphold me with Thy free spirit.

Then will I teach transgressors Thy ways;

And sinners shall be converted unto Thee.

O Lord, open Thou my lips;

And my mouth shall show forth Thy praise.

Selection 12

(From PSALM 103)

Bless the Lord, O my soul:

And all that is within me, bless His Holy Name.

Bless the Lord, O my soul;

And forget not all His benefits:

Who forgiveth all thine iniquities;

Who healeth thy diseases;

Who redeemeth thy life from destruction;

Who crowneth thee with loving kindness and tender mercies.

The Lord is merciful and gracious,

Slow to anger, and plenteous in mercy.

He hath not dealt with us after our sins;

Nor rewarded us according to our iniquities.

For as the heaven is high above the earth,

So great is His mercy toward them that fear Him.

As far as the east is from the west,

So far hath He removed our transgressions from us.

Like as a father pitieth his children,

So the Lord pitieth them that fear Him.

For He knoweth our frame;

He remembereth that we are dust.

As for man, his days are as grass:

As a flower of the field, so he flourisheth.

For the wind passeth over it, and it is gone;

And the place thereof shall know it no more.

But the mercy of the Lord is from everlasting to everlasting upon them that fear Him,

And His righteousness unto children's children;

TO SUCH AS KEEP HIS COVENANT, AND TO THOSE THAT REMEMBER HIS COMMANDMENTS TO DO THEM.

Selection 13

(A MISSIONARY RESPONSE)

Why do the heathen rage,

And the people imagine a vain thing?

The Lord said unto me, Thou art my son; this day have I begotten thee.
Ask of Me, and I will give thee the nations for thine inheritance, and the uttermost parts of the earth for thy possession.

And it shall be said in that day, Lo, this is our God; we have waited for Him; we will be glad and rejoice in His salvation.

The Lord hath made bare His holy arm in the eyes of all the nations;

And all the ends of the earth shall see the salvation of our God.

Enlarge the place of thy tent; spare not: lengthen thy cords and strengthen thy stakes.

For thou shalt spread abroad on the right hand and on the left; and thy seed shall possess the nations.

Awake, awake, put on strength, O arm of the Lord.

Awake, as in the days of old, the generations of ancient times.

And the ransomed of the Lord shall return, and come with singing unto Zion;

And everlasting joy shall be upon their heads: they shall obtain gladness and joy, and sorrow and sighing shall flee away.

Selection 14

(From I JOHN 3)

Behold, what manner of love the Father hath bestowed upon us,

That we should be called the sons of God.

Beloved, now are we the sons of God, and it doth not yet appear what we shall be:

But we know that when He shall appear, we shall be like Him; for we shall see Him as He is.

AND EVERY MAN THAT HATH THIS HOPE IN HIM PURIFIETH HIMSELF, EVEN AS HE IS PURE.

Little children, let no man deceive you: he that doeth righteousness is righteous, even as He is righteous.

In this the children of God are manifest, and the children of the devil: whosoever doeth not righteousness is not of God, neither he that loveth not his brother.

For this is the message that ye heard from the beginning, that we should love one another.

We know that we have passed from death unto life, because we love the brethren.

And this is His commandment, That we should believe on the name of His Son Jesus Christ, and love one another, as He gave us commandment.

And he that keepeth His commandments dwelleth in Him, and He in him.

And hereby we know that He abideth in us, by the Spirit which He hath given us.

AND THIS COMMANDMENT HAVE WE FROM HIM, THAT HE WHO LOVETH GOD LOVE HIS BROTHER ALSO. HE THAT LOVETH NOT KNOWETH NOT GOD: FOR GOD IS LOVE.

Selection 15

(From ISAIAH 55)

Ho, every one that thirsteth, come ye to the waters; and he that hath no money, come ye, buy and eat;

Yea, come, buy wine and milk without money, and without price.

Seek ye the Lord while He may be found,
Call ye upon Him while He is near:

Let the wicked forsake his way, and the unrighteous man his thoughts: and let him return unto the Lord, and He will have mercy upon him;

And to our God, for He will abundantly pardon.

For My thoughts are not your thoughts,
Neither are your ways My ways, saith the Lord.

FOR AS THE HEAVENS ARE HIGHER THAN THE EARTH, SO ARE MY WAYS HIGHER THAN YOUR WAYS,

AND MY THOUGHTS THAN YOUR THOUGHTS.

Selection 16

(THE BIRTH OF JESUS)

And there were in the same country shepherds abiding in the field,

Keeping watch over their flocks by night.

And, lo, the angel of the Lord came upon them, and the glory of the Lord shone round about them:

And they were sore afraid.

And the angel said unto them, Fear not: for behold, I bring you good tidings of great joy, which shall be to all people.

For unto you is born this day in the city of David a Saviour, which is Christ the Lord.

And suddenly there was with the angel a multitude of the heavenly host, praising God, and saying,

GLORY TO GOD IN THE HIGHEST, AND ON EARTH PEACE, GOOD WILL TOWARD MEN.

Now lettest Thou Thy servant depart in peace, O Lord, according to Thy word;

For mine eyes have seen Thy salvation, which Thou hast prepared before the face of all peoples;

A light for revelation to the Gentiles, and the glory of Thy people Israel.

NOW UNTO THE KING, ETERNAL, INCORRUPTIBLE, INVISIBLE, THE ONLY GOD, BE HONOR AND GLORY FOR EVER AND EVER. AMEN.

Selection 17

(A SONG OF SALVATION)

Sing unto the Lord a new song, and His praise from the end of the earth.

Sing, O heavens; and be joyful, O earth; and break forth into singing, O mountains:

For the Lord hath comforted His people,

And will have compassion upon His afflicted.

Blessed be the Lord, the God of Israel;

For He hath visited and wrought redemption for His people.

The people that walked in darkness have seen a great light:

They that dwelt in the land of the shadow of death, upon them hath the light shined.

For unto us a child is born, unto us a son is given; and the government shall be upon His shoulder:

And His name shall be called Wonderful, Counsellor, Mighty God, Everlasting Father, Prince of Peace.

Of the increase of His government and of peace there shall be no end, upon the throne of David, and upon His kingdom, to establish it,

And to uphold it with judgment and with righteousness from henceforth even for ever.

And in that day thou shalt say, I will give thanks unto Thee, O Lord.

Behold, God is my salvation; I will trust, and will not be afraid:

FOR THE LORD JEHOVAH IS MY STRENGTH AND SONG;

AND HE IS BECOME MY SALVATION.

Selection 18

(PRAISE AND BENEDICTION)

Who shall separate us from the love of Christ? shall tribulation, or anguish, or persecution, or famine, or nakedness, or peril, or sword?

Nay, in all these things we are more than conquerors through Him that loved us.

For I am persuaded that neither death, nor life, nor angels, nor principalities, nor things present, nor things to come, nor powers, nor height, nor depth, nor any other creature, shall be able to separate us from the love of God, which is in Christ Jesus our Lord.

Blessed be the God and Father of our Lord Jesus Christ, who according to His great mercy begat us again unto a living hope by the resurrection of Jesus Christ from the dead,

Unto an inheritance incorruptible, and undefiled, and that fadeth not away, reserved in heaven for you, who by the power of God are guarded through faith unto a salvation ready to be revealed in the last time.

Now unto Him that is able to do exceeding abundantly above all that we ask or think, according to the power that worketh in us, unto Him be the glory in the church and in Christ Jesus unto all generations for ever and ever.

Now our Lord Jesus Christ Himself, and God our Father who loved us and gave us eternal comfort and good hope through grace, comfort your hearts and stablish them in every good work and word.

Worthy is the Lamb that hath been slain to receive the power, and riches, and wisdom, and might, and honor, and glory, and blessing.

UNTO HIM THAT SITTETH ON THE THRONE, AND UNTO THE LAMB, BE BLESSING, AND HONOR, AND GLORY, AND DOMINION, FOR EVER AND EVER. AMEN.

Index to First Lines

Index to First Lines

Index to First Lines

Titles of Hymns

Our Workers' Library

Cloth bindings; 35 cents each, post-paid.

THE OFFICERS' HAND-BOOK
By Amos R. Wells. A complete manual for presidents, secretaries, and treasurers of young people's societies.

THE MISSIONARY MANUAL
By Amos R. Wells. A complete hand-book of methods for missionary work.

FUEL FOR MISSIONARY FIRES
By Belle M. Brain. Practical plans for missionary committees.

PRAYER-MEETING METHODS
By Amos R. Wells. The most comprehensive collection of prayer-meeting plans ever made.

SOCIAL EVENINGS
By Amos R. Wells. This is the most widely used collection of games and social entertainments ever published.

SOCIAL TO SAVE
By Amos R. Wells. A companion volume to "Social Evenings." A mine of enjoyment for the society and home.

OUR UNIONS
By Amos R. Wells. Wholly devoted to Christian Endeavor unions of all kinds.

WEAPONS FOR TEMPERANCE WARFARE
By Belle M. Brain. Full of ammunition for temperance meetings.

NEXT STEPS
By Rev. W. F. McCauley. A storehouse of suggestions for every Christian Endeavor worker.

CITIZENS IN TRAINING
By Amos R. Wells. A complete manual of Christian citizenship.

EIGHTY PLEASANT EVENINGS
A book of social entertainments intended for societies and for individual use.

United Society of Christian Endeavor

Tremont Temple, Boston, Mass.
155 La Salle Street, Chicago, Ill.